INTRODUCTION TO THE SERIES

THE FIRST EIGHTEEN MONTHS—AND AFTER

ALTHOUGH no locomotive designs prepared by the new organisation have appeared during the first eighteen months of British Railways, there are indications of the future developments which may be expected.

The arrears of locomotive construction which accrued during the war years have not yet been fully recovered. The restricted supplies of steel allotted to the railways have been devoted primarily to repairs, which have often been of a drastic nature, as a result of the exceptional wear which motive power underwent during the war. Even within the modest allowance of steel which can be spared for new construction, it is often a long process to obtain the exact sizes and specifications required for a particular job, so that more than ever before the material needed for new batches of locomotives must be ordered two or three years in advance. Consequently the Railway Executive decided at an early stage that existing locomotive programmes up to 1950 must be completed.

In the meantime, preparation of the new standard designs was begun ; but decisions formerly taken by the C.M.E. are now discussed by committees specialising in various aspects of design and development, so that the work is likely to be comparatively slow. It is expected that the first new designs will appear in 1951, and even then considerable experimental work may precede large-scale construction. The completion of the Rugby Testing Station and the Mobile Test Units have provided facilities for detailed examination of the work of a locomotive, and the new national designs will be subjected to exhaustive trial. In this connection it is interesting to recall that the development of Churchward's basic designs on the G.W.R. took some ten years (with the aid of the Swindon test plant) and that roughly the same period (allowing for the war years) was required for the perfection of the range of L.M.S. standard types of Sir William Stanier and his successors.

It has been stated by the R.E. that the first two designs will be a large express engine and a mixed traffic class. Although these will incorporate characteristic features from the four Groups, as well as some new ones, they will be influenced by the L.N.E.R. " A1 " and " B1 " classes. This is surprising and encouraging ; the key positions in the locomotive departments of the R.E. are held by former L.M.S. officers, and it may have been natural for them to perpetuate the designs of their parent company. However, it seems that the new classes will be designed impartially.

The results of the 1948 locomotive exchanges showed a marked advantage in coal consumption to the L.M.S. and L.N.E.R.

[*H. C. Casserley*

Ex-Vale of Rheidol narrow gauge 2-6-2T No. 8

[*H. C. Casserley*

Ex-Welshpool & Llanfair narrow gauge 0-6-0T No. 822 *The Earl*

Above : 0-4-0ST No. 1 *Hercules*
[*H. C. Casserley*

Left : Ex-Cardiff Rly. 0-4-0ST No. 1338
[*A. R. Venning*

Below : Ex-Powlesland & Mason 0-4-0ST No. 935
[*R. M. Casserley*

Above : Ex-Whitland & Cardigan 0-6-0ST No. 1331

[L. Elsey

Right : Ex-B.P.G.V. 0-6-0ST No. 2194 Kidwelly

[A. R. Venning

Below : Ex-B.P.G.V. 0-6-0T No. 2167

[H. C. Casserley

Left : Ex-Alexandra (Newport & S. Wales) Docks 2-6-2T No. 1205
[*P. L. Melvill*

Below : "4500" Class 2-6-2T No. 4571
[*H. C. Casserley*

Left : "4400" Class 2-6-2T No. 4402
[*D. G. Carter*

locomotives, when burning the types of coal usual on those systems. The " B1 " acquitted itself well against the older-established 4-6-0s of the other groups, but the " A1 " Pacific was not then available in sufficient numbers for the exchange workings, and its merits cannot therefore have been assessed from these trials. The new designs will presumably follow L.N.E.R. practice in having a parallel boiler on the 4-6-0, three cylinders in the Pacific, and round-top fireboxes on both.

At least until such time as work on the larger B.R. designs is complete, construction of smaller locomotives of pre-nationalisation designs may continue for some years. The L.M.S. Class "4" 2-6-0 has been tried on the E.R., and it is rumoured that locomotives of that class are to be built in the E.R. shops. There would also be scope for the use of these locomotives on the S.R., where much passenger work on secondary lines is performed by locomotives of great antiquity.

The R.E. is faced with declining receipts and increasing expenses. Amongst the latter, motive power costs are a major item. The cost of locomotive coal has increased some 150 per cent since before the war, and its quality has deteriorated considerably. Labour costs have also increased greatly. The predominant influence in the new designs will therefore be economy of operation. One of the chief weaknesses of the steam locomotive is its low availability compared with other forms of motive power ; that is, the small number of hours for which it can work trains continuously day by day. Fire cleaning, emptying the smokebox of ashes, and taking coal and water are the most frequent interruptions within the day's work, and boiler washouts the most frequent cause of stoppages for longer periods.

Efforts to increase the availability of the steam locomotive were in progress at the time of nationalisation, and these will be important factors influencing the new designs. Rocking grates, hopper ashpans and self-cleaning smokeboxes, which reduce daily shed requirements, feed water treatment (such as " T.I.A.") with continuous blow-down valves, which lengthen the periods between boiler washouts, will almost certainly become standard features. Roller bearings, which reduce axlebox wear and lessen the risk of hot boxes, are under extensive trial, and may be adopted generally. High footplating, cut away in the vicinity of the cylinders, gives improved access to the motion for inspection and repairs, and has already become standard on the recent L.M.S. and L.N.E.R. designs, but the extreme austerity of the S.R. " Q1 " 0-6-0 is unlikely to be repeated.

The future of poppet valve gears will be decided in the light of current experiments with the Caprotti gear on L.M.R. Class " 5 " 4-6-0s, and with an improved form of Lentz gear (giving infinitely variable cut-off) on N.E.R. "D49" 4-4-0 No. 62764. If these fittings can show an economy in fuel consumption or (as seems more likely) reduced maintenance costs, the fluctuating fortunes of the poppet valve in Britain may take a more favourable turn than ever seemed possible in the late 1930s. In the absence of a more general use of poppet valves, it is unlikely that there will be any serious competitor to the large-diameter, long-travel piston valve with outside Walschaerts valve gear. Inaccessibility for maintenance seems a sufficient objection to following Mr. Bulleid's practice of fitting the whole valve gear inside, encased in an oil bath.

It may not be feasible to use identical versions of the standard classes on all the Regions. This applies particularly to the use of coal, for the locomotive exchanges emphasised that the fireboxes and blast arrangements of the former G.W. locomotives, designed for soft Welsh coal, were not well suited to burning hard Northern coal regularly. It will be interesting to see whether any individuality is retained in the locomotives of the W.R. In general it is to be expected that larger grates will be provided than was usual in pre-war years, to allow for the lower quality of coal which is now usual. In this connection it is also interesting to note that the Pacifics tested in the express passenger exchanges showed an economy over the 4-6-0s against which they were tried, and from which they differed dimensionally chiefly in their much larger grates.

The L.M.R. Class "4" 2-6-0 shows in some respects the exterior pattern which may be expected in the national designs, if development follows the lines suggested above. Despite the advanced nature of this design, some semblance of the appearance of the traditional British locomotive is retained, for which the aesthete, viewing the wartime productions of the S.R., may be thankful. Remember, too, that many designs, such as the Urie "N15" 4-6-0, have been considered outrageous at their debut, although later they have been accepted as handsome locomotives.

The outlook for the revolutionary designs of steam locomotive is not good. Increased complication can be justified only if it brings some appreciable benefit. Thus roller bearings may reduce axlebox troubles, and thermic syphons increase the steaming capacity of boilers burning low grade coal, sufficiently to justify their use ; but clasp brakes, totally enclosed valve gears and feed water heaters are amongst the fittings which are unlikely to justify the expense of maintaining them.

Whether or not so complete a breakaway from the Stephenson locomotive as Mr. Bulleid's "Leader" class will offer a solution to the problem of steam locomotive availability remains to be seen. Five of these locomotives are under construction, and their appearance, long delayed by manufacturing difficulties, is now imminent. The design aims at producing a steam unit with the high availability and operating characteristics of an electric locomotive.

But it is with other forms of motive power that the chief competition to the conventional steam locomotive is developing. The Diesel-electric locomotive has swept across the United States at a phenomenal rate, and it is only on a few lines in coal-producing districts that steam is still the universal motive power. The world's fastest trains are all Diesel-hauled and their running includes such feats as those of the Burlington locomotives which, in a working day of 14 hours, cover 874 miles on the Twin-City " Zephyrs " (the world's fastest trains), and repeat this for 80 to 90 days consecutively. These performances are far ahead of the best which steam can produce. Diesel power is also used on most American railways now for freight work.

In this country the Diesel shunter has already become almost standard for yards in which shunting is continuous, but the number of workings on which main-line Diesel units could be used so intensively as in America is small. Nevertheless, until further improvements are made in steam locomotive availability, the Diesel is a most attractive prospect. In addition to its high availability, the Diesel has also a marked advantage over the steam locomotive in efficiency and fuel costs, despite the fact that its fuel is imported. Several years' experience with the L.M.R. Diesels and with those under construction for the other Regions will be needed before the future of this type of motive power can be accurately assessed.

Another competitor to the steam locomotive will shortly appear—the gas turbine. In its initial form this will burn oil, and will be closely comparable with the Diesel. Like that type of unit, it will drive through an electric generator and motors, and therefore have the acceleration of an electric locomotive. Within ten years the coal-burning gas turbine may be a practicable proposition for traction purposes (it is already in the experimental stage in America), and this will be an even greater attraction in Britain, lacking, as it will, the objection of burning imported fuel.

Ordinary electrification is already assured of further development here. The S.R. electric locomotives have recently entered regular passenger service, and by 1951 the Manchester-Sheffield electrification will be in operation with locomotive haulage. This latter scheme will be of great importance to B.R., and upon it may hinge the whole future of main line electrification on Regions other than the Southern. But several years will elapse before the long-term benefits of that scheme can be assessed.

The writer would suggest that the future of the steam locomotive on B.R. is assured for some ten years, during which time a considerable number of the new standard types will be built. If, within that time, the steam locomotive can be improved as a traffic unit, it may hold its own, but it will be hard pressed to compete with the Diesel, gas turbine and electric locomotives, which by that time should have passed the experimental stage. Even if the steam locomotive were then superseded for new construction, it would be some 25-30 years at least before it disappeared completely.

A. F. COOK

LOCOMOTIVE SUPERINTENDENTS AND CHIEF MECHANICAL ENGINEERS OF THE G.W.R. & W.R.

Sir Daniel Gooch	1837—1864
Joseph Armstrong	1854—1864* 1864—1877
George Armstrong .. .. (*Bro. of J. Armstrong*)	1864— 1877—1892*
William Dean	—1877* 1877—1902
G. J. Churchward	1902—1921
Charles B. Collett	1922—1941
F. W. Hawksworth	1941—

* In charge of standard gauge locomotives at Stafford Road Works, Wolverhampton, with wide powers in design and construction. The exact dates of Geo. Armstrong's and Dean's terms of service there cannot be definitely ascertained from existing records.

POWER AND WEIGHT CLASSIFICATION

Since 1920 Western Region locomotives have been classified for power and weight by a letter on a coloured disc on the cab side. The letter represents the power of the locomotive, and is approximately proportional to the tractive effort as under :

Power class	*Tractive effort lb.*	*Power class*	*Tractive effort lb.*
Special	Over 38,000	B	18,501-20,500
E	33,001-38,000	A	16,500-18,500
D	25,001-33,000	Un-	
C	20,501-25,000	grouped	Below 16,500

The colour of the circle represents the routes over which the engine may work. Red engines are limited to the main lines and lines capable of carrying the heaviest locomotives ; blue engines are allowed over additional routes, yellow engines over nearly the whole system and uncoloured engines are more or less unrestricted. The double red circles on the " King " class represent special restrictions for these engines.

NOTES ON THE USE OF THIS BOOK

1. This booklet lists British Railways locomotives numbered between 1 and 9999 in service at May 30th, 1949. This range of numbers covers Western Region (ex-G.W.R.) engines with the following exceptions :

(i) Diesel and forthcoming gas turbine locomotives, which are dealt with in the ABC OF BRITISH RAILWAYS LOCOMOTIVES NOS. 10000-39999.

(ii) British Railways Class " WD " 2-8-0 locomotives in service on the Western Region. These are listed in the ABC OF BRITISH RAILWAYS LOCOMOTIVES Part 4—60000-90774.

2. With the exception of Diesel locomotives, Western Region locomotives retain their original Great Western numbers. Where locomotives have been renumbered under the continued Great Western schemes involving a partial renumbering of former South Wales companies' engines, the former numbers of locomotives affected are shown in brackets in the following lists. All the formerly renumbered oil-burning locomotives are being reconverted to coal-burning and will reassume their original numbers, by which they are listed in this book.

3. Throughout the book the dimensions shown for each class are only typical examples and should not be taken as applying to every engine of the class.

4. The following is a list of abbreviations used to indicate the pre-grouping owners of certain Western Region locomotives :

AD	Alexandra (Newport and South Wales) Docks & Railway
BR	Barry Railway
BM	Brecon and Merthyr Railway
BP&GV	Burry Port & Gwendraeth Valley Rly.
Cam.R.	Cambrian Railways
Car.R.	Cardiff Railway
CMDP	Cleobury Mortimer and Ditton Priors Light Railway
LMM	Llanelly & Mynydd Mawr Railway
MSWJ	Midland and South Western Junction Railway
NB	Neath and Brecon Railway
PM	Powlesland & Mason (Contractor)
RR	Rhymney Railway
SHT	Swansea Harbour Trust
TV	Taff Vale Railway
V of R	Cambrian Railways (Vale of Rheidol)
WCPR	Weston, Clevedon & Portishead Rly.
W & C	Whitland & Cardigan
W & L	Cambrian Railways (Welshpool and Llanfair)

NUMERICAL LIST OF LOCOMOTIVES

The tables on pages 12-14 show engine number, wheel arrangement and pre-grouping owner or Western Region Class. For abbreviations see page 11. Where no initials are shown, the locomotive is of G.W.R. origin.

1 0-4-0T† Hercules
5 Portishead 0-6-0T W.C. & P.R.
7 2-6-2T V.of R.*
8 2-6-2T V.of R.*
9 2-6-2T V.of R.* (1213)
28 0-6-0T CMDP
29 0-6-0T CMDP
31 0-6-2T RR
32 0-6-2T RR
33 0-6-2T RR
34 0-6-2T RR
35 0-6-2T RR
36 0-6-2T RR
37 0-6-2T RR
38 0-6-2T RR
39 0-6-2T RR
40 0-6-2T RR
41 0-6-2T RR
42 0-6-2T RR
43 0-6-2T RR
44 0-6-2T RR
46 0-6-2T RR
52 0-6-2T RR
53 0-6-2T RR
55 0-6-2T RR
56 0-6-2T RR
57 0-6-2T RR
58 0-6-2T RR
59 0-6-2T RR
60 0-6-2T RR
61 0-6-2T RR
63 0-6-2T RR
64 0-6-2T RR
65 0-6-2T RR
66 0-6-2T RR
67 0-6-2T RR
68 0-6-2T RR
69 0-6-2T RR
70 0-6-2T RR
72 0-6-2T RR
73 0-6-2T RR
74 0-6-2T RR
75 0-6-2T RR
76 0-6-2T RR
77 0-6-2T RR
78 0-6-2T RR
79 0-6-2T RR
80 0-6-2T RR
81 0-6-2T RR
82 0-6-2T RR
90 0-6-0T RR (604)
91 0-6-0T RR (605)
92 0-6-0T RR (606)
93 0-6-0T RR (608)
94 0-6-0T RR (609)
95 0-6-0T RR (610)
100 A1 4-6-0 4073 Class
111 4-6-0 4073 Class
155 0-6-2T Car. R.
193 0-6-0T TV (792)
194 0-6-0T TV (793)
195 0-6-0T TV (794)
203 0-6-2T TV (310)
204 0-6-2T TV (311)
205 0-6-2T TV (313)
207 0-6-2T TV (315)
208 0-6-2T TV (317)
209 0-6-2T TV (318)
210 0-6-2T TV (319)
211 0-6-2T TV (320)
215 0-6-2T TV (321)
216 0-6-2T TV (324)
217 0-6-2T TV (333)
219 0-6-2T TV (414)
220 0-6-2T TV (420)
231 0-6-2T BR
236 0-6-2T TV
240 0-6-2T BR
258 0-6-2T BR
262 0-6-2T BR
263 0-6-2T BR
265 0-6-2T BR
267 0-6-2T BR
269 0-6-2T BR
270 0-6-2T BR
271 0-6-2T BR
272 0-6-2T BR
274 0-6-2T BR
276 0-6-2T BR
278 0-6-2T TV
279 0-6-2T TV
281 0-6-2T TV
282 0-6-2T TV
284 0-6-2T TV
285 0-6-2T TV
286 0-6-2T TV
287 0-6-2T TV
288 0-6-2T TV
289 0-6-2T TV
290 0-6-2T TV
291 0-6-2T TV
292 0-6-2T TV
293 0-6-2T TV
294 0-6-2T TV
295 0-6-2T TV
296 0-6-2T TV
297 0-6-2T TV
299 0-6-2T TV
303 0-6-2T TV (401)

* Built to V. of R. design by G.W.R., 1923. 1′ 11½″ gauge

† Purchased by British Railways from Ystalyfera Tin Works.

304 0-6-2T TV (402)
305 0-6-2T TV (403)
308 0-6-2T TV (408)
314 0-6-2T TV
322 0-6-2T TV (441)
332 0-6-2T BM
335 0-6-2T TV
337 0-6-2T TV
343 0-6-2T TV
344 0-6-2T TV
345 0-6-2T TV
346 0-6-2T TV
347 0-6-2T TV
348 0-6-2T TV
349 0-6-2T TV
351 0-6-2T TV
352 0-6-2T TV
356 0-6-2T TV
357 0-6-2T TV
359 Hilda 0-6-0T LMM
360 0-6-2T TV
361 0-6-2T TV
362 0-6-2T TV
364 0-6-2T TV
365 0-6-2T TV
366 0-6-2T TV
367 0-6-2T TV
368 0-6-2T TV
370 0-6-2T TV
371 0-6-2T TV
372 0-6-2T TV
373 0-6-2T TV
374 0-6-2T TV
375 0-6-2T TV
376 0-6-2T TV
377 0-6-2T TV
378 0-6-2T TV
379 0-6-2T TV
380 0-6-2T TV
381 0-6-2T TV
382 0-6-2T TV
383 0-6-2T TV
384 0-6-2T TV
385 0-6-2T TV
386 0-6-2T TV
387 0-6-2T TV
388 0-6-2T TV
389 0-6-2T TV
390 0-6-2T TV
391 0-6-2T TV
393 0-6-2T TV
394 0-6-2T TV
397 0-6-2T TV
398 0-6-2T TV
399 0-6-2T TV
404 0-6-2T TV
406 0-6-2T TV
409 0-6-2T TV
422 0-6-2T BM (21)
425 0-6-2T BM (698)
426 0-6-2T BM (888)
428 0-6-2T BM (1113)
432 0-6-2T BM (1373)
433 0-6-2T BM (1374)
434 0-6-2T BM (1375)
438 0-6-2T TV
439 0-6-2T TV
440 0-6-2T TV
611 0-6-0T RR
666 0-6-0T AD
667 0-6-0T AD
681 0-6-0T Car. R.
682 0-6-0T Car. R.
683 0-6-0T Car. R.
684 0-6-0T Car. R.
696 0-4-0T PM
779 0-4-0T PM
784 0-6-0T BR
803 0-6-0T LMM
822 The Earl 0-6-0T* W. & L.
823 Countess 0-6-0T* W & L.
844 0-6-0 Cam. R.
849 0-6-0 Cam. R.
855 0-6-0 Cam. R.
864 0-6-0 Cam. R.
873 0-6-0 Cam. R.
887 0-6-0 Cam. R.
892 0-6-0 Cam. R.
893 0-6-0 Cam. R.
894 0-6-0 Cam. R.
895 0-6-0 Cam. R.
896 0-6-0 Cam. R.
907 0-6-0T 1701 Class†
935 0-4-0T PM
942 0-4-0T PM
992 0-6-0T 1901 Class

* 2′ 6″ Narrow gauge. † Built Swindon 1895.

" County " Class
4-6-0 1000 Class

Introduced 1945.
Weights : Loco. 76 tons 17 cwt.
Tender 49 tons 0 cwt.
Pressure : 280 lb. Cyls.: $18\frac{1}{2}'' \times 30''$
Driving Wheels: 6′ 3″. T.E.: 32,580 lb.

1000 County of Middlesex
1001 County of Bucks
1002 County of Berks
1003 County of Wilts
1004 County of Somerset
1005 County of Devon
1006 County of Cornwall

1007 County of Brecknock
1008 County of Cardigan
1009 County of Carmarthen
1010 County of Carnarvon
1011 County of Chester
1012 County of Denbigh
1013 County of Dorset
1014 County of Glamorgan
1015 County of Gloucester
1016 County of Hants
1017 County of Hereford
1018 County of Leicester
1019 County of Merioneth
1020 County of Monmouth
1021 County of Montgomery
1022 County of Northampton
1023 County of Oxford
1024 County of Pembroke
1025 County of Radnor
1026 County of Salop
1027 County of Stafford
1028 County of Warwick
1029 County of Worcester

Total 30

1098 0-4-0T SHT
1101 0-4-0T 1101 Class
1102 0-4-0T 1101 Class
1103 0-4-0T 1101 Class
1104 0-4-0T 1101 Class
1105 0-4-0T 1101 Class
1106 0-4-0T 1101 Class
1140 0-4-0T SHT (701)
1141 0-4-0T SHT (929)
1142 0-4-0T SHT (943)
1143 0-4-0T SHT (968)
1144 0-4-0T SHT (974)
1146 0-6-0T SHT (1085)
1147 0-6-0T SHT (1086)
1205 2-6-2T AD
1206 2-6-2T AD
1331 0-6-0T W. & C.
1334 2-4-0 MSWJ
1335 2-4-0 MSWJ
1336 2-4-0 MSWJ
1338 0-4-0T Car. R.
1361 0-6-0T 1361 Class
1362 0-6-0T 1361 Class
1363 0-6-0T 1361 Class
1364 0-6-0T 1361 Class
1365 0-6-0T 1361 Class
1366 0-6-0T 1366 Class
1367 0-6-0T 1366 Class
1368 0-6-0T 1366 Class
1369 0-6-0T 1366 Class
1370 0-6-0T 1366 Class
1371 0-6-0T 1366 Class
1372 0-6-2T BM

Totals :

AD 0-6-0T	**2**
AD 2-6-2T	**2**
BR 0-6-0T	**1**
BR 0-6-2T	**13**
Cam. R. 0-6-0	**11**
Car. R. 0-4-0T	**1**
Car. R. 0-6-0T	**4**
Car. R. 0-6-2T	**1**
CMDP 0-6-0T	**2**
LMM 0-6-0T	**2**
MSWJ 2-4-0	**3**
PM 0-4-0T	**4**
RR 0-6-0T	**7**
RR 0-6-2T	**43**
SHT 0-4-0T	**6**
SHT 0-6-0T	**3**
TV 0-6-0T	**3**
TV 0-6-2T	**92**
V. of R. 2-6-2T	**3**
WCPR 0-6-0T	**1**
W & L 0-6-0T	**2**
W & C 0-6-0T	**1**
1101 Class	**6**
1361 Class	**5**
1366 Class	**6**

(*BM 0-6-2T continued with No.* 1668)
(1701 *Class continued with No.* 1705)
(1901 *Class continued with No.* 1903)

Above : "8100" Class 2-6-2T No. 8106

[C. R. L. Coles

Right "3150" Class 2-6-2T No. 3190

[L. Elsey

Below : "6100" Class 2-6-2T No. 6163

[C. C. B. Herbert

" Bulldog " Class 4-4-0 No. 3451 *Pelican* [B. V. Franey

Ex-M.S.W.J. 2-4-0 No. 1335 [G. L. Hoare

" 9000 " Class 4-4-0 No. 9012 [*H. C. Casserley*

" Duke " Class 4-4-0 No. 9054 *Cornubia* [*H. C. Casserley*

" 5600 " Class 0-6-2T No. 5629 [F. F. Moss

" 1400 " Class 0-4-2T No. 1407 [M. W. Earley

0-4-2T 1400 Class

Introduced 1932.
Weight: 41 tons 6 cwt.
Pressure: 165 lb. Cyls.: 16"×24"
Driving Wheels: 5' 2". T.E.: 13,900 lb.
FITTED FOR AUTO-TRAIN WORKING

1400	1419	1438	1457
1401	1420	1439	1458
1402	1421	1440	1459
1403	1422	1441	1460
1404	1423	1442	1461
1405	1424	1443	1462
1406	1425	1444	1463
1407	1426	1445	1464
1408	1427	1446	1465
1409	1428	1447	1466
1410	1429	1448	1467
1411	1430	1449	1468
1412	1431	1450	1469
1413	1432	1451	1470
1414	1433	1452	1471
1415	1434	1453	1472
1416	1435	1454	1473
1417	1436	1455	1474
1418	1437	1456	

(Class continued with No. 5800)

NOTE: Locomotives numbered between 1531-2186 except Nos. 1668/70, 1925, 2007/48, 2162/58/76, are pannier tanks converted from saddle tanks.

0-6-0T 1501 Class

(Built at Wolverhampton, 1879-80)

1531 | 1542

(Class continued with No. 1742)

0-6-2T BM Rly.

1668 | 1670

Total 12

0-6-0T 1701 Class

(Class continued from No. 907)
(Built at Swindon, 1891-2)

1705	1715*	1720	1731
1709			

(Class continued with No. 1752)

0-6-0T 1501 Class

(Class continued from No. 1542)
(Built at Wolverhampton, 1892)

1742 | 1747

(Class continued with No. 1773)

0-6-0T 1701 Class

(Class continued from No. 1731)
(Built at Swindon, 1892-3)

1752 | 1754 | 1760 | 1764

(Class continued with No. 1799)

0-6-0T 1501 Class

(Class continued from No. 1749)
(Built at Wolverhampton, 1893-4)

1773 | 1782 | 1789

Total 7

0-6-0T 1701 Class

(Class continued from No. 1764)
(Built at Swindon, 1895)

1799

(Class continued with No. 1855)

0-6-0T 1701 Class

(Class continued from No. 1799)
(Built at Swindon, 1890-5)

1855	1862	1878	1891
1858	1863	1884	1896
1861	1870	1888	

Total 22

* Standard G.W. locomotive, sold out of stock to the Neath & Brecon Rly., and later reinstated.

0-6-0T 1901 Class

(Class continued from No. 992)

(Built at Wolverhampton, 1881-95)

1903	1945	1990	2009
1907	1949	1991	2010
1909	1957	1993	2011
1912	1964	1996	2012
1917	1965	2000	2013
1919	1967	2001	2014
1925*	1968	2002	2016
1930	1969	2004	2017
1935	1973	2006	2018
1941	1979	2007*	2019
1943	1989	2008	

Total 44

0-6-0T 2021 Class

(Built at Wolverhampton, 1897-1905)

2021	2053	2086	2115
2022	2054	2088	2117
2023	2055	2089	2121
2025	2056	2090	2122
2026	2059	2091	2123
2027	2060	2092	2124
2029	2061	2093	2126
2030	2063	2094	2127
2031	2064	2095	2129
2032	2065	2096	2130
2033	2066	2097	2131
2034	2067	2098	2132
2035	2068	2099	2134
2037	2069	2100	2135
2038	2070	2101	2136
2039	2071	2102	2137
2040	2072	2104	2138
2042	2073	2106	2140
2043	2075	2107	2141
2044	2076	2108	2144
2045	2079	2109	2146
2047	2080	2110	2147
2048*	2081	2111	2148
2050	2082	2112	2150
2051	2083	2113	2151
2052	2085	2114	2152

2153	2155	2159	2160
2154	2156		

Total 110

0-6-0T BPGV Rly.

2162	2166	2168	2176
2165	2167		

(Class continued with No. 2192)

0-6-0T 2181 Class

(Built at Wolverhampton, 1899-1905)

2181	2184	2187	2189
2182	2185	2188	2190
2183	2186		

Total 10

0-6-0T BPGV Rly.

(Continued from No. 2176)

2192 Ashburnham
2193 Burry Port
2194 Kidwelly
2195
2196 Gwendraeth
2197 Pioneer
2198

Total 13

Note.—The ex-B.P.B.V.R. locomotives comprise several different types.

0-6-0 2251 Class

Introduced 1930.
Weights: Loco. 43 tons 8 cwt.
Tender 36 tons 15 cwt.
Pressure: 200 lb. Cyls.: 17½" × 24"
Driving Wheels: 5' 2" T.E.: 20,155 lb.

2200	2206	2212	2218
2201	2207	2213	2219
2202	2208	2214	2220
2203	2209	2215	2221
2204	2210	2216	2222
2205	2211	2217	2223

* Saddle tank. Remainder of classes pannier tanks.

2224	2243	2262	2281
2225	2244	2263	2282
2226	2245	2264	2283
2227	2246	2265	2284
2228	2247	2266	2285
2229	2248	2267	2286
2230	2249	2268	2287
2231	2250	2269	2288
2232	2251	2270	2289
2233	2252	2271	2290
2234	2253	2272	2291
2235	2254	2273	2292
2236	2255	2274	2293
2237	2256	2275	2294
2238	2257	2276	2295
2239	2258	2277	2296
2240	2259	2278	2297
2241	2260	2279	2298
2242	2261	2280	2299

(*Class continued with No. 3200*)

0-6-0 2301 Class*

Introduced 1883.
Weights : Loco. 36 tons 16 cwt.
Tender 34 tons 5 cwt.
Pressure : 180 lb. Cyls.: {17″ × 24″ / 17½″ × 24″}
Driving Wheels : 5′ 2″
T.E.: {17,120 lb. / 18,140 lb.}

2322	2401	2460	2534
2323	2407	2462	2537
2327	2408	2464	2538
2339	2409	2468	2541
2340	2411	2474	2543
2343	2414	2482	2551
2349	2426	2483	2556
2350	2431	2484	2568
2351	2444	2513	2572
2354	2445	2515	2573
2382	2449	2516	2578
2385	2452	2523	2579
2386	2458	2532	

Total 51

* Built at Wolverhampton.

"Aberdare" Class
2-6-0 2600 Class

Introduced 1900.
Weights : Loco. 56 tons 15 cwt.
Tender 47 tons 14 cwt.
Pressure : 200 lb. Cyls.: 18″ × 26″
Driving Wheels: 4′ 7½″ T.E.: 25,800 lb.

2620	2651	2655	2667

Total 4

0-6-0T 2700 Class

Introduced 1896.
Weight : 45 tons 13 cwt.
Pressure : 180 lb. Cyls.: 17½″ × 24″
Driving Wheels: 4′ 7½″ T.E.: 20,260 lb.

2702*	2719*	2754	2787
2704*	2721	2757	2790
2707*	2722	2760	2791
2708*	2738	2761	2792
2712*	2743	2771	2794
2713*	2744	2772	2798
2715*	2745	2780	2799
2716*	2753	2786	

Total 31

2-8-0 2800 Class

Introduced 1903.
Weights : Loco. {75 tons 10 cwt. / 76 tons 5 cwt.†}
Tender 40 tons 0 cwt.
Pressure : 225 lb. Cyls.: 18½″ × 30″
Driving Wheels: 4′ 7½″ T.E.: 35,380 lb.

2800	2811	2822	2833
2801	2812	2823	2834
2802	2813	2824	2835
2803	2814	2825	2836
2804	2815	2826	2837
2805	2816	2827	2838
2806	2817	2828	2839
2807	2818	2829	2840
2808	2819	2830	2841
2809	2820	2831	2842
2810	2821	2832	2843

† Nos. 2884-99 and 38XX series.

2844	2858	2872	2886
2845	2859	2873	2887
2846	2860	2874	2888
2847	2861	2875	2889
2848	2862	2876	2890
2849	2863	2877	2891
2850	2864	2878	2892
2851	2865	2879	2893
2852	2866	2880	2894
2853	2867	2881	2895
2854	2868	2882	2896
2855	2869	2883	2897
2856	2870	2884	2898
2857	2871	2885	2899

(Class continued with No. 3800)

"Saint" Class

4-6-0 2900 Class

Introduced 1902.
Weights : Loco. 72 tons 0 cwt.
Tender 40 tons 0 cwt.
Pressure : 225 lb. Cyls.: 18½" × 30"
Driving Wheels: 6' 8½" T.E.: 24,395 lb.

2902 Lady of the Lake
2903 Lady of Lyons
2906 Lady of Lynn
2908 Lady of Quality
2912 Saint Ambrose
2915 Saint Bartholomew
2920 Saint David
2924 Saint Helena
2926 Saint Nicholas
2927 Saint Patrick
2929 Saint Stephen
2930 Saint Vincent
2931 Arlington Court
2932 Ashton Court
2933 Bibury Court
2934 Butleigh Court
2936 Cefntilla Court
2937 Clevedon Court
2938 Corsham Court
2939 Croome Court
2940 Dorney Court
2941 Easton Court
2942 Fawley Court
2943 Hampton Court
2944 Highnam Court
2945 Hillingdon Court
2946 Langford Court
2947 Madresfield Court
2948 Stackpole Court
2949 Stanford Court
2950 Taplow Court
2951 Tawstock Court
2952 Twineham Court
2953 Titley Court
2954 Tockenham Court
2955 Tortworth Court
2979*Quentin Durward
2981*Ivanhoe
2987*Bride of Lammermoor

Total 39

* Converted from 4-4-2.

2-8-0 R.O.D. Class

Purchased from Govt. 1919.
Weights : Loco. 73 tons 11 cwt.
Tender 47 tons 14 cwt.
Pressure : 185 lb. Cyls.: 21" × 26"
Driving Wheels: 4' 8" T.E.: 32,200 lb.

3010	3020	3029	3040
3011	3022	3031	3041
3012	3023	3032	3042
3014	3024	3033	3043
3015	3025	3034	3044
3016	3026	3036	3047
3017	3028	3038	3048
3018			

Total 29

2-6-2T 3100 Class

Introduced 1938. Rebuilt from 3150 Class (Nos. 3173/56/81/55/79 respectively).
Weight : 81 tons 9 cwt.
Pressure : 225 lb. Cyls.: 18½" × 30"
Driving Wheels: 5' 3" T.E.: 31,170 lb.

3100	3102	3103	3104
3101			

Total 5

2-6-2T 3150 Class

Introduced 1907.
Weight : 81 tons 12 cwt.
Pressure : 200 lb. Cyls.: 18½″ × 30″
Driving Wheels: 5′ 8″ T.E.: 25,670 lb.

3150	3163	3172	3183
3151	3164	3174	3185
3153	3167	3176	3186
3154	3168	3177	3187
3157	3169	3178	3188
3159	3170	3180	3189
3160	3171	3182	3190
3161			

Total 29

0-6-0 2251 Class

(Class continued from 2299)

3200	3205	3210	3215
3201	3206	3211	3216
3202	3207	3212	3217
3203	3208	3213	3218
3204	3209	3214	3219

Total 120

"Bulldog" Class
4-4-0 3300 Class

Introduced 1898.
Weights : Loco. 51 tons 16 cwt.
Tender 40 tons 0 cwt.
Pressure : 200 lb. Cyls.: 18″ × 26″
Driving Wheels: 5′ 8″ T.E.: 21,060 lb.

3341 Blasius
3363 Alfred Baldwin
3364 Frank Bibby
3377
3382
3383
3386
3393 Australia
3401 Vancouver
3406 Calcutta
3407 Madras
3418 Sir Arthur Yorke
3419
3426
3432
3438
3444 Cormorant
3447 Jackdaw
3449 Nightingale
3450 Peacock
3451 Pelican
3453 Seagull
3454 Skylark
3455 Starling

Total 24

0-4-2T 517 Class

3574	3575

Total 2

2-4-0T 3500 Class

3561	3586	3588	3599
3582			

Total 5

0-6-0T 5700 Class

Introduced 1929.
Weight : 49 tons 0 cwt.
Pressure : 200 lb. Cyls.: 17½″ × 24″
Driving Wheels: 4′ 7½″ T.E.: 22,515 lb.

3600	3620	3640	3660
3601	3621	3641	3661
3602	3622	3642	3662
3603	3623	3643	3663
3604	3624	3644	3664
3605	3625	3645	3665
3606	3626	3646	3666
3607	3627	3647	3667
3608	3628	3648	3668
3609	3629	3649	3669
3610	3630	3650	3670
3611	3631	3651	3671
3612	3632	3652	3672
3613	3633	3653	3673
3614	3634	3654	3674
3615	3635	3655	3675
3616	3636	3656	3676
3617	3637	3657	3677
3618	3638	3658	3678
3619	3639	3659	3679

5700 Class—*continued*

3680	3710	3740	3770
3681	3711	3741	3771
3682	3712	3742	3772
3683	3713	3743	3773
3684	3714	3744	3774
3685	3715	3745	3775
3686	3716	3746	3776
3687	3717	3747	3777
3688	3718	3748	3778
3689	3719	3749	3779
3690	3720	3750	3780
3691	3721	3751	3781
3692	3722	3752	3782
3693	3723	3753	3783
3694	3724	3754	3784
3695	3725	3755	3785
3696	3726	3756	3786
3697	3727	3757	3787
3698	3728	3758	3788
3699	3729	3759	3789
3700	3730	3760	3790
3701	3731	3761	3791
3702	3732	3762	3792
3703	3733	3763	3793
3704	3734	3764	3794
3705	3735	3765	3795
3706	3736	3766	3796
3707	3737	3767	3797
3708	3738	3768	3798
3709	3739	3769	3799

(*Class continued with No. 4600*)

2-8-0 2800 Class

(*Class continued from 2899*)

3800	3811	3822	3833
3801	3812	3823	3834
3802	3813	3824	3835
3803	3814	3825	3836
3804	3815	3826	3837
3805	3816	3827	3838
3806	3817	3828	3839
3807	3818	3829	3840
3808	3819	3830	3841
3809	3820	3831	3842
3810	3821	3832	3843

3844	3850	3856	3862
3845	3851	3857	3863
3846	3852	3858	3864
3847	3853	3859	3865
3848	3854	3860	3866
3849	3855	3861	

Total 167

" Star " Class
4-6-0 (4 Cyl.) 4000 Class

Introduced 1907 (based on 4-4-2 prototype built 1906)
Weights : Loco. 75 tons 12 cwt.
Tender 46 tons 14 cwt.
Pressure : 225 lb. Cyls.: 15" × 26"
Driving Wheels: 6' 8½" T.E.: 27,800 lb.

4003 Lode Star
4007 Swallowfield Park
4012 Knight of the Thistle
4013 Knight of St. Patrick
4015 Knight of St. John
4017 Knight of Liége
4018 Knight of the Grand Cross
4019 Knight Templar
4020 Knight Commander
4021 British Monarch

4022	4025	4028
4023	4026	4030

4031 Queen Mary
4033 Queen Victoria
4034 Queen Adelaide
4035 Queen Charlotte
4036 Queen Elizabeth
4038 Queen Berengaria
4039 Queen Matilda
4040 Queen Boadicea
4041 Prince of Wales
4042 Prince Albert
4043 Prince Henry
4044 Prince George
4045 Prince John
4046 Princess Mary
4047 Princess Louise
4048 Princess Victoria
4049 Princess Maud
4050 Princess Alice
4051 Princess Helena

4000 Class—*continued*

4052 Princess Beatrice
4053 Princess Alexandra
4054 Princess Charlotte
4055 Princess Sophia
4056 Princess Margaret
4057 Princess Elizabeth
4058 Princess Augusta
4059 Princess Patricia
4060 Princess Eugénie
4061 Glastonbury Abbey
4062 Malmesbury Abbey

Total 46

"Castle" Class
4-6-0 (4 Cyl.) 4073 Class

Introduced 1923.
Weights: Loco. 79 tons 17 cwt.
Tender 46 tons 14 cwt.
Pressure: 225 lb. Cyls.: 16" × 26"
Driving Wheels: 6' 8½" T.E.: 31,625 lb.

100 A1 Lloyds
111 Viscount Churchill
4000 North Star
4016 The Somerset Light Infantry (Prince Albert's)
4032 Queen Alexandra
4037 The South Wales Borderers
4073 Caerphilly Castle
4074 Caldicot Castle
4075 Cardiff Castle
4076 Carmarthen Castle
4077 Chepstow Castle
4078 Pembroke Castle
4079 Pendennis Castle
4080 Powderham Castle
4081 Warwick Castle
4082 Windsor Castle
4083 Abbotsbury Castle
4084 Aberystwyth Castle
4085 Berkeley Castle
4086 Builth Castle
4087 Cardigan Castle
4088 Dartmouth Castle
4089 Donnington Castle
4090 Dorchester Castle
4091 Dudley Castle
4092 Dunraven Castle
4093 Dunster Castle
4094 Dynevor Castle
4095 Harlech Castle
4096 Highclere Castle
4097 Kenilworth Castle
4098 Kidwelly Castle
4099 Kilgerran Castle

(Class continued with No. 5000)

2-6-2T 5100 Class

Introduced 1929*
Weight: 78 tons 9 cwt.
Pressure: 200 lb. Cyls.: 18" × 30"
Driving Wheels: 5' 8" T.E.: 24,300 lb.

4100	4120	4140	4160
4101	4121	4141	4161
4102	4122	4142	4162
4103	4123	4143	4163
4104	4124	4144	4164
4105	4125	4145	4165
4106	4126	4146	4166
4107	4127	4147	4167
4108	4128	4148	4168
4109	4129	4149	4169
4110	4130	4150	4170†
4111	4131	4151	4171†
4112	4132	4152	4172†
4113	4133	4153	4173†
4114	4134	4154	4174†
4115	4135	4155	4175†
4116	4136	4156	4176†
4117	4137	4157	4177†
4118	4138	4158	4178†
4119	4139	4159	4179†

* Nos. 5100/11-48 modified from locomotives Nos. 3100/11-48 built 1905-6.

†To be constructed.

(Class continued with No. 5101)

2-8-0T 4200 Class

Introduced 1910.
Weight: 82 tons 2 cwt.
Pressure: 200 lb. Cyls.: 19" × 30"
Driving Wheels: 4' 7½" T.E.: 33,170 lb.

4200	4203	4207	4211
4201	4206	4208	4212

4200 Class—*continued*

4213	4237	4262	4282
4214	4238	4263	4283
4215	4241	4264	4284
4217	4242	4265	4285
4218	4243	4266	4286
4221	4246	4267	4287
4222	4247	4268	4288
4223	4248	4269	4289
4224	4250	4270	4290
4225	4251	4271	4291
4226	4252	4272	4292
4227	4253	4273	4293
4228	4254	4274	4294
4229	4255	4275	4295
4230	4256	4276	4296
4231	4257	4277	4297
4232	4258	4278	4298
4233	4259	4279	4299
4235	4260	4280	
4236	4261	4281	

(*Class continued with No.* 5200)

2-6-0 4300 Class

Introduced 1911.
Weights : Loco. { 65 tons 6 cwt.* / 62 tons 0 cwt.
Tender 40 tons 0 cwt.
Pressure : 200 lb. Cyls.: 18½″ × 30″
Driving Wheels: 5′ 8″ T.E.: 25,670 lb.

4303	4326	4358	4377
4318	4337	4375	4381

(*Class continued with No.* 5300)
* "93XX" series.

2-6-2T 4400 Class

Introduced 1904.
Weight : 56 tons 13 cwt.
Pressure : 180 lb. Cyls.: 17″ × 24″
Driving Wheels: 4′ 1½″ T.E.: 21,440 lb.

4400	4403	4406	4409
4401	4404	4407	4410
4402	4405	4408	

Total 11

2-6-2T 4500 Class

Introduced 1906.
Weight : { 57 tons.† / 61 tons 0 cwt.
Pressure : 200 lb. Cyls.: 17″ × 24″
Driving Wheels: 4′ 7½″ T.E.: 21,250 lb.

4500	4525	4550	4575
4501	4526	4551	4576
4502	4527	4552	4577
4503	4528	4553	4578
4504	4529	4554	4579
4505	4530	4555	4580
4506	4531	4556	4581
4507	4532	4557	4582
4508	4533	4558	4583
4509	4534	4559	4584
4510	4535	4560	4585
4511	4536	4561	4586
4512	4537	4562	4587
4513	4538	4563	4588
4514	4539	4564	4589
4515	4540	4565	4590
4516	4541	4566	4591
4517	4542	4567	4592
4518	4543	4568	4593
4519	4544	4569	4594
4520	4545	4570	4595
4521	4546	4571	4596
4522	4547	4572	4597
4523	4548	4573	4598
4524	4549	4574	4599

(*Class continued with No.* 5500)
† Nos. 4500-4574.

0-6-0T 5700 Class

(*Class continued from* 3799)

4600	4612	4624	4636
4601	4613	4625	4637
4602	4614	4626	4638
4603	4615	4627	4639
4604	4616	4628	4640
4605	4617	4629	4641
4606	4618	4630	4642
4607	4619	4631	4643
4608	4620	4632	4644
4609	4621	4633	4645
4610	4622	4634	4646
4611	4623	4635	4647

Right : " 1901 " Class 0-6-0ST No. 1925 (*cf.* No. 2012, page 57)

[*D. G. Carter*

Below : Ex-Rhymney 0-6-2T No. 63

[*P. L. Melvill*

Right : Ex-Rhymney -6-2T No. 44

[*H. C. Casserley*

[M. W. Earley

Above : " King " Class 4-6-0 No. 6024 *King Edward I*

Below : " County " Class 4-6-0 No. 1017 *County of Hereford* [F. F. Moss

Top : " Castle " Class 4-6-0 No. 4091 *Dudley Castle* [*W. J. Reynolds*
Centre : " Castle " Class 4-6-0 No. 5081 *Lockheed-Hudson* with high-sided tender [*P. Ransome-Wallis*
Bottom : " Star " Class 4-6-0 No. 4013 *Knight of St. Patrick* [*E. Treacy*

Above : Down Weston-super-Mare express near Hayes, headed by one of the famous " City " Class, now extinct, No. 3441 *City of Winchester* [*H. Gordon Tidey*
Below . A blue-liveried " King " Class 4-6-0, No. 6009 *King Charles II*, speeds westward past Twyford with the " Cornish Riviera Express " [*E. C. Ive*

RN
'E
R
9

Above : " Star " Class 4-6-0 No. 4021, bearing its former name *King Edward*, near Twyford with a down West of England express [*H. Gordon Tidey*

Below : " County " Class 4-6-0 No. 1021 *County of Montgomery* takes water from Goring troughs. The train is an up Bristol express [*E. C Ive*

" 4300 " Class 2-6-0 No. 6325 [B. V. Franey

" 4300 " Class 2-6-0 No. 9304 (with side windowcab) [H. C. Casserley

" 2600 " Class 2-6-0 No. 2620 [F F. Moss

" Saint " Class 4-6-0 No. 2939 *Croome Court* [W. J. Reynolds

" Manor " Class 4-6-0 No. 7808 *Cookham Manor* [H. C. Casserley

" Grange " Class 4-6-0 No. 6877 *Llanfair Grange* [M. W. Earley

Above : "7200" Class 2-8-2T No. 7240

[*H. C. Casserley*

Left : "9400" Class 0-6-0PT No. 9407

[*R. Jelves*

Below : "4200" Class 2-8-0T No. 4225

[*H. C. Casserley*

5700 Class— *continued*

4648	4661	4674	4687
4649	4662	4675	4688
4650	4663	4676	4689
4651	4664	4677	4690
4652	4665	4678	4691
4653	4666	4679	4692
4654	4667	4680	4693
4655	4668	4681	4694
4656	4669	4682	4695
4657	4670	4683	4696
4658	4671	4684	4697
4659	4672	4685	4698
4660	4673	4686	4699

(*Class continued with No. 5700*)

2-8-0 4700 Class

Introduced 1919.
Weights : Loco. 82 tons 0 cwt.
Tender 16 tons 14 cwt.
Pressure : 225 lb. Cyls.: 19" × 30"
Driving Wheels: 5' 8" T.E.: 30,460 lb.

4700	4703	4705	4707
4701	4704	4706	4708
4702			

Total 9

"Hall" Class
4-6-0 4900 Class

Introduced 1928.
Weights : Loco. 75 tons 0 cwt.
Tender 46 tons 14 cwt.
Pressure : 225 lb. Cyls.: $18\frac{1}{2}$" × 30"
Driving Wheels: 6' 0" T.E.: 27,275 lb.

4900 Saint Martin
4901 Adderley Hall
4902 Aldenham Hall
4903 Astley Hall
4904 Binnegar Hall
4905 Barton Hall
4906 Bradfield Hall
4907 Broughton Hall
4908 Broome Hall
4909 Blakesley Hall
4910 Blaisdon Hall
4912 Berrington Hall
4913 Baglan Hall
4914 Cranmore Hall
4915 Condover Hall
4916 Crumlin Hall
4917 Crosswood Hall
4918 Dartington Hall
4919 Donnington Hall
4920 Dumbleton Hall
4921 Eaton Hall
4922 Enville Hall
4923 Evenley Hall
4924 Eydon Hall
4925 Eynsham Hall
4926 Fairleigh Hall
4927 Farnborough Hall
4928 Gatacre Hall
4929 Goytrey Hall
4930 Hagley Hall
4931 Hanbury Hall
4932 Hatherton Hall
4933 Himley Hall
4934 Hindlip Hall
4935 Ketley Hall
4936 Kinlet Hall
4937 Lanelay Hall
4938 Liddington Hall
4939 Littleton Hall
4940 Ludford Hall
4941 Llangedwyn Hall
4942 Maindy Hall
4943 Marrington Hall
4944 Middleton Hall
4945 Milligan Hall
4946 Moseley Hall
4947 Nanhoran Hall
4948 Northwick Hall
4949 Packwood Hall
4950 Patshull Hall
4951 Pendeford Hall
4952 Peplow Hall
4953 Pitchford Hall
4954 Plaish Hall
4955 Plaspower Hall
4956 Plowden Hall
4957 Postlip Hall
4958 Priory Hall
4959 Purley Hall
4960 Pyle Hall
4961 Pyrland Hall

4900 Class—*continued*

4962 Ragley Hall
4963 Rignall Hall
4964 Rodwell Hall
4965 Rood Ashton Hall
4966 Shakenhurst Hall
4967 Shirenewton Hall
4968 Shotton Hall
4969 Shrugborough Hall
4970 Sketty Hall
4971 Stanway Hall
4972 Saint Brides Hall
4973 Sweeney Hall
4974 Talgarth Hall
4975 Umberslade Hall
4976 Warfield Hall
4977 Watcombe Hall
4978 Westwood Hall
4979 Wootton Hall
4980 Wrottesley Hall
4981 Abberley Hall
4982 Acton Hall
4983 Albert Hall
4984 Albrighton Hall
4985 Allesley Hall
4986 Aston Hall
4987 Brockley Hall
4988 Bulwell Hall
4989 Cherwell Hall
4990 Clifton Hall
4991 Cobham Hall
4992 Crosby Hall
4993 Dalton Hall
4994 Downton Hall
4995 Easton Hall
4996 Eden Hall
4997 Elton Hall
4998 Eyton Hall
4999 Gopsal Hall

(*Class continued with No.* 5900)

"Castle" Class
4-6-0 (4 Cyl.) 4073 Class

(*Continued from* 4099)

5000 Launceston Castle
5001 Llandovery Castle
5002 Ludlow Castle
5003 Lulworth Castle
5004 Llanstephan Castle
5005 Manorbier Castle
5006 Tregenna Castle
5007 Rougemont Castle
5008 Raglan Castle
5009 Shrewsbury Castle
5010 Restormel Castle
5011 Tintagel Castle
5012 Berry Pomeroy Castle
5013 Abergavenny Castle
5014 Goodrich Castle
5015 Kingswear Castle
5016 Montgomery Castle
5017 St. Donats Castle
5018 St. Mawes Castle
5019 Treago Castle
5020 Trematon Castle
5021 Whittington Castle
5022 Wigmore Castle
5023 Brecon Castle
5024 Carew Castle
5025 Chirk Castle
5026 Criccieth Castle
5027 Farleigh Castle
5028 Llantilio Castle
5029 Nunney Castle
5030 Shirburn Castle
5031 Totnes Castle
5032 Usk Castle
5033 Broughton Castle
5034 Corfe Castle
5035 Coity Castle
5036 Lyonshall Castle
5037 Monmouth Castle
5038 Morlais Castle
5039 Rhuddlan Castle
5040 Stokesay Castle
5041 Tiverton Castle
5042 Winchester Castle
5043 Earl of Mount Edgcumbe
5044 Earl of Dunraven
5045 Earl of Dudley
5046 Earl Cawdor
5047 Earl of Dartmouth
5048 Earl of Devon
5049 Earl of Plymouth

4073 Class—*continued*

5050 Earl of St. Germans
5051 Earl Bathurst
5052 Earl of Radnor
5053 Earl Cairns
5054 Earl of Ducie
5055 Earl of Eldon
5056 Earl of Powis
5057 Earl Waldegrave
5058 Earl of Clancarty
5059 Earl St. Aldwyn
5060 Earl of Berkeley
5061 Earl of Birkenhead
5062 Earl of Shaftesbury
5063 Earl Baldwin
5064 Bishop's Castle
5065 Newport Castle
5066 Wardour Castle
5067 St. Fagans Castle
5068 Beverston Castle
5069 Isambard Kingdom Brunel
5070 Sir Daniel Gooch
5071 Spitfire
5072 Hurricane
5073 Blenheim
5074 Hampden
5075 Wellington
5076 Gladiator
5077 Fairey Battle
5078 Beaufort
5079 Lysander
5080 Defiant
5081 Lockheed-Hudson
5082 Swordfish
5083 Bath Abbey
5084 Reading Abbey
5085 Evesham Abbey
5086 Viscount Horne
5087 Tintern Abbey
5088 Llanthony Abbey
5089 Westminster Abbey
5090 Neath Abbey
5091 Cleeve Abbey
5092 Tresco Abbey
5093 Upton Castle
5094 Tretower Castle
5095 Barbury Castle
5096 Bridgwater Castle
5097 Sarum Castle
5098 Clifford Castle
5099 Compton Castle

(*Class continued with No. 7000*)

2-6-2T 5100 Class

(*Continued from 4179*)

5101	5137	5160	5180
5102	5138	5161	5181
5103	5139	5162	5182
5104	5140	5163	5183
5105	5141	5164	5184
5106	5142	5165	5185
5107	5143	5166	5186
5108	5144	5167	5187
5109	5147	5168	5188
5110	5148	5169	5189
5112	5150	5170	5190
5113	5151	5171	5191
5114	5152	5172	5192
5122	5153	5173	5193
5125	5154	5174	5194
5129	5155	5175	5195
5132	5156	5176	5196
5134	5157	5177	5197
5135	5158	5178	5198
5136	5159	5179	5199†

Total 160

2-8-0T 4200 Class

(*Continued from 4299*)

5200	5207	5214	5221
5201	5208	5215	5222
5202	5209	5216	5223
5203	5210	5217	5224
5204	5211	5218	5225
5205	5212	5219	5226
5206	5213	5220	5227

† Including 10 to be constructed.

4200 Class—*continued*

5228	5238	5247	5256
5229	5239	5248	5257
5230	5240	5249	5258
5231	5241	5250	5259
5232	5242	5251	5260
5233	5243	5252	5261
5234	5244	5253	5262
5235	5245	5254	5263
5236	5246	5255	5264
5237			

Total 151

2-6-0 4300 Class

(Continued from 4381)

5300	5326	5353	5378
5303	5327	5355	5379
5305	5328	5356	5380
5306	5330	5357	5381
5307	5331	5358	5382
5309	5332	5359	5384
5310	5333	5360	5385
5311	5334	5361	5386
5312	5335	5362	5388
5313	5336	5364	5390
3514	5337	5365	5391
5315	5338	5367	5392
5316	5339	5368	5393
5317	5341	5369	5394
5318	5344	5370	5395
5319	5345	5371	5396
5321	5346	5372	5397
5322	5347	5373	5398
5323	5348	5375	5399
5324	5350	5376	
5325	5351	5377	

(Class continued with No. 6300)

0-6-0T 5400 Class

Introduced 1931.
Weight : 46 tons 12 cwt.
Pressure : 165 lb. Cyls.: $16\frac{1}{2}'' \times 24''$
Driving Wheels: 5′ 2″ T.E.: 14,780 lb.

FITTED FOR AUTO TRAIN WORKING

5400	5401	5402	5403
5404	5410	5416	5422
5405	5411	5417	5423
5406	5412	5418	5424
5407	5413	5419	
5408	5414	5420	
5409	5415	5421	

Total 25

2-6-2T 4500 Class

(Continued from 4599)

5500	5519	5538	5557
5501	5520	5539	5558
5502	5521	5540	5559
5503	5522	5541	5560
5504	5523	5542	5561
5505	5524	5543	5562
5506	5525	5544	5563
5507	5526	5545	5564
5508	5527	5546	5565
5509	5528	5547	5566
5510	5529	5548	5567
5511	5530	5549	5568
5512	5531	5550	5569
5513	5532	5551	5570
5514	5533	5552	5571
5515	5534	5553	5572
5516	5535	5554	5573
5517	5536	5555	5574
5518	5537	5556	

Total 175

0-6-2T 5600 Class

Introduced 1924.
Weight : 68 tons 12 cwt.
Pressure : 200 lb. Cyls.: $18'' \times 26''$
Driving Wheels: 4′ $7\frac{1}{2}''$ T.E.: 25,800 lb.

5600	5608	5616	5624
5601	5609	5617	5625
5602	5610	5618	5626
5603	5611	5619	5627
5604	5612	5620	5628
5605	5613	5621	5629
5606	5614	5622	5630
5607	5615	5623	5631

5600 Class—*continued*

5632	5649	5666	5683
5633	5650	5667	5684
5634	5651	5668	5685
5635	5652	5669	5686
5636	5653	5670	5687
5637	5654	5671	5688
5638	5655	5672	5689
5639	5656	5673	5690
5640	5657	5674	5691
5641	5658	5675	5692
5642	5659	5676	5693
5643	5660	5677	5694
5644	5661	5678	5695
5645	5662	5679	5696
5646	5663	5680	5697
5647	5664	5681	5698
5648	5665	5682	5699

(Class continued with No. 6600)

0-6-0T 5700 Class

Introduced 1929.
Weight: 49 tons 0 cwt.
Pressure: 200 lb. Cyls.: $17\frac{1}{2}'' \times 24''$
Driving Wheels: $4'\ 7\frac{1}{2}''$ T.E.: 22,515 lb.

(Continued from 4699)

5700	5719	5738	5757
5701	5720	5739	5758
5702	5721	5740	5759
5703	5722	5741	5760
5704	5723	5742	5761
5705	5724	5743	5762
5706	5725	5744	5763
5707	5726	5745	5764
5708	5727	5746	5765
5709	5728	5747	5766
5710	5729	5748	5767
5711	5730	5749	5768
5712	5731	5750	5769
5713	5732	5751	5770
5714	5733	5752	5771
5715	5734	5753	5772
5716	5735	5754	5773
5717	5736	5755	5774
5718	5737	5756	5775
5776	5782	5788	5794
5777	5783	5789	5795
5778	5784	5790	5796
5779	5785	5791	5797
5780	5786	5792	5798
5781	5787	5793	5799

(Class continued with No. 6700)

0-4-2T 1400 Class

NOT FITTED FOR AUTO TRAIN WORKING

(Continued from 1474)

5800	5805	5810	5815
5801	5806	5811	5816
5802	5807	5812	5817
5803	5808	5813	5818
5804	5809	5814	5819

Total 95

"Hall" Class
4-6-0 4900 Class

(Continued from 4999)

5900 Hinderton Hall
5901 Hazel Hall
5902 Howick Hall
5903 Keele Hall
5904 Kelham Hall
5905 Knowsley Hall
5906 Lawton Hall
5907 Marble Hall
5908 Moreton Hall
5909 Newton Hall
5910 Park Hall
5911 Preston Hall
5912 Queen's Hall
5913 Rushton Hall
5914 Ripon Hall
5915 Trentham Hall
5916 Trinity Hall
5917 Westminster Hall
5918 Walton Hall
5919 Worsley Hall
5920 Wycliffe Hall
5921 Bingley Hall
5922 Caxton Hall

4900 Class—*continued*

5923 Colston Hall
5924 Dinton Hall
5925 Eastcote Hall
5926 Grotrian Hall
5927 Guild Hall
5928 Haddon Hall
5929 Hanham Hall
5930 Hannington Hall
5931 Hatherley Hall
5932 Haydon Hall
5933 Kingsway Hall
5934 Kneller Hall
5935 Norton Hall
5936 Oakley Hall
5937 Stanford Hall
5938 Stanley Hall
5939 Tangley Hall
5940 Whitbourne Hall
5941 Campion Hall
5942 Doldowlod Hall
5943 Elmdon Hall
5944 Ickenham Hall
5945 Leckhampton Hall
5946 Marwell Hall
5947 Saint Benet's Hall
5948 Siddington Hall
5949 Trematon Hall
5950 Wardley Hall
5951 Clyffe Hall
5952 Cogan Hall
5953 Dunley Hall
5954 Faendre Hall
5955 Garth Hall
5956 Horsley Hall
5957 Hutton Hall
5958 Knolton Hall
5959 Mawley Hall
5960 Saint Edmund Hall
5961 Toynbee Hall
5962 Wantage Hall
5963 Wimpole Hall
5964 Wolseley Hall
5965 Woollas Hall
5966 Ashford Hall
5967 Bickmarsh Hall
5968 Cory Hall
5969 Honington Hall
5970 Hengrave Hall
5971 Merevale Hall
5972 Olton Hall
5973 Rolleston Hall
5974 Wallsworth Hall
5975 Winslow Hall
5976 Ashwicke Hall
5977 Beckford Hall
5978 Bodinnick Hall
5979 Cruckton Hall
5980 Dingley Hall
5981 Frensham Hall
5982 Harrington Hall
5983 Henley Hall
5984 Linden Hall
5985 Mostyn Hall
5986 Arbury Hall
5987 Brocket Hall
5988 Bostock Hall
5989 Cransley Hall
5990 Durford Hall
5991 Gresham Hall
5992 Horton Hall
5993 Kirby Hall
5994 Roydon Hall
5995 Wick Hall
5996 Mytton Hall
5997 Sparkford Hall
5998 Trevor Hall
5999 Wollaton Hall

(*Class continued with No. 6900*)

"King" Class
4-6-0 (4 Cyl.) 6000 Class

Introduced 1927.
Weights : Loco. 89 tons 0 cwt.
Tender 46 tons 14 cwt.
Pressure : 250 lb. Cyls.: $16\frac{1}{4}'' \times 28''$
Driving Wheels: 6' 6" T.E.: 40,300 lb.

6000 King George V
6001 King Edward VII
6002 King William IV
6003 King George IV
6004 King George III
6005 King George II
6006 King George I
6007 King William III
6008 King James II

6000 Class—*continued*

6009 King Charles II
6010 King Charles I
6011 King James I
6012 King Edward VI
6013 King Henry VIII
6014 King Henry VII
6015 King Richard III
6016 King Edward V
6017 King Edward IV
6018 King Henry VI
6019 King Henry V
6020 King Henry IV
6021 King Richard II
6022 King Edward III
6023 King Edward II
6024 King Edward I
6025 King Henry III
6026 King John
6027 King Richard I
6028 King George VI
6029 King Edward VIII

Total 30

2-6-2T 6100 Class

Introduced 1931.
Weight : 78 tons 9 cwt.
Pressure : 225 lb. Cyls.: 18″ × 30″
Driving Wheels: 5′ 8″ T.E.: 27,340 lb.

6100	6118	6136	6153
6101	6119	6137	6154
6102	6120	6138	6155
6103	6121	6139	6156
6104	6122	6140	6157
6105	6123	6141	6158
6106	6124	6142	6159
6107	6125	6143	6160
6108	6126	6144	6161
6109	6127	6145	6162
6110	6128	6146	6163
6111	6129	6147	6164
6112	6130	6148	6165
6113	6131	6149	6166
6114	6132	6150	6167
6115	6133	6151	6168
6116	6134	6152	6169
6117	6135		

Total 70

2-6-0 4300 Class

(*Continued from 5399*)

6300	6326	6351	6376
6301	6327	6352	6377
6302	6328	6353	6378
6303	6329	6354	6379
6304	6330	6355	6380
6305	6331	6356	6381
6306	6332	6357	6382
6307	6333	6358	6383
6308	6334	6359	6384
6309	6335	6360	6385
6310	6336	6361	6386
6311	6337	6362	6387
6312	6338	6363	6388
6313	6339	6364	6389
6314	6340	6365	6390
6316	6341	6366	6391
6317	6342	6367	6392
6318	6343	6368	6393
6319	6344	6369	6394
6320	6345	6370	6395
6321	6346	6371	6396
6322	6347	6372	6397
6323	6348	6373	6398
6324	6349	6374	6399
6325	6350	6375	

(*Class continued with No. 7300*)

0-6-0T 6400 Class

Introduced 1931.
Weight : 45 tons 12 cwt.
Pressure : 165 lb. Cyls.: 16½″ × 24″
Driving Wheels: 4′ 7½″ T.E.: 16,510 lb.

FITTED FOR AUTO TRAIN WORKING

6400	6410	6420	6430
6401	6411	6421	6431
6402	6412	6422	6432
6403	6413	6423	6433
6404	6414	6424	6434
6405	6415	6425	6435
6406	6416	6426	6436
6407	6417	6427	6437
6408	6418	6428	6438
6409	6419	6429	6439

Total 40

0-6-2T 5600 Class

(Continued from 5699)

6600	6625	6650	6675
6601	6626	6651	6676
6602	6627	6652	6677
6603	6628	6653	6678
6604	6629	6654	6679
6605	6630	6655	6680
6606	6631	6656	6681
6607	6632	6657	6682
6608	6633	6658	6683
6609	6634	6659	6684
6610	6635	6660	6685
6611	6636	6661	6686
6612	6637	6662	6687
6613	6638	6663	6688
6614	6639	6664	6689
6615	6640	6665	6690
6616	6641	6666	6691
6617	6642	6667	6692
6618	6643	6668	6693
6619	6644	6669	6694
6620	6645	6670	6695
6621	6646	6671	6696
6622	6647	6672	6697
6623	6648	6673	6698
6624	6649	6674	6699

Total 200

0-6-0T 5700 Class

Note.—Nos. 6700-69 differ from remainder of 5700 class in that they are fitted with vacuum brake equipment.

(Continued from 5799)

6700	6712	6724	6736
6701	6713	6725	6737
6702	6714	6726	6738
6703	6715	6727	6739
6704	6716	6728	6740
6705	6717	6729	6741
6706	6718	6730	6742
6707	6719	6731	6743
6708	6720	6732	6744
6709	6721	6733	6745
6710	6722	6734	6746
6711	6723	6735	6747

6748	6754	6760	6766
6749	6755	6761	6767
6750	6756	6762	6768
6751	6757	6763	6769
6752	6758	6764	
6753	6759	6765	

(Class continued with No. 7700)

" Grange " Class
4-6-0 6800 Class

Introduced 1936.
Weights: Loco. 74 tons 0 cwt.
Tender 40 tons 0 cwt.
Pressure: 225 lb. Cyls.: $18\frac{1}{2}'' \times 30''$
Driving Wheels: 5′ 8″ T.E. 28,875 lb

6800 Arlington Grange
6801 Aylburton Grange
6802 Bampton Grange
6803 Bucklebury Grange
6804 Brockington Grange
6805 Broughton Grange
6806 Blackwell Grange
6807 Birchwood Grange
6808 Beenham Grange
6809 Burghclere Grange
6810 Blakemere Grange
6811 Cranbourne Grange
6812 Chesford Grange
6813 Eastbury Grange
6814 Enbourne Grange
6815 Frilford Grange
6816 Frankton Grange
6817 Gwenddwr Grange
6818 Hardwick Grange
6819 Highnam Grange
6820 Kingstone Grange
6821 Leaton Grange
6822 Manton Grange
6823 Oakley Grange
6824 Ashley Grange
6825 Llanvair Grange
6826 Nannerth Grange
6827 Llanfrechfa Grange
6828 Trellech Grange
6829 Burmington Grange

Top : " Hal " Class 4-6-0 No. 4900 *Saint Martin* (note lower pitch of boiler and detail modifications compared with No. 4946 (centre)

[*M. W. Earley*

Centre : " Hall " Class 4-6-0 No. 4946 *Moseley Hall*

[*W. Beckerlegge*

Bottom : " Modified Hall " Class 4-6-0 No. 6996 *Blackwell Hall*

[*M. W. Earley*

Above :
''2251''
Class 0-6-0
No. 2282
[*B. V. Franey*

Left :
''2301''
Class 0-6-0
No. 2572
[*P. Ransome-Wallis*

Below :
Ex-Cambrian
0-6-0 No. 887
[*H. C. Casserley*

Above : R.O.D. Class 2-8-0 No. 3031
[*M. W. Earley*

Right : " 2800 " Class 2-8-0 No. 2818
[*P. Ransome-Wallis*

Below : " 4700 " Class 2-8-0 No 4706
[*B. V. Franey*

Diesel Railcar No. 11, which incorporates W.C. facilities [S. C. Townroe

Diesel Railcar No. 4, which carries buffet as well as W. C. facilities [H. C. Casserley

6800 Class—*continued*

6830 Buckenhill Grange
6831 Bearley Grange
6832 Brockton Grange
6833 Calcot Grange
6834 Dummer Grange
6835 Eastham Grange
6836 Estevarney Grange
6837 Forthampton Grange
6838 Goodmoor Grange
6839 Hewell Grange
6840 Hazeley Grange
6841 Marlas Grange
6842 Nunhold Grange
6843 Poulton Grange
6844 Penydd Grange
6845 Paviland Grange
6846 Ruckley Grange
6847 Tidmarsh Grange
6848 Toddington Grange
6849 Walton Grange
6850 Cleeve Grange
6851 Hurst Grange
6852 Headbourne Grange
6853 Morehampton Grange
6854 Roundhill Grange
6855 Saighton Grange
6856 Stowe Grange
6857 Tudor Grange
6858 Woolston Grange
6859 Yiewsley Grange
6860 Aberporth Grange
6861 Crynant Grange
6862 Derwent Grange
6863 Dolhywel Grange
6864 Dymock Grange
6865 Hopton Grange
6866 Morfa Grange
6867 Peterston Grange
6868 Penrhos Grange
6869 Resolven Grange
6870 Bodicote Grange
6871 Bourton Grange
6872 Crawley Grange
6873 Caradoc Grange
6874 Haughton Grange
6875 Hindford Grange
6876 Kingsland Grange
6877 Llanfair Grange
6878 Longford Grange
6879 Overton Grange

Total 80

"Hall" Class

4-6-0 4900 Class

(*Continued from* 5999)

6900 Abney Hall
6901 Arley Hall
6902 Butlers Hall
6903 Belmont Hall
6904 Charfield Hall
6905 Claughton Hall
6906 Chicheley Hall
6907 Davenham Hall
6908 Downham Hall
6909 Frewin Hall
6910 Gossington Hall
6911 Holker Hall
6912 Helmster Hall
6913 Levens Hall
6914 Langton Hall
6915 Mursley Hall
6916 Misterton Hall
6917 Oldlands Hall
6918 Sandon Hall
6919 Tylney Hall
6920 Barningham Hall
6921 Borwick Hall
6922 Burton Hall
6923 Croxteth Hall
6924 Grantley Hall
6925 Hackness Hall
6926 Holkham Hall
6927 Lilford Hall
6928 Underley Hall
6929 Whorlton Hall
6930 Aldersey Hall
6931 Aldborough Hall
6932 Burwarton Hall
6933 Birtles Hall
6934 Beachamwell Hall
6935 Browsholme Hall

4900 Class—*continued*

6936 Breccles Hall
6937 Conyngham Hall
6938 Corndean Hall
6939 Calveley Hall
6940 Didlington Hall
6941 Fillongley Hall
6942 Eshton Hall
6943 Farnley Hall
6944 Fledborough Hall
6945 Glasfryn Hall
6946 Heatherden Hall
6947 Helmingham Hall
6948 Holbrooke Hall
6949 Haberfield Hall
6950 Kingsthorpe Hall
6951 Impney Hall
6952 Kimberley Hall
6953 Leighton Hall
6954 Lotherton Hall
6955 Lydcott Hall
6956 Mottram Hall
6957 Norcliffe Hall
6958 Oxburgh Hall

Total 258

" Modified Hall " Class*
4-6-0 6959 Class

Introduced 1944.
Weights : Loco. 75 tons 16 cwt.
Tender 46 tons 14 cwt.
Pressure : 225 lb. Cyls.: 18½" × 30"
Driving Wheels: 6' 0" T.E.: 27,275 lb.

6959 Peatling Hall
6960 Raveningham Hall
6961 Stedham Hall
6962 Soughton Hall
6963 Throwley Hall
6964 Thornbridge Hall
6965 Thirlestaine Hall
6966 Witchingham Hall
6967 Willesley Hall
6968 Woodcock Hall
6969 Wraysbury Hall
6970 Whaddon Hall
6971 Athelhampton Hall
6972 Beningbrough Hall
6973 Bricklehampton Hall
6974 Bryngwyn Hall
6975 Capesthorne Hall
6976 Graythwaite Hall
6977 Grundisburgh Hall
6978 Haroldstone Hall
6979 Helperly Hall
6980 Llanrumney Hall
6981 Marbury Hall
6982 Melmerby Hall
6983 Otterington Hall
6984 Owsden Hall
6985 Parwick Hall
6986 Rydal Hall
6987 Sherrington Hall
6988 Swithland Hall
6989 Wightwick Hall
6990 Witherslack Hall
6991 Acton Burnell Hall
6992 Arborfield Hall
6993 Arthog Hall
6994 Baggrave Hall
6995 Benthall Hall
6996 Blackwell Hall
6997 Bryn-Ivor Hall
6998 Burton Agnes Hall
6999 Capel Dewi Hall

(*Class continued with No.* 7900)

" Castle " Class
4-6-0 7000 Class

(Fitted with mechanical lubricators)
(*Continued from* 5099)

7000 Viscount Portal
7001 Sir James Milne
7002 Devizes Castle
7003 Elmley Castle
7004 Eastnor Castle
7005 Lamphey Castle

* With redesigned boiler, increased superheating surface, "one-piece" main frame, plate-frame bogie and cylinders individually cast.

Class **7000**—*continued*

7006 Lydford Castle
7007 Great Western
7008 Swansea Castle
7009 Athelney Castle
7010 Avondale Castle
7011 Banbury Castle
7012 Barry Castle
7013 Bristol Castle
7014 Caerhays Castle
7015 Carn Brea Castle
7016 Chester Castle
7017 G. J. Churchward
7018 Drysllwyn Castle
7019 Fowey Castle
7020 Gloucester Castle
7021 Haverfordwest Castle
7022 Hereford Castle
7023 Penrice Castle
7024 Powis Castle
7025 Sudeley Castle
7026 Tenby Castle
7027 Thornbury Castle
7028*
7029*
7030*
7031*
7032*
7033*
7034*
7035*
7036*
7037*

Total 161

* To be constructed. Names not yet announced.

2-8-2T — 7200 Class

Introduced 1934, rebuilt from 4200 class 2-8-0T.
Weight: 92 tons 2 cwt.
Pressure: 200 lb. Cyls.: 19"×30"
Driving Wheels: 4' 7½" T.E.: 33,170 lb.

7200	7203	7206	7209
7201	7204	7207	7210
7202	7205	7208	7211

7212	7223	7234	7245
7213	7224	7235	7246
7214	7225	7236	7247
7215	7226	7237	7248
7216	7227	7238	7249
7217	7228	7239	7250
7218	7229	7240	7251
7219	7230	7241	7252
7220	7231	7242	7253
7221	7232	7243	
7222	7233	7244	

Total 54

2-6-0 — 4300 Class

(Continued from 6399)

7300	7306	7312	7318
7301	7307	7313	7319
7302	7308	7314	7320
7303	7309	7315	7321
7304	7310	7316	
7305	7311	7317	

(Class continued with No. 9300)

0-6-0T — 7400 Class

Introduced 1936.
Weight: 45 tons 9 cwt.
Pressure: 180 lb. Cyls.: 16½"×24"
Driving Wheels: 4' 7½" T.E.: 18,010 lb.

7400	7413	7426	7438
7401	7414	7427	7439
7402	7415	7428	7440
7403	7416	7429	7441
7404	7417	7430	7442
7405	7418	7431	7443
7406	7419	7432	7444
7407	7420	7433	7445
7408	7421	7434	7446
7409	7422	7435	7447
7410	7423	7436	7448
7411	7424	7437	7449
7412	7425		

Total 50

NOTE.—Not all this Class are yet in service.

0-6-0T 5700 Class

(Continued from 6759)

7700	7725	7750	7775
7701	7726	7751	7776
7702	7727	7752	7777
7703	7728	7753	7778
7704	7729	7754	7779
7705	7730	7755	7780
7706	7731	7756	7781
7707	7732	7757	7782
7708	7733	7758	7783
7709	7734	7759	7784
7710	7735	7760	7785
7711	7736	7761	7786
7712	7737	7762	7787
7713	7738	7763	7788
7714	7739	7764	7789
7715	7740	7765	7790
7716	7741	7766	7791
7717	7742	7767	7792
7718	7743	7768	7793
7719	7744	7769	7794
7720	7745	7770	7795
7721	7746	7771	7796
7722	7747	7772	7797
7723	7748	7773	7798
7724	7749	7774	7799

(Class continued with No. 8700)

" Manor " Class
4-6-0 7800 Class

Introduced 1938.
Weights : Loco. 68 tons 18 cwt.
Tender 40 tons 0 cwt.
Pressure : 225 lb. Cyls.: 18" × 30"
Driving Wheels: 5' 8" T.E.: 27,340 lb.

7800 Torquay Manor
7801 Anthony Manor
7802 Bradley Manor
7803 Barcote Manor
7804 Baydon Manor
7805 Broome Manor
7806 Cockington Manor
7807 Compton Manor
7808 Cookham Manor
7809 Childrey Manor
7810 Draycott Manor
7811 Dunley Manor
7812 Erlestoke Manor
7813 Freshford Manor
7814 Fringford Manor
7815 Fritwell Manor
7816 Frilsham Manor
7817 Garsington Manor
7818 Granville Manor
7819 Hinton Manor
7820*
7821*
7822*
7823*
7824*
7825*
7826*
7827*
7828*
7829*

Total 20

* To be constructed. Names not yet announced.

" Modified Hall " Class
4-6-0 6959 Class

(Continued from No. 6999)

7900 St. Peter's Hall
7901 Dodington Hall
7902 Eaton Mascot Hall
7903 Foremarke Hall
7904 Fountains Hall
7905 Fowey Hall
7906 Fron Hall
7907 Hart Hall
7908 Henshall Hall
7909 Heveningham Hall
7910 Hown Hall
7911 Lady Margaret Hall
7912 Little Linford Hall
7913 Little Wyrley Hall
7914 Lleweni Hall
7915 Mere Hall
7916 Mobberley Hall
7917 North Aston Hall
7918 Rhose Wood Hall
7919 Runter Hall

6959 Class—*continued*

7920 Coney Hall
7921 Salesbury Hall
7922 Salford Hall
7923 Speke Hall
7924 Thornycroft Hall
7925 Westol Hall
7926 Willey Hall
7927 Willington Hall
7928 Wolf Hall
7929 Wyke Hall

Total 71

Note.—Not all of these engines are yet in service.

2-6-2T 8100 Class

Introduced 1938, rebuilt from 5100 class
Weight : 76 tons 11 cwt.
Pressure : 225 lb. Cyls.: 18″×30″
Driving Wheels: 5′ 6″ T.E.: 28,165 lb.

8100	8103	8106	8108
8101	8104	8107	8109
8102	8105		

Total 10

0-6-0T 5700 Class

(*Continued from 7799*)

8700	8720	8740	8760
8701	8721	8741	8761
8702	8722	8742	8762
8703	8723	8743	8763
8704	8724	8744	8764
8705	8725	8745	8765
8706	8726	8746	8766
8707	8727	8747	8767
8708	8728	8748	8768
8709	8729	8749	8769
8710	8730	8750	8770
8711	8731	8751	8771
8712	8732	8752	8772
8713	8733	8753	8773
8714	8734	8754	8774
8715	8735	8755	8775
8716	8736	8756	8776
8717	8737	8757	8777
8718	8738	8758	8778
8719	8739	8759	8779

8780	8785	8790	8795
8781	8786	8791	8796
8782	8787	8792	8797
8783	8788	8793	8798
8784	8789	8794	8799

(*Class continued with No. 9600*)

4-4-0 9000 Class

Introduced 1936.
Weights : Loco. 49 tons 0 cwt.
Tender 40 tons 0 cwt.
Pressure : 180 lb. Cyls.: 18″×26″
Driving Wheels: 5′ 8″ T.E.: 18,955 lb.

9000	9009	9016	9024
9001	9010	9017	9025
9002	9011	9018	9026
9003	9012	9020	9027
9004	9013	9021	9028
9005	9014	9022	
9008	9015	9023	

Total 26

(Nos. 3200-3228 until 1946)

"Duke" Class
4-4-0 3252 Class

Introduced 1895 by William Dean
Weights : Loco. 47 tons 6 cwt.
Tender 34 tons 5 cwt.
Pressure : 180 lb. Cyls.: 18″×26″
Driving Wheels: 5′ 8″ T.E.: 18,955 lb.

9054 Cornubia
9064 Trevithick
9065 Tre Pol and Pen
9072
9073 Mounts Bay
9076
9083 Comet
9084 Isle of Jersey
9087 Mercury
9089

Total 10

2-6-0 4300 Class

(Continued from 7321)

9300	9305	9310	9315
9301	9306	9311	9316
9302	9307	9312	9317
9303	9308	9313	9318
9304	9309	9314	9319

Total 231

0-6-0T 9400 Class

Introduced 1947.
Weight: 55 tons 7 cwt.
Pressure: 200 lb. Cyls.: 17½"×24"
Driving Wheels: 4' 7½" T.E.: 22,515 lb.

9400	9403	9406	9409
9401	9404	9407	
9402	9405	9408	

Total 10

0-6-0T 5700 Class

(Continued from 8799)

9600	9612	9624	9636
9601	9613	9625	9637
9602	9614	9626	9638
9603	9615	9627	9639
9604	9616	9628	9640
9605	9617	9629	9641
9606	9618	9630	9642
9607	9619	9631	9643
9608	9620	9632	9644
9609	9621	9633	9645
9610	9622	9634	9646
9611	9623	9635	9647

9648	9682	9733	9767
9649	9700*	9734	9768
9650	9701*	9735	9769
9651	9702*	9736	9770
9652	9703*	9737	9771
9653	9704*	9738	9772
9654	9705*	9739	9773
9655	9706*	9740	9774
9656	9707*	9741	9775
9657	9708*	9742	9776
9658	9709*	9743	9777
9659	9710*	9744	9778
9660	9711	9745	9779
9661	9712	9746	9780
9662	9713	9747	9781
9663	9714	9748	9782
9664	9715	9749	9783
9665	9716	9750	9784
9666	9717	9751	9785
9667	9718	9752	9786
9668	9719	9753	9787
9669	9720	9754	9788
9670	9721	9755	9789
9671	9722	9756	9790
9672	9723	9757	9791
9673	9724	9758	9792
9674	9725	9759	9793
9675	9726	9760	9794
9676	9727	9761	9795
9677	9728	9762	9796
9678	9729	9763	9797
9679	9730	9764	9798
9680	9731	9765	9799
9681	9732	9766	

Total 853

* Fitted with condensing apparatus.

STREAM-LINED DIESEL RAIL-CARS

Car No.	Date	Engines	Total b.h.p.	Seats
1	1934	1	121	69
2-4*	1934	2	242	44
5-7	1935	2	242	70
8, 9	1936	2	242	70
10-12†	1936	2	242	63
13-16	1936	2	242	70
17‡	1936	2	242	—
18§	1937	2	242	70
19-32	1940	2	210	48
33	1941	2	210	48
34‡	1941	2	210	—
35-36‖	1941	4	420	104
37-38‖	1942	4	420	104

* Buffet and lavatory facilities.
† Lavatory facilities.
‡ Parcels cars.
§ Experimentally geared to haul trailer car, became prototype of subsequent designs.

‖ Twin-coach units with buffet and lavatory facilities. Adjoining statistics apply per 2-car unit. When new, some of these units worked as 3-car rakes by the addition of an ordinary 70 ft. corridor coach.

1	6	12	17	22	27	32	37
2	7	13	18	23	28	33	38
3	8	14	19	24	29	34	
4	10	15	20	25	30	35	
5	11	16	21	26	31	36	

SERVICE LOCOS.

Petrol

0-4-0 : 23, 24, 26 and 27

Total 4

BRITISH RAILWAYS POWER CLASSIFICATION

Western Region locomotives are classified as follows under the new British Railways scheme, based on the former L.M.S.R. code :

7P "King"
6P "Castle"
5P "Star"
4P "Saint"; B.M. 4 ft. 6 in., R.R. "R," "RI," "M" and "A", Cdf. R. No. 155, T.V. "A" 0-6-2Ts
3P "Bulldog"; R.R. "P" and "PI" Classes.
2P "Duke"; "9000"; "6400."
1P "3500"; "1400"; "517"; "5400."
6MT "County."
5MT "Hall"; "Grange"; "Manor."
4MT "4300"; T.V. "04" 0-6-2T; A.D. 2-6-2T; "3100"; "4500"; "5100"; "6100"; "8100."
3MT "2251"; B.M. 5 ft. 0-6-2T; "4400."
2MT Cam. R. 0-6-0; "2301."
1MT MSWJ 2-4-0.
8F "2800"; "4200" (Nos. 5205-64 only); "7200."
7F R.O.D.; "4700"; "4200" (to No. 5204 only).
5F "5600."
4F "Aberdare"; R.R. "S" and "SI" 0-6-0T; Car. R. Nos. 681-4; "5700"; "9400."
3F B.R. "B" 0-6-2T; A.D. 0-6-0T; "1701"; "1101."
2F C.M.D.P. 0-6-0T; L.M.M. No. 803; "655"; "1501"; "1901"; "2021"; "2181"; B.P.G.V. Nos. 2162/5-8; "7400."
1F L.M.M. No. 359; T.V. "H"; S.H.T. Nos. 1142/6/7; "1366"; B.P.G.V. Nos. 2176/92/6/8.
0F W.C.P. No. 5; W. & C. No. 1331; B.P.G.V. Nos. 2193-5/7; P.M. 0-4-0T; S.H.T. Nos. 1140/1/3/4; Car. R. No. 1338.

PRINCIPAL DIMENSIONS OF WESTERN REGION ENGINES

(Tractive Effort calculated to nearest 5lb.)

Class	Type	Designer	Intro-duced	Weight (full) Loco. T. Cwt.	Weight (full) Tender T. Cwt.	Press-ure Lb. per sq. in.	Cylinders (2 unless otherwise shown)	Driving Wheels	T.E. at 85% lb.	Power Class	Route Restriction Colour
517*	0-4-2T	G. Armstrong	1868	35 4	—	165	16″ × 24″	5′ 2″	13,900	—	—
1000	4-6-0	Hawksworth	1945	76 17	19 0	280	18½″ × 30″	6′ 3″	32,580	D	Red
1101	0-4-0T	Collett	1926	38 4	—	170	16″ × 24″	3′ 9½″	19,510	B	Red
1361	0-6-0ST	Churchward	1910	35 4	—	150	16″ × 20″	3′ 8″	14,835	—	—
1366	0-6-0PT	Collett	1934	35 15	—	165	16″ × 20″	3′ 8″	16,320	—	—
1400	0-4-2T	Collett	1932	41 6	—	165	16″ × 24″	5′ 2″	13,900	—	—
1501	0-6-0PT	Dean & G. Armstrong (Wolv'n.)	1878	42 17	—	165	17″ × 24″	4′ 7½″	17,525	A	Blue**
1701	0-6-0PT	Dean (Swindon)	1891††	46 13	—	180	17″ × 24″	4′ 7½″	19,120	A	Blue
1901	0-6-0PT	Dean & G. Armstrong (Wolv'n.)	1881	36 3	—	165	16″ × 24″	4′ 1½″	17,410	—	—
2021 2181§	0-6-0PT	Dean (Wolv'n.)	1897	39 15	—	165	16½″ × 24″	4′ 1½″	18,515	A	—
2251	0-6-0	Collett	1930	43 8	36 15	200	17½″ × 24″	5′ 2″	20,155	B	Yellow
2301	0-6-0	Dean	1883	36 16	34 5	180	17″ × 24″ 17½″ × 24″	5′ 2″ 5′ 2″	17,120 18,140	A	—
2600	2-6-0	Dean	1900	56 15	47 14	200	18″ × 26″	4′ 7½″	25,800	D	Blue
2700	0-6-0PT	Dean†	1896	45 13	—	180	17½″ × 24″	4′ 7½″	20,260	A	Blue
2800	2-8-0	Churchward	1903	75 10 76 5	40 0	225	18½″ × 30″	4′ 7½″	35,380	E	Blue
2900	4-6-0	Churchward‡	1902	72 0	40 0	225	18½″ × 30″	6′ 8½″	24,395	C	Red
3100	2-6-2T	Collett	1938	81 9	—	225	18½″ × 30″	5′ 3″	31,170	E	Red
3150	2-6-2T	Churchward	1907	81 12	—	200	18½″ × 30″	5′ 8″	25,670	D	Red
3252	4-4-0	Dean	1895	47 6	34 5	180	18″ × 26″	5′ 8″	18,955	B	Yellow

* Wolverhampton-built in 1895-7.
† Nos. 2701-20 built at Wolverhampton, 1896-7.
‡ Pioneer engine No. 2900 (originally No. 100) designed by Dean, built 1902.
§ 2021 Class with altered brake gear.
** Nos. 1742/5/7/9/73/80/2/9 bear colour "Yellow"
†† Embodying earlier engines.

One of the twin-coach units, cars Nos. 35-36, working with an ordinary coach. These railcars are fitted with buffet and W.C. [M. W. *Earley*

Diesel Railcar No. 34, a parcels car [*British Railways*

'1366" Class 0-6-0PT No. 1366 [Donovan E. H. Box

"6400" Class 0-6-0PT No. 6400 [L. Elsey

" 1701 " Class 0-6-0PT No. 907 [P. L. Melvill

" 1901 " Class 0-6-0PT No. 2012 (*cf.* No. 1925, page 2") [H. C. Casserley

" 2021 " Class 0-6-0PT No. 2151 [H. C. Casserley

Left : " 1501 " Class 0-6-0PT No. 1782
[*D. W. Backhouse*

Centre : " 5700 " Class 0-6-0PT No. 9715
[*F. F Moss*

Bottom : " 5700 " Class 0-6-0PT No. 9706 (fitted with condensing gear)
[*B. V. Franey*

Class	Type	Designer	Introduced	Weight (full) Loco. T. Cwt.	Weight (full) Tender T. Cwt.	Pressure Lb. per sq. in.	Cylinders (2 unless otherwise shown)	Driving Wheels	T.E. at 85% Lb.	Power Class	Route Restriction Colour
3300	4-4-0	Dean	1898	51 16	40 0	200	18″ × 26″	5′ 8″	21,060	B	Blue
3500	2-4-0T	Dean	1899	41 7	—	165	16″ × 24″	5′ 2″	13,900	—	Yellow
4000	4-6-0	Churchward	1906	75 12	46 14	225	15″ × 26″ (4)	6′ 8½″	27,800	D	Red
4073	4-6-0	Collett	1923	79 17	46 14	225	16″ × 26″ (4)	6′ 8½″	31,625	D	Red
4200	2-8-0T	Churchward	1910	82 2	—	200	19″ × 30″	4′ 7½″	33,170	E	Red
4300	2-6-0	Churchward	1911	62 0 65 6	40 0	200	18½″ × 30″	5′ 8″	25,670	D	Blue Red§
4400	2-6-2T	Churchward*	1904	56 13	—	180	17″ × 24″	4′ 1½″	21,440	C	—
4500	2-6-2T	Churchward†	1906	61 0	—	200	17″ × 24″	4′ 7½″	21,250	C	Yellow
4700	2-8-0	Churchward	1919	82 0	46 14	225	19″ × 30″	5′ 8″	30,460	D	Red
4900	4-6-0	Collett	1928	75 0	46 14	225	18½″ × 30″	6′ 0″	27,275	D	Red
5100	2-6-2T	Collett	1929	78 9	—	200	18″ × 30″	5′ 8″	24,300	D	Blue
5400	0-6-0PT	Collett	1931	46 12	—	165	16½″ × 24″	5′ 2″	14,780	—	Yellow
5600	0-6-2T	Collett	1924	68 12	—	200	18″ × 26″	4′ 7½″	25,800	D	Red
5700	0-6-0PT	Collett	1929	49 0	—	200	17½″ × 24″	4′ 7½″	22,515	C	Blue
6000	4-6-0	Collett	1927	89 0	46 14	250	16¼″ × 28″ (4)	6′ 6″	40,300	Spcl.	Double Red
6100	2-6-2T	Collett	1931	78 9	—	225	18″ × 30″	5′ 8″	27,340	D	Blue
6400	0-6-0PT	Collett	1931	45 12	—	165	16½″ × 24″	4′ 7½″	16,510	A	Yellow
6800	4-6-0	Collett	1936	74 0	40 0	225	18½″ × 30″	5′ 8″	28,875	D	Red
6959	4-6-0	Hawksworth	1944	76 16	46 14	225	18½″ × 30″	6′ 0″	27,275	D	Red
7200	2-8-2T	Collett	1934	92 12	—	200	19″ × 30″	4′ 7½″	33,170	E	Red
7400	0-6-0PT	Collett	1936	45 9	—	180	16½″ × 24″	4′ 7½″	18,010	A	Yellow
7800	4-6-0	Collett	1938	68 18	40 0	225	18″ × 30″	5′ 8″	27,340	D	Blue
8100	2-6-2T	Collett	1938	76 11	—	225	18″ × 30″	5′ 6″	28,165	D	Blue
9000	4-4-0	Collett‡	1936	49 0	40 0	180	18″ × 26″	5′ 8″	18,955	B	Yellow
9400	0-6-0T	Hawksworth	1947	55 7	—	200	17½″ × 24″	4′ 7½″	22,515	C	Red
R.O.D.	2-8-0	Robinson, G.C.R.	1917**	73 11	48 6	185	21″ × 26″	4′ 8″	32,200	D	Blue

* Nos. 4401-10 built at Wolverhampton, 1905.

† Nos. 4500-19. last engines built at Wolverhampton, 1906-8.

‡ New class rebuilt from obsolescent Dean engines.

§ Engines numbered in 93XX series.

** Date of initial wartime contract for Railway Operating Division. The design originated with G.C.R., 1911.

LOCOMOTIVE RUNNING SHEDS STENCILLED ABBREVIATIONS

Depot	*Code*
Aberdare	ABDR
Aberbeeg	ABEEG
Banbury	BAN
Birkenhead	BHD
Brecon	BCN
Bristol	
Bath Road	BRD
St. Philips Marsh	SPM
Cardiff	CDF
Cardiff Valleys	
Abercynon	CV(AYN)
Barry	CV (BRY)
Caeharris	CH
Cardiff East Dcks.	CED
Cathays	CHYS
Ferndale	CV (FDL)
Merthyr	MTHR
Radyr Jct.	RYR
Rhymney	RHY
Treherbert	THT
Carmarthen	CARM
Cheltenham	CHEL
Chester	CHR
Croes Newydd	CNYD
Crewe	CRW
Danygraig	DG
Didcot	DID
Duffryn Yard	DYD
Exeter	EXE
Fishguard (Goodwick)	FGD
Gloucester	GLO
Hereford	HFD
Kidderminster	KDR
Laira (Plymouth)	LA
Leamington	LMTN
Llandore	LDR
Llanelly	LLY
Llantrisant	LTS
Lydney	LYD
Machynlleth	MCH
Neath	NEA
Newport Dock	PILL
Newport Ebbw Jct.	NPT
Newton Abbot	NA
Neyland	NEY
Old Oak Common	PDN
Oswestry	OSW
Oxford	OXF
Oxley	OXY
Penzance	PZ
Pontypool Road	PPRD
Reading	RDG
Severn Tunnel Jct.	STJ
Shrewsbury	SALOP
Slough	SLO
Southall	SHL
St. Blazey	SBZ
Stourbridge	STB
Swansea East Dock	SED
Swindon	SDN
Taunton	TN
Tondu	TDU
Truro	TR
Tyseley	TYS
Wellington	WLN
Westbury	WES
Weymouth	WEY
Wolverhampton (Stafford Road)	SRD
Worcester	WOS
Whitland	WTD
Yeovil	YEO

THE ABC OF BRITISH RAILWAYS LOCOMOTIVES

EDITED BY A. F. COOK AND O. J. MORRIS

PART 2—Nos. 10000-39999

LONDON:

Ian Allan Ltd

NOTES ON THE USE OF THIS BOOK

INTERNAL COMBUSTION LOCOMOTIVES

In accordance with the usual British practice the wheel arrangement of Diesel and petrol locomotives are defined by the Whyte system (*i.e.*, 0–6–6–0) and electric locomotives by the letter system (*i.e.*, Co+Co).

SOUTHERN REGION STEAM LOCOMOTIVES

(1) This section of the book is divided into four parts:—

- (*a*) An alphabetical list of classes, with dimensions and subdivisions, and a summary of locomotives in the class.
- (*b*) A numerical list of locomotives showing the class of each.
- (*c*) A list of named engines in numerical order.
- (*d*) A table of dimensions and tender details.

(2) The aim of the book is that 1(*a*) above shall provide a ready reference to particulars of individual locomotives in a class: and that 1(*b*) shall be used for observation purposes. In the numerical list (1(*b*)) named engines are denoted by an asterisk and for details of locomotive names the reader should look up the engine in 1(*c*), which lists named locomotives in numerical order.

(3) The following notes are a guide to the system of reference marks and other details given in the lists of dimensions shown for each class in the alphabetical list of classes.

- (*a*) In the lists of dimensions "Su" indicates a superheated locomotive.
- (*b*) Locomotives are fitted with two inside cylinders, slide valves and Stephenson link motion, except where otherwise shown, *e.g.*, (O) indicates outside cylinders and "P.V." piston valves.
- (*c*) Owing to the complication of tender allocations on this Region a separate list of tenders is appended on p. 60. The reference numbers to tender types in the lists of dimensions are purely for the reader's guidance, and have no official significance.
- (*d*) The letter "S" in front of a number indicates a Service Locomotive. On the S.R. (only) this marking appears on the locomotive.
- (*e*) (W) before a number indicates an Isle of Wight locomotive. The "W" is no longer painted on the locomotives, but may still be seen on the bunker numberplate of some of them.
- (*f*) The date on which a design of locomotive first appeared is indicated by "Introduced." If the oldest surviving locomotive was built at a later date, that also is indicated.

(4) The list of locomotives in service has been checked to June 30th, 1949.

BRITISH RAILWAYS
INTERNAL COMBUSTION LOCOMOTIVES

0-6-6-0 Diesel Electric
LONDON MIDLAND REGION

Introduced 1947 : English Electric Co. and H. A. Ivatt, main line passenger design for L.M.S.R.
Weight : 121 tons 10 cwt.
Driving Wheels : 3′ 6″.
T.E. : 41,400 lb.
Engine : English Electric Co. 16 cyls. 1,600 h.p.
Motors : Six nose-suspended motors, single reduction gear drive.

10000 10001

Total 2

0-6-0 Diesel Electric
LONDON MIDLAND REGION

Introduced 1936 : English Electric–Hawthorn Leslie design for L.M.S.R.
Weight : 51 tons.* / 47 tons.†
Driving Wheels : 4′ 0½″.
T.E. : 30,000 lb.
Engine : English Electric 6 cyl. 350 h.p.
Motors : Two nose-suspended motors, single reduction gear drive.

12000* 12001* 12002†

Total 3

0-6-0 Diesel Electric
LONDON MIDLAND REGION

Introduced 1939 : English Electric and Stanier design for L.M.S.R., development of previous design with jackshaft drive.
Weight : 54 tons 16 cwt.
Driving Wheels : 4′ 3″.
T.E. : 33,000 lb.
Engine : English Electric, 6 cyls. 350 h.p.
Motors : Single motor ; jackshaft drive

12003	12011	12019	12026
12004	12012	12020	12027
12005	12013	12021	12028
12006	12014	12022	12029
12007	12015	12023	12030
12008	12016	12024	12031
12009	12017	12025	12032
12010	12018		

Total 30

0-6-0 Diesel Electric
LONDON MIDLAND REGION

Introduced 1945 : English Electric and Stanier design for L.M.S.R., development of previous design with double reduction gear drive.
Weight : 50 tons.
Driving Wheels : 4′ 0½″.
T.E. : 33,000 lb.
Engine : English Electric, 6 cyls. 350 h.p.
Engine : Two nose-suspended motors, double reduction gear drive.

12033	12042	12051	12060
12034	12043	12052	12061
12035	12044	12053	12062
12036	12045	12054	12063
12037	12046	12055	12064
12038	12047	12056	12065
12039	12048	12057	12066
12040	12049	12058	12067
12041	12050	12059	12068

N.B.—Locos of this class are still being delivered.

0-6-0 Diesel Electric
LONDON MIDLAND REGION

Introduced 1934 : Armstrong-Whitworth design for L.M.S.R.
Weight : 40 tons 10 cwt.
Driving Wheels : 3′ 6″.
T.E. : 24,000 lb.
Engine : Armstrong Sulzer 6 cyl. 250 h.p.
Motors : Single motor, jackshaft drive.

13000

Total 1

0-6-0 Diesel Electric
EASTERN REGION

Introduced 1944 : English Electric and Thompson design for L.N.E.R., (L.N.E.R. version of L.M.S. 12033 series).
Weight : 51 tons.
Driving Wheels : 4′ 0″.
T.E. : 32.000 lb.
Engine : English Electric, 6 cyl. 350 h.p.
Motors : Two nose-suspended motors, double reduction gear.

15000 15001 15002 15003

Total 4

0-6-0 Diesel Electric
EASTERN REGION

Introduced 1949 : Brush design for E.R.
Weight : 51 tons.
Driving Wheels : 4′ 0″.
T.E. : 32,000 lb.
Engine : Petter 4 cyl. 360 h.p.

15004 **Total 1**

0-4-0 Petrol (Class Y11)
EASTERN REGION

Introduced 1921 : Motor, Rail and Tram Car Co., design (purchased by N.B.R. and L.N.E.R.).
Weight : 8 tons.
Driving Wheels : 3′ 1″.
Engine : 4 cyl. 40 h.p. petrol.
Drive : Chains and two speed gear box.
(Original B.R. numbers in brackets.)

15098 (68188) 15099 (68189)

Total 2

0-6-0 Diesel Electric
WESTERN REGION

Introduced 1936 : Hawthorn Leslie and English Electric design for G.W.R. (G.W.R. version of L.M.S.R. Nos. 12000/1).
Weight : 51 tons 10 cwt.
Driving Wheels : 4′ 1″.
T.E. : 30,000 lb.
Engine : English Electric 6 cyl. 350 h.p.
Motors : Two nose-suspended motors, single reduction gear drive.

15100 **Total 1**

0-6-0 Diesel Electric
WESTERN REGION

Introduced 1948 : English Electric and Hawksworth design for Western Region (W.R. version of L.M.S. 12033 series).
Weight : 46 tons 9 cwt.
Driving Wheels : 4′ 0½″.
T.E. : 33,500 lb.
Engine : English Electric 6 cyl. 350 h.p.
Motors: Two nose-suspended motors, single reduction gear drive.

15101	15103	15105
15102	15104	15106

Total 6

0-6-0 Diesel Electric
SOUTHERN REGION

Introduced 1937 : English Electric and Bulleid design for S.R.
Weight : 55 tons 5 cwt.
Driving Wheels : 4′ 6″.
T.E. : 30,000 lb.
Engine : English Electric 6 cyl. 350 h.p.
Motors : Two nose-suspended motors, single reduction gear drive.

15201 15202 15203

Total 3

0-6-0 Diesel Electric
SOUTHERN REGION

Introduced 1949 : English Electric and Bulleid design for S.R. (S.R. version of L.M.S.R. 12033 series, but designed for higher speeds).
Weight : 49 tons.
Driving Wheels : 4′ 6″.
T.E. : 24,000 lb.
Engine : English Electric 6 cyl. 350 h.p.
Motors: Two nose-suspended motors, double reduction gear drive.

15210	15214	15218	15222
15211	15215	15219	15223
15212	15216	15220	15224
15213	15217	15221	

N.B.—Locos. of this class are still being delivered.

LOCOMOTIVES NOT YET IN SERVICE

L.M.R. Fell Diesel Mechanical, 1,600 h.p. 4-8-4.

10100

S.R. Diesel Electric, 1,600 h.p.

From 10200

L.M.R. Diesel Electric, 800 h.p.

From 10800

Diesel Mechanical, 400 h.p.

From 11000

W.R. Brown Boveri and Metropolitan Vickers Gas Turbine with electric transmission.

18000 18001

NOTE—There are a number of Diesel locomotives in the Service or Departmental stock of the Regions, but these have not been included in this section.

BRITISH RAILWAYS ELECTRIC LOCOMOTIVES

Co + Co Class CC

SOUTHERN REGION

*Introduced 1941 : Raworth & Bulleid design for S.R.
†Introduced 1948 : Later design with detail differences.
Weight : 99 tons 14 cwt.* / 104 tons 14 cwt.†
T.E. : 40,000 lb.
Voltage : 600 D.C.
Current Collection : Overhead and third rail, with flywheel-driven generator for gaps in third rail.

20001* 20002* 20003†

Total 3

Bo + Bo Class EM1

EASTERN & NORTH-EASTERN REGIONS

Introduced 1941 : Metropolitan Vickers and Gresley design for L.N.E.R.
Weight : 87 tons 18 cwt.
Driving Wheels : 4′ 2″.
T.E. : 45,000 lb.
Voltage : 1,500 D.C.
Current Collection : overhead.

26000

Total 1

Bo + Bo Class EB1

NORTH-EASTERN REGION

Introduced 1914 : Raven freight design for N.E.R. (stored at Darlington since cessation of electric working on Sheldon-Newport line in 1934).
*Introduced 1946 : L.N.E.R. rebuild of N.E.R. design for banking work on Manchester-Wath line.
Weight : 74 tons 8 cwt.
Driving Wheels : 4′ 0″.
T.E. : 28,000 lb.
Voltage : 1,500 D.C.
Current collection : overhead.

26490	26493	26496	26498*
26491	26494	26497	26499
26492	26495		

Total 10

Bo + Bo Class ES1

NORTH-EASTERN REGION

Built 1902 : Brush & Thomson-Houston shunting design for N.E.R.
Weight : 46 tons.
Voltage : 600 D.C.
T.E. : 25,000 lb.

26500 26501

Total 2

2-Co-2 Class EE1

NORTH-EASTERN REGION

Introduced 1922 : Metropolitan Vickers experimental express design for N.E.R.
Weight : 110 tons 1 cwt.
Driving Wheels : 6′ 8″.
T.E. : 28,000 lb.
Voltage : 1,500 D.C.
Current collection : overhead.

26999

Total 1

NOTE—Service locomotives 74S and 75S are electric, but have not been included in this section of the B.R. list

SUMMARY OF SOUTHERN REGION STEAM LOCOMOTIVE CLASSES

(In alphabetical order)

WITH HISTORICAL NOTES & DIMENSIONS

0-6-0T Class A1 & A1X

***A1** Introduced 1872: Stroudley L.B.S.C. "Terrier," later fitted with Marsh boiler, retaining original type smokebox (survivor built 1875).

†**A1X** Introduced 1911: Rebuild of A1 with Marsh boiler and extended smokebox.

‡**A1X** Loco. with increased cylinder diameter.

Weight: { 27 tons 10 cwt.* / 28 tons 5 cwt.†‡

Pressure: 150 lb. Cyls. { 12″ × 20″† / 14$\frac{3}{16}$″ × 20″‡

Driving Wheels: 4′ 0″.

T.E.: { 7,650 lb.*† / 10,695 lb.‡

*680S

†377**S**, 515**S**, 32640/4/6/7/55/9/61/2/70/7/8.

‡32636

Totals: A1 1
A1X 14

4-4-0 Class B1

Introduced 1910: Wainwright rebuild with domed boiler and extended smokebox of Stirling S.E.R. domeless Class B (originally introduced 1898).

Weight: Loco. 45 tons 2 cwt.

Tender: type 6.

Pressure: 170 lb. Cyls.: 18″ × 26″

Driving Wheels: 7′ 0″.

T.E.: 14,490 lb.

31217, 31443/6/8/51/2.

Total 6

0-4-0T Class B4

*Introduced 1891: Adams L.S.W. design for dock shunting.

†Introduced 1908: Drummond K14 locos., with smaller boiler and detail alterations.

‡Adams locos. fitted with Drummond boiler.

§Drummond loco. fitted with Adams boiler.

Weight: { 33 tons 9 cwt.*‡ / 32 tons 18 cwt.†§

Pressure: 140 lb. Cyls (O): 16″ × 22″

Driving Wheels: 3′ 9$\frac{3}{4}$″.
T.E.: 14,650 lb.

*30086/7/9/93/4/6, 30102.
†30082/3 ‡30088 §30084

Total 11

4-4-0 Classes B4 & B4X

***B4** Introduced 1899: R. J. Billinton L.B.S.C. design.

†**B4X** Introduced 1922: L. B. Billinton design, incorporating parts from B4.

Weights: Loco. { 51 tons 10 cwt.* / 58 tons 1 cwt.†

Tender type: { 7* / 22†

Pressure: { 180 lb.* / 180 lb. Su.†

Cyls. { 19″ × 26″.* / 20″ × 26″.†

Driving Wheels: 6′ 9″.

T.E.: { 17,730 lb.* / 19,645 lb.†

P.V. (B4X).

*32054/62/3/8/74.
†32043/5/50/2/5/6/60/7/70–3.

Totals: Class B4 5
Class B4X 12

4-6-2 Class BB

(see Class WC & BB)

0-6-0 Class C

Introduced 1900: Wainwright S.E.C. design.
Weight: Loco. 43 tons 16 cwt.
Tender type: 10.
Pressure: 160 lb. Cyls.: 18½″ × 26″
Driving Wheels: 5′ 2″.
T.E.: 19.520 lb.

31004/18/33/7/8/54/9/61/3/8/71/86/90, 31102/12/3/50/91, 31218/9/21/3/5/7/9/34/42–5/52/3/5–7/60/7/8/70-2/7/80/7/91/3/4/7/8, 31317, 31461/80/1/6/95/8, 31508/10/3/72/3/5/6/8–85/8–90/2/3, 31681–4/6–95, 31711–25.

Total 105

0-6-0 Classes C2 & C2X

***C2** Introduced 1893: R. J. Billinton L.B.S.C. design.
†**C2X** Introduced 1908: Marsh rebuild of C2 with larger C3-type boiler, extended smokebox, etc.
Weights: Loco. { 39 tons 10 cwt.* / 45 tons 5 cwt.†
Tender type: 4.
Pressure: { 160 lb.* / 170 lb.†
Cyls.: 17½″ × 26″.
Driving Wheels: 5′ 0″.
T.E.: { 18,050 lb.* / 19,175 lb.†

*32436, 32533.

†32434/7/8/40–51, 32521–9/32/4–41/3–54.

Totals: C2 2
C2X 45

0-6-0 Class C3

Introduced 1906: Marsh L.B.S.C. design.
Weight: Loco. 47 tons 10 cwt.
Tender type: 5, 8.
Pressure: 170 lb. Cyls.: 17½″ × 26″
Driving Wheels: 5′ 0″.
T.E.: 19,175 lb.

32300–3/6. **Total 5**

0-4-0T Class C14

Introduced 1913: Urie rebuild as shunting locos. of Drummond L.S.W. motor-train 2–2–0T (originally introduced 1906).
Weight: 25 tons 15 cwt.
Pressure: 150 lb.
Cyls. (O): 14″ × 14″.
Driving Wheels: 3′ 0″.
T.E.: 9,720 lb.
Walschaerts gear.

77S, 30588/9. **Total 3**

4-4-0 Classes D & D1

***D** Introduced 1901: Wainwright S.E.C. design, with round-top fire-box, some later fitted with extended smokebox.
†**D1** Introduced 1921: Maunsell rebuild of Class D, with superheated Belpaire boiler, and long-travel piston valves.
Weights: { 50 tons* / 52 tons 4 cwt.†
Tender type: { 13.* / 11.†
Pressure: { 175 lb.* / 180 lb. Su.†
Cyls.: 19″ × 26″.
Driving Wheels: 6′ 8″.
T.E.: { 17,450 lb.* / 17,950 lb.†

*31057/75/92, 31477/88/90/3/6, 31501/49/74/7/86/91, 31728–34/7/8/40/4/6/8/50.

†31145, 31246/7, 31470/87/9/92/4, 31502/5/9/45, 31727/35/6/9/41/3/5/9.

Total: Class D 28
Class D1 20

0-4-2T Classes D1 & D1/M

***D1** Introduced 1873: Stroudley L.B.S.C. design, reboilered by Marsh.
†**D1/M** Introduced 1909: D1 fitted for push-and-pull working (reclassified D1/M by S.R.).
‡**D1** Introduced 1947: D1 fitted for oil pumping.
Weight: 43 tons 10 cwt.
Pressure: 170 lb. Cyls.: 17″ × 24″
Driving Wheels: 5′ 6″.
T.E.: 15,185 lb.

*32274
†32215/34/52/3, 32359
‡701S.
Total : D1 2 D1/M 5

0-4-4T Class D3

Introduced 1892 : R. J. Billinton L.B.S.C. design, later reboilered by Marsh and fitted from 1934 for push-and-pull working.
Weight : 52 tons.
Pressure : 170 lb. Cyls. : 17½" × 26"
Driving Wheels : 5' 6".
T.E. : 17,435 lb.

32364/5/8/72/6/8–80/4–6/8/90/1/3/4. **Total 16**

4-4-0 Class D15

Introduced 1912 : Drummond L.S.W. design, superheated by Urie from 1915.
Weight Loco. 61 tons 11 cwt.
Tender type : 17.
Pressure : 180 lb. Su.
Cyls. : 20" × 26".
Driving Wheels : 6' 7".
T.E. : 20,140 lb.
Walschaerts gear, P.V.

30463–72. **Total 10**

4-4-0 Classes E & E1

*E Introduced 1905 : Wainwright S.E.C. design with Belpaire boiler.
†E Introduced 1912 : Rebuilt with superheater in original boiler.
‡E1 Introduced 1919 : Maunsell rebuild of E, with larger superheated Belpaire boiler and long-travel piston valves.

Weight : Loco. { 52 tons 5 cwt.* / 53 tons 10 cwt.† / 53 tons 9 cwt.‡
Tender type : { 13.* / 13.† / 12.‡
Pressure : { 180 lb.* / 160 lb Su.† / 180 lb. Su.‡
Cyls. : { 19" × 26".* / 20½" × 26".† / 19" × 26".‡
T.E. : { 18,410 lb.* / 19,050 lb.† / 18,410 lb.‡
Driving Wheels : 6' 6".

*31157/9/66/75/6, 31273, 31315, 31491, 31514–6/47/87.
†31036, 31275.
‡31019/67, 31160/5/79, 31497, 31504/6/7/11.

Total : Class E 15
Class E1 10

0-6-0T Class E1

Introduced 1874 : Stroudley L.B.S.C. design, reboilered by Marsh.
Weight : 44 tons 3 cwt.
Pressure : 170 lb. Cyls. : 17" × 24"
Driving Wheels : 4' 6".
T.E. : 18,560 lb.

32097, 32112/3/7–9/33/8/9/41/2/5/7/51/6/60/2, 32689/90/1/4, (W) 1–4.

Total 25

0-6-2T Class E1/R

Introduced 1927 : Maunsell rebuild of Stroudley E1, with radial trailing axle and larger bunker for passenger service in West of England.
Weight : 50 tons 5 cwt.
Pressure : 170 lb. Cyls. : 17" × 24"
Driving Wheels : 4' 6".
T.E. : 18,560 lb.

32094–6, 32124/35, 32608/10/95–7.

Total 10

0-6-0T Class E2

*Introduced 1913 : L. B. Billinton L.B.S.C. design.
†Introduced 1915 : Later locos. with tanks extended further forward.
Weight : { 52 tons 15 cwt.* / 53 tons 10 cwt.†
Pressure : 170 lb. Cyls. : 17½" × 26"
Driving Wheels : 4' 6".
T.E. : 21,305 lb.

*32100–4.
†32105–9.

Total 10

L.M.R. 0–6–6–0 Diesel Electric No. 10001 [*Basil A. Young*

S.R. 0–6–0 Diesel Electric No. 15213 [*A. S. H. Tayler*

L.M.R. 0–6–0 Diesel Electric No. 12028 [*H. C. Casserley*

S.R. Class CC Electric Locomotive No. 20002 [*A. S. H. Tayler*

S.R. Class CC Electric Locomotive No. 20003 [*M. P. Mileham*

N.E.R. Class ESI Electric Locomotive No. 26501 [*B. V. Franey*

Class H16 4–6–2T No. 30520 [C. C. B. Herbert

Class J2 4–6–2T No. 32326 [H. C. Casserley

Class S11 4-4-0 No. 30399 [H. C. Casserley

Class L12 4-4-0 No. 30432 [W. Gilburt

Class D15 4-4-0 No. 30469 [A. F. Cook

0-6-2T Class E3

Introduced 1894: R. J. Billinton L.B.S.C. design, development of Stroudley "West Brighton" (introduced 1891), reboilered and fitted with extended smokebox, 1918 onwards; cylinder diameter reduced from 18" by S.R.
Weight: 56 tons 10 cwt.
Pressure: {160 lb. / 170 lb.*}
Cyls.: 17½" × 26"
Driving Wheels: 4' 6"
T.E.: {20,055 lb. / 21,305 lb.*}

*32165–70.
32453–6/8–61/2.

Total 15

0-6-2T Classes E4 & E4X

***E4** Introduced 1897: R. J. Billinton L.B.S.C. design, development of E3 with larger wheels, cylinder diameter reduced from 18" by S.R., but retaining original type smokebox.
†**E4** Introduced 1910: Reboilered with Marsh boiler and extended smokebox.
‡**E4X** Introduced 1909: E4 reboilered with larger I2 4-4-2T type boiler.
Weights: {56 tons 15 cwt.* / 57 tons 10 cwt.† / 59 tons 5 cwt.‡}
Pressure: 170 lb. Cyls.: 17½" × 26"
Driving Wheels: 5' 0"
T.E.: 19,175 lb.

*32468.
†32463–5/7/9–76/9–82/4–8/90–99, 32500–20/56–66/77–82.
‡32466/77/8/89.

Totals E4 70
E4X 4

NOTE

To understand the system of reference marks used in this book, it is essential to read the notes on page 2.

0-6-2T Classes E5 & E5X

*‡**E5** Introduced 1902: R. J. Billinton L.B.S.C. design, development of E4 with larger wheels and firebox, cylinder diameter reduced from 18" by S.R.
†**E5X** Introduced 1911: E5 reboilered with larger C3-type boiler.
Weights: {60 tons.* / 64 tons 5 cwt.†}
Pressure: {160 lb.* / 175 lb.‡ / 170 lb.†}
Cyls.: 17½" × 26"
Driving Wheels: 5' 6"
T.E.: {16,410 lb.* / 17,945 lb.‡ / 17,435 lb.†}

*‡32399, 32400/2/4–6, 32567/8/71/3–5/83–5/7/8/90–4.
†32401, 32570/6/86.

Totals: E5 22 E5X 4

0-6-2T Classes E6 & E6X

*‡**E6** Introduced 1904: R. J. Billinton L.B.S.C. design, development of E5 with smaller wheels.
†**E6X** Introduced 1911: E6 reboilered with larger C3-type boiler.
Weights: {61 tons.* / 63 tons.†}
Pressure: {160 lb.* / 175 lb.‡ / 170 lb.†}
Cyls.: 18" × 26"
Driving Wheels: 4' 6"
T.E.: {21,215 lb.* / 23,205 lb.‡ / 22,540 lb.†}

*‡32408–10/2–8.
†32407/11.

Totals: E6 10 E6X 2

0-6-0T Class G6

*Introduced 1894: Adams L.S.W. design, later additions by Drummond, but with Adams type boiler.
†Introduced 1925: Fitted with Drummond type boiler.
Weight: 47 tons 13 cwt.
Pressure: 160 lb. Cyls.: 17½" × 24"
Driving Wheels: 4' 10"
T.E.: 17,235 lb.

*30162, 30238/58/60/2/3/5/6/8/70 /2/5–7, 30353/4.
†30160, 30259/69/74, 30349/54.

Total 21

4-8-0T Class G16

Introduced 1921 : Urie L.S.W. "Hump" loco.
Weight : 95 tons 2 cwt.
Pressure : 180 lb. Su.
Cyls. (O) : 22″ × 28″
Driving Wheels : 5′ 1″
T.E. : 33,990 lb.
Walschaerts gear, P.V.

30492–5 **Total 4**

0-4-4T Class H

Introduced 1904. Wainwright S.E.C. design.
*Introduced 1949. Fitted for push-and-pull working.
Weight : 54 tons 8 cwt.
Pressure : 160 lb. Cyls. : 18″ × 26″
Driving Wheels : 5′ 6″
T.E. : 17,360 lb.

31005, 31158/61/2/4/77/84/93, 31239/59/61/3/5/6/9/74/6/8/9/95, 31305–11/9–22/4/6–9, 31500/3/12/7–9/21/2/30–3/40–4/6/8/50–4.
*31016, 31182, 31520/3.

Total 60

4-4-2 Class H1

*Introduced 1905 : Marsh L.B.S.C. design, later superheated and re-cylindered.
†Introduced 1947 : Rebuilt experimentally with sleeve valves.
Weight : Loco. 68 tons 5 cwt.
Tender type : 15.
Pressure : 200 lb. Su.
Cyls. : (O) 19″ × 26″.*
Driving Wheels : 6′ 7½″
T.E. : 20,070 lb.*

*32037/8 †32039

Total 3

4-4-2 Class H2

Introduced 1911 : Marsh L.B.S.C. design, superheated development of H1 with large cylinders.
Weight : Loco. 68 tons 5 cwt.
Tender type : 15.
Pressure : 200 lb. Su.
Cyls. : (O) 21″ × 26″
Driving Wheels : 6′ 7½″
T.E. : 24,520 lb.
P.V. :

32421/2, 32424–6.

Total 5

4-6-0 Class H15

*Introduced 1914 : Urie L.S.W. design, fitted with "Maunsell" superheater from 1927, replacing earlier types (30490 built saturated).
†Introduced 1915 : Urie rebuild with two outside cylinders of Drummond E14, 4-cyl. 4-6-0 introduced 1907, retaining original boiler retubed and fitted with superheater.
‡Introduced 1924 : Maunsell locos. with N15 type boiler and smaller tenders.
§Introduced 1924 : Maunsell rebuild of Drummond F13 4-cyl. 4–6–0 introduced 1905, with detail differences from rebuild of E14.
¶Introduced 1927 : Urie loco. (built 1914 saturated) rebuilt with later N15 class boiler, with smaller firebox.

Weight : Loco. { 81 tons 5 cwt.* / 82 tons 1 cwt.† / 79 tons 19 cwt.‡¶ / 80 tons 11 cwt.§ }
Tender type : 29, 31, 36, 39.
Pressure : { 180 lb. Su.*‡¶ / 175 lb. Su.†§ }
Cyls. : 21″ × 28″
Driving Wheels : 6′ 0″
T.E. : { 26,240 lb *‡¶ / 25,510 lb.†§ }
Walschaerts gear, P.V.

*30482–90
†30335
‡30473–8, 30521–4
§30330–4
¶30491

Total 26

4-6-2T Class H16

Introduced 1921 : Urie L.S.W. design for heavy freight traffic.
Weight : 96 tons 8 cwt.
Pressure : 180 lb. Su.
Cyls. : (O) 21″ × 28″
Driving Wheels : 5′ 7″
T.E. : 28,200 lb.
Walschaerts valve gear, P.V.

30516–20 **Total 5**

4-4-2T Class I1X

*Introduced 1925 : Maunsell rebuild with I3 class non-superheater boiler of Marsh L.B.S.C. I1 class (introduced 1906).
†Introduced 1929 : Maunsell rebuild of later I1 locos., with shorter coupled wheelbase (introduced 1907).
Weight : 71 tons 18 cwt.
Pressure : 180 lb. Cyls. : 17½″ × 26″
Driving Wheels : 5′ 6″
T.E. : 18,450 lb.

*32595/6, 32602/3
†32002/5/8/9

Total 8

4-4-2T Class I3

*Introduced 1907 : Marsh L.B.S.C. design with slide valves, rebuilt 1919 with superheater and extended smokebox.
†Introduced 1908 : Marsh L.B.S.C. design with piston valves and smaller wheels, 32026-30/75/6 originally saturated, remainder built superheated.
‡Introduced 1912 : L. B. Billinton modification of 1908 design, built superheated with larger cylinders.
Weight : {75 tons 10 cwt.* / 76 tons†‡}
Pressure : 180 lb. Su.
Cyls. : {19″ × 26″* / 20″ × 26″† / 21″ × 26″‡}
Driving Wheels : {6′ 9″* / 6′ 7½″†‡}
T.E. : {17,730 lb.* / 20,015 lb.† / 22,065 lb.‡}

*32021
†32022/3/5/6–30/75–81.
‡32082–91

Total 26

0-6-4T Class J

Introduced 1913 : Wainwright S.E.C. design.
Weight : 70 tons 4 cwt.
Pressure : 160 lb. Su.
Cyls. : 19½″ × 26″
Driving Wheels : 5′ 6″
T.E. : 20,370 lb.
P.V.

31595–9 **Total 5**

4-6-2T Classes J1 & J2

*J1 Introduced 1910 : Marsh L.B.S.C. design.
†J2 Introduced 1912 : L. B. Billinton development of J1 with Walschaerts valve gear and detail differences.
Weight : 89 tons.
Pressure : 170 lb. Su.
Cyls. : (O) 21″ × 26″
Driving Wheels : 6′ 7″
T.E. : 20,840 lb.
P.V. :

*32325 †32326

Total : Class J1 1
Class J2 1

2-6-0 Class K

Introduced 1913 : L. B. Billinton L.B.S.C. design.
Weight : Loco. 63 tons 15 cwt.
Tender type : 24.
Pressure : 180 lb. Su.
Cyls. . (O) 21″ × 26″
Driving Wheels : 5′ 6″
T.E. : 26,580 lb.
P.V. :

32337–53 **Total 17**

4-4-0 Class K10

Introduced 1901. Drummond L.S.W. design, development of C8 express 4-4-0 for mixed traffic work.
Weight : Loco. 46 tons 14 cwt.
Tender types : 18, 20, 28.
Pressure : 175 lb. Cyls. : 18½″ × 26″
Driving Wheels : 5′ 7″
T.E. : 19,755 lb.

30137/40–2/4/51, 30329/41/5/82, 30329/41 5 82/4/6/9/90/1.

Total 15

0-8-0T Class KES

ntroduced 1904: Hawthorn Leslie design for K.E.S.R., taken over by S.R. 1932, and later rebuilt with L.B.S.C. boiler.
Weight: 47 tons 10 cwt.
Pressure: 160 lb.
Cyls.: (O) 16″ × 24″
Driving Wheels: 4′ 3″
T.E.: 16,385l›

30949 **Total 1**

4-4-0 Class L

Introduced 1914: Wainwright S.E.C. design, with detail alterations by Maunsell.
Weight: Loco. 57 tons 9 cwt.
Tender type: 14.
Pressure: 180 lb. Su.
Cyls.: 19½″ × 26″
Driving Wheels: 6′ 8″
T.E.: 18,910 lb.
P.V.

31760–81 **Total 22**

4-4-0 Class L1

Introduced 1926: Post-grouping development of L, with long-travel valves, side window cab and detail alterations
Weight: Loco. 57 tons 16 cwt.
Tender type: 19.
Pressure: 180 lb. Su.
Cyls.: 19½″ × 26″
Driving Wheels: 6′ 8″
T.E.: 18,910 lb.
P.V.

31753–9/82–9

Total 15

4-4-0 Class L11

Introduced 1903. Drummond L.S.W. design, development of K10 with T9-type boiler, with larger firebox.
Weight: Loco. 50 tons 11 cwt.
Tender types: 18, 28, 32.
Pressure: 175 lb. Cyls.: 18½″ × 26″
Driving Wheels: 5′ 7″
T.E.: 19,755 lb.

30134/48/54–9/61/3–75, 30405–14/35–8/41/2.

Total 38

4-4-0 Class L12

Introduced 1904: Drummond L.S.W. design, development of T9 with larger boiler barrel, superheated from 1915.
Weight: Loco. 55 tons 5 cwt.
Tender types: 18, 28.
Pressure: 175 lb. Su.
Cyls.: 19″ × 26″
Driving Wheels: 6′ 7″
T.E.: 17,675 lb.

30415–34 **Total 20**

0-6-6-0T "Leader" Class

Introduced 1949: Bulleid double-bogie design, with chain-coupled wheels.
Pressure: 280 lb Su.
Cyls.: (6) 12¼″ × 15″
Driving Wheels: 5′ 1″
T.E.: 26,350 lb.
Sleeve valves with modified Bulleid valve gear.

36001–5

N.B.—Locos. of this class are still being delivered.

4-6-0 Class LN

*Introduced 1926: Maunsell design, cylinders and tender modified by Bulleid from 1938, and fitted with multiple-jet blast pipe and large chimney.
†Introduced 1929: Loco. fitted experimentally with smaller driving wheels.
‡Introduced 1929: Loco. fitted experimentally with longer boiler barrel.
Weights: Loco. { 83 tons 10 cwt.*† / 84 tons 16 cwt.‡ }
Tender type: 38.
Pressure: 220 lb. Su.
Cyls.: (4) 16½″ × 26″
Driving Wheels: { 6′ 7″*‡ / 6′ 3″† }
T.E. { 33,510 lb.*‡ / 35,300 lb.† }
Walschaerts gear, P.V.

*30850–8/61–5.
†30859 ‡30860

Total 16

0-4-4T Class M7

*Introduced 1897: Drummond L.S.W. M7 design.
†Introduced 1903: Drummond X14 design, with increased front overhang, steam reverser and detail alterations, now classified M7 (30254 originally M7).
‡Introduced 1925: X14 design fitted for push-and-pull working.
Weights: {60 tons 4 cwt.* / 60 tons 3 cwt.† / 62 tons 0 cwt.‡}
Pressure: 175 lb. Cyls.: 18½" × 26"
Driving Wheels: 5' 7"
T.E.: 19,755 lb.

*30022–6/31–44, 30112, 30241–53/5/6, 30318–24/56/7, 30667–71/3–6.
†30029/30, 30123/4/7/30/2/3, 30254, 30374–8, 30479.
‡30021/7/8/45–60, 30104–11/25/8/9/31, 30328/79, 30480/1.

Total 103

4-6-2 Class MN

*Introduced 1941: Bulleid design.
†Introduced 1948: Loco. rebuilt with mechanical stoker.
Weight: Loco. 94 tons 15 cwt.
Tender types: 33, 34, 42.
Pressure: 280 lb. Su.
Cyls.: (3) 18" × 24"
Driving Wheels: 6' 2"
T.E.: 37,515 lb.
Bulleid valve gear, P.V.

*35001–4/6–30
†35005

Total 30

2-6-0 Classes N & N1

*N Introduced 1917: Maunsell S.E.C. mixed traffic design.
†N1 Introduced 1922: 3-cylinder development of N.
Weight: Loco. {61 tons 4 cwt.* / 64 tons 5 cwt.†}
Tender type: 16, 25.
Pressure: 200 lb. Su.
Cyls.: {(O) 19" × 28"* / (3) 16" × 28"†}
Driving Wheels: 5' 6"
T.E.: {26,035 lb.* / 27,695 lb.†}
Walschaert gear, P.V.

*31400–14, 31810–21/3–75
†31822/76–80

Totals: Class N 80
Class N1 6

4-6-0 Class N15

*Introduced 1918: Urie L.S.W. design.
†Introduced 1928: Locos. with cylinders of reduced diameter.
‡Introduced 1925: Maunsell locos. with long-travel valves, increased boiler pressure, smaller fireboxes, and tenders from Drummond G14 4–6–0's.
§Introduced 1925: Later locos, with detail alterations and increased weight.
||Introduced 1925: Locos. with modified cabs to suit Eastern Section and new bogie tenders.
¶Introduced 1926: Locos. with detail alterations and six-wheeled tenders for Central Section.
Weight: Loco. {80 tons 7 cwt.*† / 79 tons 18 cwt.‡ / 80 tons 19 cwt.§|| / 81 tons 17 cwt.¶}
Tender types: 21, 29, 36, 37.
Pressure: {180 lb. Su.*† / 200 lb Su.‡§||¶}
Cyls.: {(O) 22" × 28"* / (O) 21" × 28"† / (O) 20½" × 28"‡§||¶}
Driving Wheels: 6' 7"
T.E.: {26,245 lb.* / 23,915 lb.† / 25,320 lb. §‡||¶}
Walschaerts gear, P.V.
NOTE: Nos. 30736/7/41/52/5 are fitted with multiple jet blastpipe and large diameter chimney.

*30755	†30736–54
‡30453–7	§30448–52
||30763–92	¶30793–30806

Total 74

4-6-0 Class N15X

Introduced 1934: Maunsell rebuild of L. B. Billinton L.B.S.C. Class L 4–6–4T (introduced 1914).
Weight: Loco. 73 tons 2 cwt.
Tender type: 36.
Pressure: 180 lb. Su.
Cyls.: (O) 21" × 28"
Driving Wheels: 6' 9"
T.E.: 23,325 lb.
Walschaerts gear, P.V.

32327–33

Total 7

0-6-0 Class O1

*Introduced 1903 : Wainwright rebuild with domed boiler and new cab of Stirling S.E.R. Class O 0-6-0 (introduced 1878, oldest survivor built 1882).
†Introduced 1903 : Locos. with smaller driving wheels.
Weight : Loco. 41 tons 1 cwt.
Tender types : 1, 43.
Pressure : 150 lb. Cyls. : 18" × 26"
Driving Wheels : {5' 2"* / 5' 1"†}
T.E. : {17,325 lb.* / 17,610 lb.†}

*31039/44/64–6/80/93, 31108/23, 31248/58, 31369/70/3/4/7/9–81/3–5/90/1/5, 31425/9/30/2/4, †31041/8, 31238.

Total 33

0-4-4T Class O2

*Introduced 1889 : Adams L.S.W. design.
†Introduced 1923 : Fitted with Westinghouse brake for I.O.W., bunkers enlarged from 1932.
‡Fitted with Drummond-type boiler.
§Fitted for push-and-pull working.
Weight : {46 tons 18 cwt.*‡ / 48 tons 8 cwt.†}
Pressure : 160 lb. Cyls. : 17½" × 24"
Driving Wheels : 4' 10"
T.E. : 17,235 lb.

*30177/9/92/3/7/9, 30200/3/12/6/24/9–32/6.
† (W)14–34 †§ (W)35/6.
‡30204/13/21/3/5/33.
‡§30182/3, 30207.

Total 48

0-6-0T Class P

Introduced 1909 : Wainwright S.E.C. design for push-and-pull work, now used for shunting.
Weight : 28 tons 10 cwt.
Pressure : 160 lb. Cyls. : 12" × 18"
Driving Wheels : 3' 9½"
T.E. : 7,810 lb.

31027, 31178, 31323/5, 31555–8.

Total 8

0-6-0 Class Q

Introduced 1938 : Maunsell design, later fitted with multiple-jet blast pipe and large chimney.
Weight : Loco. 49 tons 10 cwt.
Tender type : 19.
Pressure : 200 lb. Su.
Cyls. : 19" × 26"
Driving Wheels : 5' 1"
T.E. : 26,160 lb.
P.V.

30530–49 **Total 20**

0-6-0 Class Q1

Introduced 1942 : Bulleid "Austerity" design.
Weight : Loco. 51 tons 5 cwt.
Tender type : 23.
Pressure : 230 lb. Su.
Cyls. : 19" × 26"
Driving Wheels : 5' 1"
T.E. : 30,080 lb.
P.V.

33001–40 **Total 40**

0-4-4T Classes R & R1

*R Introduced 1891 : Kirtley L.C.D. design, since rebuilt with H. class boiler.
†R1 Introduced 1900 : Locos. built for S.E.C. with enlarged bunkers, since rebuilt with H class boiler.
‡Fitted for push-and-pull working.
Weight : {48 tons 15 cwt.* / 52 tons 3 cwt.†}
Pressure : 160 lb. Cyls. : 17½" × 24"
Driving Wheels : 5' 6"
T.E. : 15,145 lb.

*31661/73/4.
†31696/8/9, 31705/8/9.
*‡31658–60/2/3/5–7/70/2/5.
†‡31697, 31700/3/4/6/10.

Total : Class R 15
Class R1 12

IMPORTANT NOTE

A careful reading of the notes on page 2 is essential to understand the use of reference marks in this book.

For full details of
BRITISH RAILWAYS CLASS "WD" 2-8-0s
running on the Southern Region,
see the
A.B.C. OF BRITISH RAILWAYS LOCOMOTIVES PT. IV. Nos. 60000–90999

0-6-0T Class R1

*Introduced 1888: Stirling S.E. design, later rebuilt with domed boiler.
†Introduced 1938: Fitted with Urie type short chimney for Whitstable branch, and fitted with or retaining original Stirling-type cab.
Weight: { 46 tons 15 cwt.* / 46 tons 8 cwt.† }
Pressure: 160 lb. Cyls.: 18″ × 26″
Driving Wheels: { 5′ 2″* / 5′ 1″† }
T.E.: { 18,480 lb.* / 18,780 lb.† }

*31047, 31128/54/74, 31335/7/40
†31010/69, 31107/47, 31339.

Total 12

0-6-0ST Class S

Introduced 1917: Maunsell rebuild of Wainwright S.E.C. C Class (built 1900) with saddle-tank.
Weight: 53 tons 10 cwt.
Pressure: 160 lb. Cyls.: 18½″ × 26″
Driving Wheels: 5′ 2″
T.E.: 19,520 lb.

31685 **Total 1**

4-4-0 Class S11

Introduced 1903: Drummond L.S.W. design, development of T9 with larger boiler barrel and smaller wheels for West of England, superheated from 1920.
Weight: Loco. 53 tons, 15 cwt.
Tender types: 17, 28
Pressure: 175 lb. Su.
Cyls: 19″ × 26″
Driving Wheels: 6′ 0″
T.E.: 19,390 lb.

30395–30404 **Total 10**

4-6-0 Class S15

*Introduced 1920: Urie L.S.W. design, development of N15 for mixed traffic work.
†Introduced 1927: Post-grouping locos. with higher pressure, smaller grate, modified footplating and other detail differences. 30833-7 with 6-wheel tenders for Central Section.
‡Introduced 1936: Later Locos. with detail differences and reduced weight.
Weight: Loco. { 79 tons 16 cwt.* / 80 tons 14 cwt.† / 79 tons 5 cwt.‡ }
Tender types: 26, 35, 37.
Pressure: { 180 lb. Su.* / 200 lb. Su.†‡ }
Cyls.: { (O) 21″ × 28″* / (O) 20½″ × 28″†‡ }
Driving Wheels: 5′ 7″
T.E.: { 28,200 lb.* / 29,855 lb.†‡ }
Walschaerts gear, P.V.

*30496–30515 †30823–37
‡30838–47

Total 45

0-6-0T Class T

Introduced 1879: Kirtley L.C.D. design (oldest survivor built 1890).
Weight: 40 tons 15 cwt.
Pressure: 160 lb. Cyls.: 17½″ × 24″
Driving Wheels: 4′ 6″
T.E.: 18,510 lb.

31602/4 500S

Total 3

0-4-4T Class T1

Introduced 1894: Adams L.S.W. design, originally designated F6, but later assimilated into Class T1 (introduced 1888).
Weight: 57 tons 2 cwt.
Pressure: 160 lb. Cyls.: 18″ × 26″
Driving Wheels: 5′ 7″
T.E.: 17,100 lb.

30001/5/7/20, 30367

Total 5

IMPORTANT NOTE

A careful reading of the notes on page 2 is essential to understand the use of reference marks in this book.

4-4-0 Class T9

*Introduced 1899 : Drummond L.S.W. design, fitted with superheater and larger cylinders by Urie from 1922.
†Introduced 1899 : Locos. with detail differences (originally fitted with firebox watertubes).
‡Introduced 1900 : Locos. with wider cab and splashers, and without coupling rod splashers (originally fitted with firebox watertubes.)

Weight : Loco. { 51 tons 18 cwt.* / 51 tons 16 cwt.† / 51 tons 7 cwt.‡ }
Tender types : 17, 18, 28.
Pressure : 175 lb. Su.
Cyls. : 19" × 26"
Driving Wheels : 6' 7"
T.E. : 17,675 lb.

*30113–22, 30280–9
†30702–19/21–33
‡30300–5/7/10–4/36–8 **Total 66**

4-6-0 Class T14

Introduced 1911 : Drummond L.S.W. design, fitted with superheater by Urie from 1915, and with Maunsell superheater, raised footplating and detail alterations from 1930.
Weight : Loco. 76 tons 10 cwt.
Tender type : 41.
Pressure : 175 lb. Su.
Cyls. : (4) 15" × 26"
Driving Wheels : 6' 7"
T.E. : 22,030 lb.
Walschaerts gear and rocking arms.

30444/6/7/61/2 **Total 5**

2-6-0 Classes U & U1

*U Introduced 1928 : Rebuild of Maunsell S.E.C. Class K ("River") 2–6–4T (introduced 1917).
†U Introduced 1928 : Locos. built as Class U, with smaller splashers and detail alterations.
‡U1 Introduced 1928 : 3-cylinder development of Class U (prototype, 31890, rebuilt from 2–6–4T, originally built 1925).

Weight : Loco. { 63 tons* / 62 tons 6 cwt.† / 65 tons 6 cwt.‡ }
Tender types : 19, 25.
Pressure : 200 lb. Su.
Cyls. : { (O) 19" × 28"*† / (3) 16" × 28"‡ }
Driving Wheels : 6' 0"
T.E. : { 23,865 lb.*† / 25,385 lb.‡ }
Walschaerts gear, P.V.

*31790–31809 †31610–39
‡31890–31910

Total : Class U 50
Class U1 21

0-6-0T Class USA

Introduced 1942 : U.S. Army Transportation Corps design, purchased by S.R. 1946, and fitted with modified cab and bunker and other detail alterations.
Weight : 46 tons 10 cwt.
Pressure : 210 lb.
Cyls. : (O) 16½" × 24"
Driving Wheels : 4' 6"
T.E. : 21,600 lb.
Walschaerts gear, P.V.

30061–74 **Total 14**

4-4-0 Class V

*Introduced 1930 : Maunsell design.
†Introduced 1938 : Fitted with multiple jet blastpipe and larger chimney by Bulleid.
Weight : Loco. 67 tons 2 cwt.
Tender type : 27.
Pressure : 220 lb. Su.
Cyls. : (3) 16½" × 26"
Driving Wheels : 6' 7"
T.E. : 25,135 lb.
Walschaerts gear, P.V.

*30902–6/8/10–2/6/22/3/5–8/32/5/6.
†30900/1/7/9/13–5/7–21/4/29–31/3/4/7–9.

Total 40

Class T9 4–4–0 No. 30708 [*E. C. Ive*

Class L11 4–4–0 No. 30156 [*H. C. Casserley*

Class B1 4–4–0 No. 31446 [*H. C. Casserley*

[P. Ransome-Wallis

Class D 4–4–0 No. 31549

[M. W. Earley

Class E 4–4–0 No. 1273 (new No. 31273)

Class E1 4-4-0 No. 31504 [*A. F. Cook*

Class L1 4-4-0 No. 1755 (new No. 31755) [*A. F. Cook*

Class L 4-4-0 No. 31767 [*M. P. Mileham*

Left : Class N1 2–6–0
No. 31909

[*C. C. B. Herbert*

Below : Class N 2–6–0
No. 31827

[*A. F. Cook*

Right : Class U 2–6–0
No. 31798

[*C. C. B. Herbert*

2-6-4T Class W

Introduced 1931 : Maunsell design, developed from Class N1 2–6–0.
Weight : 90 tons 14 cwt.
Pressure : 200 lb. Su.
Cyls. : (3) 16½″ × 28″
Driving Wheels : 5′ 6″
T.E. : 29,450 lb.
Walschaerts gear, P.V.

31911–25 **Total 15**

4-6-2 Classes WC & BB

*Introduced 1945 : Bulleid "West Country" Class.
†Introduced 1946 : Bulleid "Battle of Britain" Class.
‡Introduced 1948 : Locos. with larger tenders.
Weight : Loco. 86 tons 0 cwt.
Tender types : 30*, 30†, 40‡.
Pressure : 280 lb. Su.
Cyls. : (3) 16⅜″ × 24″
Driving Wheels : 6′ 2″
T.E. : 31,050 lb.
Bulleid valve gear, P.V.

*34001–48 †34049–70
‡34071–34105

N.B.—Locos. of this class are still being delivered.

0-8-0T Class Z

Introduced 1929 : Maunsell design for heavy shunting.
Weight : 71 tons 12 cwt.
Pressure : 180 lb. Cyls : (3) 16″ × 18″
Driving Wheels : 4′8″
T.E. : 29,375 lb.
Walschaerts gear, P.V.

30950–7 **Total 8**

0-6-0 Class 700

Introduced 1897 : Drummond L.S.W. design, superheated from 1921.
Weight : Loco. 46 tons 14 cwt.
Tender types : 17, 18.
Pressure : 180 lb. Su.
Cyls. : 19″ × 26″
Driving Wheels : 5′ 1″
T.E. : 23,540 lb.

30306/8/9/15–7/25–7/39/46/50/2/5/68, 30687–30701.

Total 30

0-6-0T Class 756

Introduced 1907 : Hawthorn Leslie design for P.D.S.W.J.
Weight : 35 tons 15 cwt.
Pressure : 170 lb.
Cyls. : (O) 14″ × 22″
Driving Wheels : 3′ 10″
T.E. : 13,545 lb.

30756 **Total 1**

0-6-2T Class 757

Introduced 1907 : Hawthorn Leslie design for P.D.S.W.J.
Weight : 49 tons 19 cwt.
Pressure : 170 lb.
Cyls. : (O) 16″ × 24″
Driving Wheels : 4′ 0″
T.E. : 18,495 lb.

30757–8 **Total 2**

0-4-0CT Class 1302

Introduced 1881 : Neilson patent crane tank for S.E.R.
Weight : 17 tons 17 cwt.
Pressure : 120 lb. Cyls : 11″ × 20
Driving Wheels : 3′ 3″
T.E. : 6,330 lb.

31302 **Total 1**

2-4-0WT Class 0298

Introduced 1874 : Beattie L.S.W. design, rebuilt by Adams (1884-92), Urie (1921-2) and Maunsell (1931-5).
Weight : 37 tons 16 cwt.
Pressure : 160 lb.
Cyls. : (O) 16½″ × 20″
Driving Wheels : 5′ 7″
T.E. : 11,050 lb.

30585–7 **Total 3**

For full details of
BRITISH RAILWAYS CLASS "WD" 2–8–0s
running on the Southern Region,
see the
A.B.C. OF BRITISH RAILWAYS LOCOMOTIVES PT. IV. Nos. 60000–90999

0-6-0 Class 0395

*Introduced 1881: Adams L.S.W. design.
†Introduced 1885: Adams "496" class, with longer front overhang.
‡Introduced 1928: Reboilered with ex-S.E.C. Class M3 4-4-0 boiler.
§Fitted with Drummond type boiler.
Weight: Loco. {37 tons 12 cwt.* / 38 tons 14 cwt.†}
Tender types: 2, 9.
Pressure: {140 lb.* / 150 lb.†}
Driving Wheels: 5′ 1″
T.E.: {15,535 lb.* / 16,645 lb.†}

*30568–72/4–8
†30566/79/81
*‡30573
*§30567
†‡30565/80
†§30564

Total 18

4-4-2T Class 0415

Introduced 1882: Adams L.S.W. design later reboilered (oldest survivor built 1883).
Weight: 55 tons 2 cwt.
Pressure: 160 lb.
Cyls.: (O) 17½″ × 24″
Driving Wheels: 5′ 7″
T.E.: 14,920 lb.

30582–4 Total 3

0-4-0ST Class 0458

Introduced 1890: Hawthorn Leslie design for Southampton Docks Co., absorbed by L.S.W., 1892.
Weight: 21 tons 2 cwt.
Pressure: 120 lb.
Cyls.: (O) 12″ × 20″
Driving Wheels: 3′ 2″
T.E.: 7,730 lb.

30458 Total 1

NUMERICAL LIST OF SOUTHERN REGION STEAM LOCOMOTIVES

(Named engines denoted by asterisk(*). See page 44).

30001	T1	30033	M7	30051	M7	30069	USA
30005	T1	30034	M7	30052	M7	30070	USA
30007	T1	30035	M7	30053	M7	30071	USA
30020	T1	30036	M7	30054	M7	30072	USA
30021	M7	30037	M7	30055	M7	30073	USA
30022	M7	30038	M7	30056	M7	30074	USA
30023	M7	30039	M7	30057	M7	30082	B4
30024	M7	30040	M7	30058	M7	30083	B4
30025	M7	30041	M7	30059	M7	30084	B4
30026	M7	30042	M7	30060	M7	30086*	B4
30027	M7	30043	M7	30061	USA	30087	B4
30028	M7	30044	M7	33002	USA	30088	B4
30029	M7	30045	M7	30063	USA	30089*	B4
30030	M7	30046	M7	30064	USA	30093*	B4
30031	M7	30047	M7	30065	USA	30094	B4
30032	M7	30048	M7	30066	USA	30096*	B4
		30049	M7	30067	USA	30102*	B4
		30050	M7	30068	USA	30104	M7

30105	M7
30106	M7
30107	M7
30108	M7
30109	M7
30110	M7
30111	M7
30112	M7
30113	T9
30114	T9
30115	T9
30116	T9
30117	T9
30118	T9
30119	T9
30120	T9
30121	T9
30122	T9
30123	M7
30124	M7
30125	M7
30127	M7
30128	M7
30129	M7
30130	M7
30131	M7
30132	M7
30133	M7
30134	L11
30137	K10
30140	K10
30141	K10
30142	K10
30144	K10
30148	L11
30151	K10
30154	L11
30155	L11
30156	L11
30157	L11
30158	L11
30159	L11
30160	G6
30161	L11
30162	G6
30163	L11
30164	L11
30165	L11
30166	L11
30167	L11
30168	L11
30169	L11
30170	L11
30171	L11
30172	L11
30173	L11
30174	L11
30175	L11
30177	O2
30179	O2
30182	O2
30183	O2
30192	O2
30193	O2
30197	O2
30199	O2
30200	O2
30203	O2
30204	O2
30207	O2
30212	O2
30213	O2
30216	O2
30221	O2
30223	O2
30224	O2
30225	O2
30229	O2
30230	O2
30231	O2
30232	O2
30233	O2
30236	O2
30238	G6
30241	M7
30242	M7
30243	M7
30244	M7
30245	M7
30246	M7
30247	M7
30248	M7
30249	M7
30250	M7
30251	M7
30252	M7
30253	M7
30254	M7
30255	M7
30256	M7
30258	G6
30259	G6
30260	G6
30262	G6
30263	G6
30265	G6
30266	G6
30268	G6
30269	G6
30270	G6
30272	G6
30274	G6
30275	G6
30276	G6
30277	G6
30280	T9
30281	T9
30282	T9
30283	T9
30284	T9
30285	T9
30286	T9
30287	T9
30288	T9
30289	T9
30300	T9
30301	T9
30302	T9
30303	T9
30304	T9
30305	T9
30306	700
30307	T9
30308	700
30309	700
30310	T9
30311	T9
30312	T9
30313	T9
30314	T9
30315	700
30316	700
30317	700
30318	M7
30319	M7
30320	M7
30321	M7
30322	M7
30323	M7
30324	M7
30325	700
30326	700
30327	700
30328	M7
30329	K10
30330	H15
30331	H15
30332	H15
30333	H15
30334	H15
30335	H15
30336	T9
30337	T9
30338	T9
30339	700
30341	K10
30345	K10
30346	700
30349	G6
30350	700
30352	700
30353	G6
30354	G6
30355	700
30356	M7
30357	M7
30367	T1
30368	700
30374	M7
30375	M7

30376	M7
30377	M7
30378	M7
30379	M7
30382	K10
30384	K10
30386	K10
30389	K10
30390	K10
30391	K10
30395	S11
30396	S11
30397	S11
30398	S11
30399	S11
30400	S11
30401	S11
30402	S11
30403	S11
30404	S11
30405	L11
30406	L11
30407	L11
30408	L11
30409	L11
30410	L11
30411	L11
30412	L11
30413	L11
30414	L11
30415	L12
30416	L12
30417	L12
30418	L12
30419	L12
30420	L12
30421	L12
30422	L12
30423	L12
30424	L12
30425	L12
30426	L12
30427	L12
30428	L12
30429	L12
30430	L12
30431	L12
30432	L12
30433	L12
30434	L12
30435	L11
30436	L11
30437	L11
30438	L11
30441	L11
30442	L11
30444	T14
30446	T14
30447	T14
30448*	N15
30449*	N15
30450*	N15
30451*	N15
30452*	N15
30453*	N15
30454*	N15
30455*	N15
30456*	N15
30457*	N15
30458*	0458
30461	T14
30462	T14
30463	D15
30464	D15
30465	D15
30466	D15
30467	D15
30468	D15
30469	D15
30470	D15
30471	D15
30472	D15
30473	H15
30474	H15
30475	H15
30476	H15
30477	H15
30478	H15
30479	M7
30480	M7
30481	M7
30482	H15
30483	H15
30484	H15
30485	H15
30486	H15
30487	H15
30488	H15
30489	H15
30490	H15
30491	H15
30492	G16
30493	G16
30494	G16
30495	G16
30496	S15
30497	S15
30498	S15
30499	S15
30500	S15
30501	S15
30502	S15
30503	S15
30504	S15
30505	S15
30506	S15
30507	S15
30508	S15
30509	S15
30510	S15
30511	S15
30512	S15
30513	S15
30514	S15
30515	S15
30516	H16
30517	H16
30518	H16
30519	H16
30520	H16
30521	H15
30522	H15
30523	H15
30524	H15
30530	Q
30531	Q
30532	Q
30533	Q
30534	Q
30535	Q
30536	Q
30537	Q
30538	Q
30539	Q
30540	Q
30541	Q
30542	Q
30543	Q
30544	Q
30545	Q
30546	Q
30547	Q
30548	Q
30549	Q
30564	0395
30565	0395
30566	0395
30567	0395
30568	0395
30569	0395
30570	0395
30571	0395
30572	0395
30573	0395
30574	0395
30575	0395
30576	0395
30577	0395
30578	0395
30579	0395
30580	0395
30581	0395
30582	0415
30583	0415
30584	0415
30585	0298
30586	0298
30587	0298
30588	C14
30589	C14

30667 M7
30668 M7
30669 M7
30670 M7
30671 M7
30673 M7
30674 M7
30675 M7
30676 M7
30687 700
30688 700
30689 700
30690 700
30691 700
30692 700
30693 700
30694 700
30695 700
30696 700
30697 700
30698 700
30699 700
30700 700
30701 700
30702 T9
30703 T9
30704 T9
30705 T9
30706 T9
30707 T9
30708 T9
30709 T9
30710 T9
30711 T9
30712 T9
30713 T9
30714 T9
30715 T9
30716 T9
30717 T9
30718 T9
30719 T9
30721 T9
30722 T9
30723 T9
30724 T9
30725 T9
30726 T9
30727 T9
30728 T9
30729 T9
30730 T9
30731 T9
30732 T9
30733 T9
30736* N15
30737* N15
30738* N15
30739* N15
30740* N15
30741* N15
30742* N15
30743* N15
30744* N15
30745* N15
30746* N15
30747* N15
30748* N15
30749* N15
30750* N15
30751* N15
30752* N15
30753* N15
30754* N15
30755* N15
30756* 756
30757* 757
30758* 757
30763* N15
30764* N15
30765* N15
30766* N15
30767* N15
30768* N15
30769* N15
30770* N15
30771* N15
30772* N15
30773* N15
30774* N15
30775* N15
30776* N15
30777* N15
30778* N15
30779* N15
30780* N15
30781* N15
30782* N15
30783* N15
30784* N15
30785* N15
30786* N15
30787* N15
30788* N15
30789* N15
30790* N15
30791* N15
30792* N15
30793* N15
30794* N15
30795* N15
30796* N15
30797* N15
30798* N15
30799* N15
30800* N15
30801* N15
30802* N15
30803* N15
30804* N15
30805* N15
30806* N15
30823 S15
30824 S15
30825 S15
30826 S15
30827 S15
30828 S15
30829 S15
30830 S15
30831 S15
30832 S15
30833 S15
30834 S15
30835 S15
30836 S15
30837 S15
30838 S15
30839 S15
30840 S15
30841 S15
30842 S15
30843 S15
30844 S15
30845 S15
30846 S15
30847 S15
30850* LN
30851* LN
30852* LN
30853* LN
30854* LN
30855* LN
30856* LN
30857* LN
30858* LN
30859* LN
30860* LN
30861* LN
30862* LN
30863* LN
30864* LN
30865* LN
30900* V
30901* V
30902* V
30903* V
30904* V
30905* V
30906* V
30907* V
30908* V
30909* V
30910* V
30911* V
30912* V
30913* V
30914* V
30915* V
30916* V

30917*	V	31044	OI	31178	P	31276	H
30918*	V	31047	RI	31179	EI	31277	C
30919*	V	31048	OI	31182	H	31278	H
30920*	V	31054	C	31184	H	31279	H
30921*	V	31057	D	31191	C	31280	C
30922*	V	31059	C	31193	H	31287	C
30923*	V	31061	C	31217	BI	31291	C
30924*	V	31063	C	31218	C	31293	C
30925*	V	31064	OI	31219	C	31294	C
30926*	V	31065	OI	31221	C	31295	H
30927*	V	31066	OI	31223	C	31297	C
30928*	V	31067	EI	31225	C	31298	C
30929*	V	31068	C	31227	C	31302	1302
30930*	V	31069	RI	31229	C	31305	H
30931*	V	31071	C	31234	C	31306	H
30932*	V	31075	D	31238	OI	31307	H
30933*	V	31080	OI	31239	H	31308	H
30934*	V	31086	C	31242	C	31309	H
30935*	V	31090	C	31243	C	31310	H
30936*	V	31092	D	31244	C	31311	H
30937*	V	31093	OI	31245	C	31315	E
30938*	V	31102	C	31246	DI	31317	C
30939*	V	31107	RI	31247	DI	31319	H
30949*	KES	31108	OI	31248	OI	31320	H
30950	Z	31112	C	31252	C	31321	H
30951	Z	31113	C	31253	C	31322	H
30952	Z	31123	OI	31255	C	31323	P
30953	Z	31128	RI	31256	C	31324	H
30954	Z	31145	DI	31257	C	31325	P
30955	Z	31147	RI	31258	OI	31326	H
30956	Z	31150	C	31259	H	31327	H
30957	Z	31154	RI	31260	C	31328	H
31004	C	31157	E	31261	H	31329	H
31005	H	31158	H	31263	H	31335	RI
31010	RI	31159	E	31265	H	31337	RI
31016	H	31160	EI	31266	H	31339	RI
31018	C	31161	H	31267	C	31340	RI
31019	EI	31162	H	31268	C	31369	OI
31027	P	31164	H	31269	H	31370	OI
31033	C	31165	EI	31270	C	31373	OI
31036	E	31166	E	31271	C	31374	OI
31037	C	31174	RI	31272	C	31377	OI
31038	C	31175	E	31273	E	31379	OI
31039	OI	31176	E	31274	H	31380	OI
31041	OI	31177	H	31275	E	31381	OI

31383	O1
31384	O1
31385	O1
31390	O1
31391	O1
31395	O1
31400	N
31401	N
31402	N
31403	N
31404	N
31405	N
31406	N
31407	N
31408	N
31409	N
31410	N
31411	N
31412	N
31413	N
31414	N
31425	O1
31429	O1
31430	O1
31432	O1
31434	O1
31443	B1
31446	B1
31448	B1
31451	B1
31452	B1
31461	C
31470	D1
31477	D
31480	C
31481	C
31486	C
31487	D1
31488	D
31489	D1
31490	D
31491	E
31492	D1
31493	D
31494	D1
31495	C
31496	D
31497	E1
31498	C
31500	H
31501	D
31502	D1
31503	H
31504	E1
31505	D1
31506	E1
31507	E1
31508	C
31509	D1
31510	C
31511	E1
31512	H
31513	C
31514	E
31515	E
31516	E
31517	H
31518	H
31519	H
31520	H
31521	H
31522	H
31523	H
31530	H
31531	H
31532	H
31533	H
31540	H
31541	H
31542	H
31543	H
31544	H
31545	D1
31546	H
31547	E
31548	H
31549	D
31550	H
31551	H
31552	H
31553	H
31554	H
31555	P
31556	P
31557	P
31558	P
31572	C
31573	C
31574	D
31575	C
31576	C
31577	D
31578	C
31579	C
31580	C
31581	C
31582	C
31583	C
31584	C
31585	C
31586	D
31587	E
31588	C
31589	C
31590	C
31591	D
31592	C
31593	C
31595	J
31596	J
31597	J
31598	J
31599	J
31602	T
31604	T
31610	U
31611	U
31612	U
31613	U
31614	U
31615	U
31616	U
31617	U
31618	U
31619	U
31620	U
31621	U
31622	U
31623	U
31624	U
31625	U
31626	U
31627	U
31628	U
31629	U
31630	U
31631	U
31632	U
31633	U
31634	U
31635	U
31636	U
31637	U
31638	U
31639	U
31658	R
31659	R
31660	R
31661	R
31662	R
31663	R
31665	R
31666	R
31667	R
31670	R
31671	R
31672	R
31673	R
31674	R
31675	R
31681	C
31682	C
31683	C
31684	C
31685	S
31686	C
31687	C
31688	C
31689	C
31690	C
31691	C
31692	C

31693	C
31694	C
31695	C
31696	R1
31697	R1
31698	R1
31699	R1
31700	R1
31703	R1
31704	R1
31705	R1
31706	R1
31708	R1
31709	R1
31710	R1
31711	C
31712	C
31713	C
31714	C
31715	C
31716	C
31717	C
31718	C
31719	C
31720	C
31721	C
31722	C
31723	C
31724	C
31725	C
31727	D1
31728	D
31729	D
31730	D
31731	D
31732	D
31733	D
31734	D
31735	D1
31736	D1
31737	D
31738	D
31739	D1
31740	D
31741	D1
31743	D1
31744	D
31745	D1
31746	D
31748	D
31749	D1
31750	D
31753	L1
31754	L1
31755	L1
31756	L1
31757	L1
31758	L1
31759	L1
31760	L
31761	L
31762	L
31763	L
31764	L
31765	L
31766	L
31767	L
31768	L
31769	L
31770	L
31771	L
31772	L
31773	L
31774	L
31775	L
31776	L
31777	L
31778	L
31779	L
31780	L
31781	L
31782	L1
31783	L1
31784	L1
31785	L1
31786	L1
31787	L1
31788	L1
31789	L1
31790	U
31791	U
31792	U
31793	U
31794	U
31795	U
31796	U
31797	U
31798	U
31799	U
31800	U
31801	U
31802	U
31803	U
31804	U
31805	U
31806	U
31807	U
31808	U
31809	U
31810	N
31811	N
31812	N
31813	N
31814	N
31815	N
31816	N
31817	N
31818	N
31819	N
31820	N
31821	N
31822	N1
31823	N
31824	N
31825	N
31826	N
31827	N
31828	N
31829	N
31830	N
31831	N
31832	N
31833	N
31834	N
31835	N
31836	N
31837	N
31838	N
31839	N
31840	N
31841	N
31842	N
31843	N
31844	N
31845	N
31846	N
31847	N
31848	N
31849	N
31850	N
31851	N
31852	N
31853	N
31854	N
31855	N
31856	N
31857	N
31858	N
31859	N
31860	N
31861	N
31862	N
31863	N
31864	N
31865	N
31866	N
31867	N
31868	N
31869	N
31870	N
31871	N
31872	N
31873	N
31874	N
31875	N
31876	N1
31877	N1
31878	N1
31879	N1
31880	N1

" Merchant Navy " 4-6-2 No. 35024 [*A. F. Cook*

" West Country " 4-6-2 No. 34011 *Tavistock* [*L. Elsey*

[*C. C. B. Herbert*
"Battle of Britain " 4-6-2 No. 34059 *Sir Archibald Sinclair*

Class No S15 4-6-0 No. 838 (new No. 30838) [W. Gilburt

Class H15 4-6-0 No. 30486 [H. C. Casserley

Class T14 4-6-0 No. 30446 [W. Gilburt

Class N15X 4-6-0 No. 32333 *Remembrance* [A. F. Cook

[C. C. B. Herbert
Class H2 4-4-2 No. 32421 *South Foreland*

Class V 4-4-0 No. 30934 *St. Lawrence* [H. C. Casserley

Above : " Lord Nelson " No. 852 *Sir Walter Raleigh* (new No. 30852) leaving Southampton with a down Bournemouth express

[*Pursey C. Short*

Below : A " Urie Arthur " with large diameter chimney—No. 30741 *Joyous Gard* heads through Clapham Junction with a down Basingstoke train

[*C. C. B. Herbert*

LORD

KIN

Right· Sma
No. 30796 S
at Salisbu

Below : "Ea
Sir Galahac
with a dow

LSONS
)
RTHURS

Scotch Arthur"
le *Savage* arrives
slow passenger

hur" No. 30456
orting Junction
England express

G. O. P. Pearce
[M. W. Earley

Urie Arthur " No. 782 *Sir Brian* (new No. 30782) at speed near Fleet with an up Southampton boat train

[C. J. Grose

Class C 0–6–0 No. 31068 [A. F. Cook

Class 700 0–6–0 No. 30339 [G. B. Seymour

Class 0395 0–6–0 No. 30571 [H. C. Casserley

Class C2X 0–6–0 No. 32440 [W. Beckerlegge

Class Q 0–6–0 No. 30541 [A. S. H. Tayler

Class Q1 0–6–0 No. 33037 [P. Ransome-Wallis

Class K 2-6-0 No. 32348 [W. Beckerlegge

Class B4X 4-4-0 No. 32071 [H.C. Casserley

Class C3 0-6-0 No. 32301 [W. Beckerlegge

31890	U1
31891	U1
31892	U1
31893	U1
31894	U1
31895	U1
31896	U1
31897	U1
31898	U1
31899	U1
31900	U1
31901	U1
31902	U1
31903	U1
31904	U1
31905	U1
31906	U1
31907	U1
31908	U1
31909	U1
31910	U1
31911	W
31912	W
31913	W
31914	W
31915	W
31916	W
31917	W
31918	W
31919	W
31920	W
31921	W
31922	W
31923	W
31924	W
31925	W
32002	I1X
32005	I1X
32008	I1X
32009	I1X
32021	I3
32022	I3
32023	I3
32025	I3
32026	I3
32027	I3
32028	I3
32029	I3
32030	I3
32037*	H1
32038*	H1
32039*	H1
32043	B4X
32045	B4X
32050	B4X
32052	B4X
32054	B4
32055	B4X
32056	B4X
32060	B4X
32062	B4
32063	B4
32067	B4X
32068	B4
32070	B4X
32071	B4X
32072	B4X
32073	B4X
32074	B4
32075	I3
32076	I3
32077	I3
32078	I3
32079	I3
32080	I3
32081	I3
32082	I3
32083	I3
32084	I3
32085	I3
32086	I3
32087	I3
32088	I3
32089	I3
32090	I3
32091	I3
32094	E1/R
32095	E1/R
32096	E1/R
32097	E1
32100	E2
32101	E2
32102	E2
32103	E2
32104	E2
32105	E2
32106	E2
32107	E2
32108	E2
32109	E2
32112	E1
32113	E1
32124	E1/R
32127	E1
32128	E1
32129	E1
32133	E1
32135	E1/R
32138	E1
32139	E1
32141	E1
32142	E1
32145	E1
32147	E1
32151	E1
32156	E1
32160	E1
32162	E1
32165	E3
32166	E3
32167	E3
32168	E3
32169	E3
32170	E3
32215	D1/M
32234	D1/M
32252	D1/M
32253	D1/M
32274	D1
32300	C3
32301	C3
32302	C3
32303	C3
32306	C3
32325	J1
32326	J2
32327*	N15X
32328*	N15X
32329*	N15X
32330*	N15X
32331*	N15X
32332*	N15X
32333*	N15X
32337	K
32338	K
32339	K
32340	K
32341	K
32342	K
32343	K
32344	K
32345	K
32346	K
32347	K
32348	K
32349	K
32350	K
32351	K
32352	K
32353	K
32359	D1/M
32364	D3
32365	D3
32368	D3
32372	D3
32376	D3
32378	D3
32379	D3
32380	D3
32384	D3
32385	D3
32386	D3
32388	D3
32390	D3
32391	D3
32393	D3
32394	D3
32399	E5

32400	E5
32401	E5X
32402	E5
32404	E5
32406	E5
32407	E6X
32408	E6
32409	E6
32410	E6
32411	E6X
32412	E6
32413	E6
32414	E6
32415	E6
32416	E6
32417	E6
32418	E6
32421*	H2
32422*	H2
32424*	H2
32425*	H2
32426*	H2
32434	C2X
32436	C2
32437	C2X
32438	C2X
32440	C2X
32441	C2X
32442	C2X
32443	C2X
32444	C2X
32445	C2X
32446	C2X
32447	C2X
32448	C2X
32449	C2X
32450	C2X
32451	C2X
32453	E3
32454	E3
32455	E3
32456	E3
32458	E3
32459	E3
32460	E3
32461	E3
32462	E3
32463	E4
32464	E4
32465	E4
32466	E4X
32467	E4
32468	E4
32469	E4
32470	E4
32471	E4
32472	E4
32473	E4
32474	E4
32475	E4
32476	E4
32477	E4X
32478	E4X
32479	E4
32480	E4
32481	E4
32482	E4
32484	E4
32485	E4
32486	E4
32487	E4
32488	E4
32489	E4X
32490	E4
32491	E4
32492	E4
32493	E4
32494	E4
32495	E4
32496	E4
32497	E4
32498	E4
32499	E4
32500	E4
32501	E4
32502	E4
32503	E4
32504	E4
32505	E4
32506	E4
32507	E4
32508	E4
32509	E4
32510	E4
32511	E4
32512	E4
32513	E4
32514	E4
32515	E4
32516	E4
32517	E4
32518	E4
32519	E4
32520	E4
32521	C2X
32522	C2X
32523	C2X
32524	C2X
32525	C2X
32526	C2X
32527	C2X
32528	C2X
32529	C2X
32532	C2X
32533	C2
32534	C2X
32535	C2X
32536	C2X
32537	C2X
32538	C2X
32539	C2X
32540	C2X
32541	C2X
32543	C2X
32544	C2X
32545	C2X
32546	C2X
32547	C2X
32548	C2X
32549	C2X
32550	C2X
32551	C2X
32552	C2X
32553	C2X
32554	C2X
32556	E4
32557	E4
32558	E4
32559	E4
32560	E4
32561	E4
32562	E4
32563	E4
32564	E4
32565	E4
32566	E4
32567	E5
32568	E5
32570	E5X
32571	E5
32573	E5
32574	E5
32575	E5
32576	E5X
32577	E4
32578	E4
32579	E4
32580	E4
32581	E4
32582	E4
32583	E5
32584	E5
32585	E5
32586	E5X
32587	E5
32588	E5
32590	E5
32591	E5
32592	E5
32593	E5
32594	E5
32595	I1X
32596	I1X
32602	I1X
32603	I1X
32608	E1/R
32610	E1/R
32636	A1X
32640	A1X
32644	A1X

32646	A1X
32647	A1X
32655	A1X
32659	A1X
32661	A1X
32662	A1X
32670	A1X
32677	A1X
32678	A1X
32689	E1
32690	E1
32691	E1
32694	E1
32695	E1/R
32696	E1/R
32697	E1/R
33001	Q1
33002	Q1
33003	Q1
33004	Q1
33005	Q1
33006	Q1
33007	Q1
33008	Q1
33009	Q1
33010	Q1
33011	Q1
33012	Q1
33013	Q1
33014	Q1
33015	Q1
33016	Q1
33017	Q1
33018	Q1
33019	Q1
33020	Q1
33021	Q1
33022	Q1
33023	Q1
33024	Q1
33025	Q1
33026	Q1
33027	Q1
33028	Q1
33029	Q1
33030	Q1
33031	Q1
33032	Q1
33033	Q1
33034	Q1
33035	Q1
33036	Q1
33037	Q1
33038	Q1
33039	Q1
33040	Q1
34001*	WC
34002*	WC
34003*	WC
34004*	WC
34005*	WC
34006*	WC
34007*	WC
34008*	WC
34009*	WC
34010*	WC
34011*	WC
34012*	WC
34013*	WC
34014*	WC
34015*	WC
34016*	WC
34017*	WC
34018*	WC
34019*	WC
34020*	WC
34021*	WC
34022*	WC
34023*	WC
34024*	WC
34025*	WC
34026*	WC
34027*	WC
34028*	WC
34029*	WC
34030*	WC
34031*	WC
34032*	WC
34033*	WC
34034*	WC
34035*	WC
34036*	WC
34037*	WC
34038*	WC
34039*	WC
34040*	WC
34041*	WC
34042*	WC
34043*	WC
34044*	WC
34045*	WC
34046*	WC
34047*	WC
34048*	WC
34049*	BB
34050*	BB
34051*	BB
34052*	BB
34053*	BB
34054*	BB
34055*	BB
34056*	BB
34057*	BB
34058*	BB
34059*	BB
34060*	BB
34061*	BB
34062*	BB
34063*	BB
34064*	BB
34065*	BB
34066*	BB
34067*	BB
34068*	BB
34069*	BB
34070*	BB
34071*	BB
34072*	BB
34073*	BB
34074*	BB
34075*	BB
34076*	BB
34077*	BB
34078*	BB
34079*	BB
34080*	BB
34081*	BB
34082*	BB
34083*	BB
34084*	BB
34085*	BB
34086*	BB
34087*	BB
34088*	BB
34089*	BB
34090*	BB
34091†	
34092†	
34093†	
34094†	
34095†	
34096†	
34097†	
34098†	
34099†	
34100†	
34101†	
34102†	
34103†	
34104†	
34105†	
35001*	MN
35002*	MN
35003*	MN
35004*	MN
35005*	MN
35006*	MN
35007*	MN
35008*	MN
35009*	MN
35010*	MN
35011*	MN
35012*	MN
35013*	MN
35014*	MN
35015*	MN
35016*	MN
35017*	MN
35018*	MN
35019*	MN

†Under Construction

35020* MN	36002† Lead.	W 15* O2	W 27* O2
35021* MN	36003† Lead.	W 16* O2	W 28* O2
35022* MN	36004† Lead.	W 17* O2	W 29* O2
35023* MN	36005† Lead.	W 18* O2	W 30* O2
35024* MN		W 19* O2	W 31* O2
35025* MN	**I.O.W.**	W 20* O2	W 32* O2
35026* MN	**LOCOS.**	W 21* O2	W 33* O2
35027* MN	W 1* E1	W 22* O2	W 34* O2
35028* MN	W 2* E1	W 23* O2	W 35* O2
35029* MN	W 3* E1	W 24* O2	W 36* O2
35030* MN	W 4* E1	W 25* O2	† Under construction.
36001 Lead.	W 14* O2	W 26* O2	

NAMED ENGINES OF THE S.R.
(in numerical order)

0-4-0T Class B4

30086 Havre
30089 Trouville
30093 St. Malo
30096 Normandy
30102 Granville

" King Arthur Class "
4-6-0 Class N15

30448 Sir Tristram
30449 Sir Torre
30450 Sir Kay
30451 Sir Lamorak
30452 Sir Meliagrance
30453 King Arthur
30454 Queen Guinevere
30455 Sir Launcelot
30456 Sir Galahad
30457 Sir Bedivere

(*continued with No.* 30736)

0-4-0ST Class 0458

30458 Ironside

" King Arthur Class "
4-6-0 Class N15
(*continued*)

30736 Excalibur
30737 King Uther
30738 King Pellinore
30739 King Leodegrance
30740 Merlin
30741 Joyous Gard
30742 Camelot
30743 Lyonnesse
30744 Maid of Astolat
30745 Tintagel
30746 Pendragon
30747 Elaine
30748 Vivien
30749 Iseult
30750 Morgan le Fay
30751 Etarre
30752 Linette
30753 Melisande
30754 The Green Knight
30755 The Red Knight

(*continued with No.* 30763)

0-6-0T Class 756

30756 A. S. Harris

0-6-2T Class 757

30757 Earl of Mount Edgcumbe
30758 Lord St. Levan

" King Arthur " Class

4-6-0 Class N15

(continued)

30763	Sir Bors de Ganis
30764	Sir Gawain
30765	Sir Gareth
30766	Sir Geraint
30767	Sir Valence
30768	Sir Balin
30769	Sir Balan
30770	Sir Prianius
30771	Sir Sagramore
30772	Sir Percivale
30773	Sir Lavaine
30774	Sir Gaheris
30775	Sir Agravaine
30776	Sir Galagars
30777	Sir Lamiel
30778	Sir Pelleas
30779	Sir Colgrevance
30780	Sir Persant
30781	Sir Aglovale
30782	Sir Brian
30783	Sir Gillemere
30784	Sir Nerovens
30785	Sir Mador de la Porte
30786	Sir Lionel
30787	Sir Menadeuke
30788	Sir Urre of the Mount
30789	Sir Guy
30790	Sir Villiars
30791	Sir Uwaine
30792	Sir Hervis de Revel
30793	Sir Ontzlake
30794	Sir Ector de Maris
30795	Sir Dinadan
30796	Sir Dodinas le Savage
30797	Sir Blamor de Ganis
30798	Sir Hectimere
30799	Sir Ironside
30800	Sir Meleaus de Lile
30801	Sir Meliot de Logres
30802	Sir Durnore
30803	Sir Harry le Fise Lake
30804	Sir Cador of Cornwall
30805	Sir Constantine
30806	Sir Galleron

" Lord Nelson " Class

4-6-0 Class LN

30850	Lord Nelson
30851	Sir Francis Drake
30852	Sir Walter Raleigh
30853	Sir Richard Grenville
30854	Howard of Effingham
30855	Robert Blake
30856	Lord St. Vincent
30857	Lord Howe
30858	Lord Duncan
30859	Lord Hood
30860	Lord Hawke
30861	Lord Anson
30862	Lord Collingwood
30863	Lord Rodney
30864	Sir Martin Frobisher
30865	Sir John Hawkins

" Schools " Class

4-4-0 Class V

30900	Eton
30901	Winchester
30902	Wellington
30903	Charterhouse
30904	Lancing
30905	Tonbridge
30906	Sherborne
30907	Dulwich
30908	Westminster
30909	St. Paul's
30910	Merchant Taylors
30911	Dover
30912	Downside
30913	Christ's Hospital
30914	Eastbourne
30915	Brighton
30916	Whitgift
30917	Ardingly
30918	Hurstpierpoint

30919	Harrow
30920	Rugby
30921	Shrewsbury
30922	Marlborough
30923	Bradfield
30924	Haileybury
30925	Cheltenham
30926	Repton
30927	Clifton
30928	Stowe
30929	Malvern
30930	Radley
30931	King's Wimbledon
30932	Blundells
30933	King's Canterbury
30934	St. Lawrence
30935	Sevenoaks
30936	Cranleigh
30937	Epsom
30938	St. Olave's
30939	Leatherhead

0-8-0T Class KES

30949	Hecate

4-4-2 Class H1

32037	Selsey Bill
32038	Portland Bill
32039	Hartland Point

" Remembrance " Class
4-6-0 Class N15X

32327	Trevithick
32328	Hackworth
32329	Stephenson
32330	Cudworth
32331	Beattie
32332	Stroudley
32333	Remembrance

4-4-2 Class H2

32421	South Foreland
32422	North Foreland
32424	Beachy Head
32425	Trevose Head
32426	St. Alban's Head

" West Country " Class
4-6-2 Class WC

34001	Exeter
34002	Salisbury
34003	Plymouth
34004	Yeovil
34005	Barnstaple
34006	Bude
34007	Wadebridge
34008	Padstow
34009	Lyme Regis
34010	Sidmouth
34011	Tavistock
34012	Launceston
34013	Okehampton
34014	Budleigh Salterton
34015	Exmouth
34016	Bodmin
34017	Ilfracombe
34018	Axminster
34019	Bideford
34020	Seaton
34021	Dartmoor
34022	Exmoor
34023	Blackmoor Vale
34024	Tamar Valley
34025	Whimple
34026	Yes Tor
34027	Taw Valley
34028	Eddystone
34029	Lundy
34030	Watersmeet
34031	Torrington
34032	Camelford
34033	Chard
34034	Honiton
34035	Shaftesbury
34036	Westward Ho !
34037	Clovelly

34038 Lynton
34039 Boscastle
34040 Crewkerne
34041 Wilton
34042 Dorchester
34043 Combe Martin
34044 Woolacombe
34045 Ottery St. Mary
34046 Braunton
34047 Callington
34048 Crediton

"Battle of Britain" Class

4-6-2 **Class BB**

34049 Anti-Aircraft Command
34050 Royal Observer Corps
34051 Winston Churchill
34052 Lord Dowding
34053 Sir Keith Park
34054 Lord Beaverbrook
34055 Fighter Pilot
34056 Croydon
34057 Biggin Hill
34058 Sir Frederick Pile
34059 Sir Archibald Sinclair
34060 25 Squadron
34061 73 Squadron
34062 17 Squadron
34063 229 Squadron
34064 Fighter Command
34065 Hurricane
34066 Spitfire
34067 Tangmere
34068 Kenley
34069 Hawkinge
34070 Manston
34071 601 Squadron
34072 257 Squadron
34073 249 Squadron
34074 46 Squadron
34075 264 Squadron
34076 41 Squadron
34077 603 Squadron
34078 222 Squadron
34079 141 Squadron
34080 74 Squadron
34081 92 Squadron
34082 615 Squadron
34083 605 Squadron
34084 253 Squadron
34085 501 Squadron
34086 219 Squadron
34087 145 Squadron
34088 213 Squadron
34089 602 Squadron
34090 Sir Eustace Missenden, Southern Railway

"Merchant Navy"

4-6-2 **Class MN**

35001 Channel Packet
35002 Union Castle
35003 Royal Mail
35004 Cunard White Star
35005 Canadian Pacific
35006 Peninsular & Oriental S.N. Co.
35007 Aberdeen Commonwealth
35008 Orient Line
35009 Shaw Savill
35010 Blue Star
35011 General Steam Navigation
35012 United States Line
35013 Blue Funnel
35014 Nederland Line
35015 Rotterdam Lloyd
35016 Elders Fyffes
35017 Belgian Marine
35018 British India Line
35019 French Line CGT
35020 Bibby Line
35021 New Zealand Line
35022 Holland-America Line
35023 Holland-Afrika Line
35024 East Asiatic Company

35025	Brocklebank Line
35026	Lamport & Holt Line
35027	Port Line
35028	Clan Line
35029	Ellerman Lines
35030	Elder Dempster Lines

0-6-0T Class E1

W 1	Medina
W 2	Yarmouth
W 3	Ryde
W 4	Wroxall

0-4-4T Class O2

W14	Fishbourne
W15	Cowes
W16	Ventnor
W17	Seaview
W18	Ningwood
W19	Osborne
W20	Shanklin
W21	Sandown
W22	Brading
W23	Totland
W24	Calbourne
W25	Godshill
W26	Whitwell
W27	Merstone
W28	Ashey
W29	Alverstone
W30	Shorwell
W31	Chale
W32	Bonchurch
W33	Bembridge
W34	Newport
W35	Freshwater
W36	Carisbrooke

SOUTHERN REGION SERVICE LOCOS.

No.	Old No.	Class	Station
†49 S	—	Shunter	Broad Clyst Sleep. Depot
*74 S	—	Bo-Bo	Durnsford R Power Stn.
*75 S	—	Bo	Waterloo & City Rly.
77 S	0745	C14	Redbridge Sleep. Depot
†343 S	—	Shunter	Eastleigh Carr. Works
†346 S	—	Inspection Car	Engin'r's Dept.
‡377 S	2635	AIX	Brighton Wks.
§400 S	—	0-4-0	S'hamptonDks.
500 S	1607	T	Meldon Quarry
515 S	L.B.S.C. 650 I.W. 9	AIX	Lancing Carr. Wks.
600 S	—	0-4-0 diesel	
680 S	L.B.S.C. 654 SEC. 751.	A I	,,
701 S	2284	D I	Fratton**

* Electric
** Ex-oil Pumping Engine
‡ Repainted 1947 in Stroudley livery
§ Fowler Diesel
† Petrol

Class W 2–6–4T No. 31916 [*L. Elsey*

Class 757 0–6–2T No. 30757 *Earl of Mount Edgcumbe* [*W. Gilburt*

Class Z 0–8–0 No. s953 (new No. 30953) [*P. L. Melvill*

Class S 0–6–0ST No. 31685 [N. F. Parker

Class M7 0–4–4T No. 30038 [C. C. B. Herbert

Class O2 0–4–4T No. 30213 [H. C. Casserley

Class R1 0–6–0T No. 31069 [W. Beckerlegge

Class H 0–4–4T No. 31521 [P. Ransome-Wallis

Class R1 0–4–4T No. 31706 [A. F. Cook

Class I3 4–4–2T No. 32079 [L. Elsey

Class E4 0–6–2T No. 32499 [W. Beckerlegge

Class E6 0–6–2T No. 32415 [H. C. Casserley

THE NEW S.R. MOTIVE POWER CLASSIFICATION

Classification	
PASSENGER TENDER	
7P	Merchant Navy
6P	Lord Nelson
5P	N15, V (Schools)
4P	H2, N15X, T14
3P	B4X, D15, H1
2P	D1, E1 (4-4-0), L, L1, L12, S11, T9
1P	B1, B4 (4-4-0), D, E
PASSENGER TANK	
4PT	J1, J2
3PT	I3
2PT	I1X, M7
1PT	D1, D1/M, D3, H, O2, 0415, R, R1 (0-4-4T), T1
0PT	A1X
MIXED TRAFFIC TENDER	
6MT	West Country, Battle of Britain
4MT	H15, K, N, N1, U, U1
1MT	K10, L11

Classification	*Class*
MIXED TRAFFIC TANK	
3MTTK	J
2MTTK	E1/R, E4, E4X, E5, E5X
1MTTK	757
FREIGHT TENDER	
7F	Austerity 2-8-0
6F	S15
5F	Q1
4F	Q, 700
3F	C, C2X, C3
2F	C2
1F	O1, 0395
FREIGHT TANK	
7FT	Z, G16
5FT	H16, W
4FT	E6, E6X
3FT	E2, E3, U.S.A.
2FT	E1, KES, G6, R1 (0-6-0T), S, T
1FT	756
0FT	B4 (0-4-0T), C14, 0298, 0458, P, 31302
UNCLASSIFIED	
	Electric Passenger
	Diesel Electric Shunter

DIMENSIONS OF BRITISH RAILWAYS DIESEL ELECTRIC LOCOMOTIVES

Region	Type	Date	Weight tons cwt.	Driving Wheels ft. ins.	H.P.	T.E.
L.M.	0–6–6–0	1947	121 10	3 6	1,600	41,400 lb.
L.M.	0–6–0	1936	{51 0 / 47 0}	4 0½	350	30,000 lb.
L.M.	0–6–0	1939	54 16	4 3	350	33,000 lb.
L.M.	0–6–0	1945	50 0	4 0½	350	33,000 lb.
L.M.	0–6–0	1934	40 10	3 6	250	24,000 lb.
E.	0–6–0	1944	51 0	4 0	350	32,000 lb.
W....	0–6–0	1936	51 10	4 1	350	30,000 lb.
W....	0–6–0	1948	46 9	4 0½	350	33,500 lb.
S.	0–6–0	1937	55 5	4 6	350	30,000 lb.
S.	0–6–0	1949	49 0	4 6	350	24,000 lb.

DIMENSIONS OF BRITISH RAILWAYS ELECTRIC LOCOMOTIVES

Region	Class	Type	Date	Weight tons cwt.	Voltage	T.E.
S.	C.C.	Co + Co	1942-5	{99 14 / 104 14}	600 D.C.	40,000 lb.
E. & N.E.	E.M.I.	Bo + Bo	1941	87 18	1,500 D.C.	45,000 lb.
N.E.	E.B.I.	Bo + Bo	1914	74 8	1,500 D.C.	28,000 lb.
N.E.	E.S.I.	Bo + Bo	1905	56 0	600 D.C.	25,000 lb.
N.E.	E.E.I.	2 - Co - 2	1922	110 1	1,500 D.C.	28,000 lb.

PRINCIPAL DIMENSIONS of SOUTHERN REGION STEAM LOCOMOTIVES

Entries in *italics* under the headings "Designers," and "Building Date," refer to engine classes listed as "Rebuilt." Unless otherwise stated, two inside cylinders are understood. The number of cylinders above two is entered in brackets—e.g. (4)—in the "cylinders" column. Superheated locos. are indicated by "Su" after the boiler pressure. The building or rebuilding dates are those of the entire class and not necessarily those of the individual engines surviving.

Class	Wheels	Designer	Building Date	Weight of Loco. tons cwt.	Boiler Pressure lb. per sq. in.	Cylinders in.	Driving Wheels	Tractive Effort at 85% B.P.
								lb.
A1	0–6–0T	Stroudley	1872–80	27 10	150	12 × 20	4" 0'	7,650
A1X	0–6–0T	*Marsh**	1911–47	28 5	150	12 × 20 $14\frac{3}{16}$ × 20	4' 0"	7,650 10,695
B1(†)	4–4–0	*Wainwright*	1910–27	45 2	170	18 × 26	7' 0"	14,490
B4	0–4–0T	Adams Drummond	1891–93 1908	33 9 32 18	140	(O)16 × 22	3' 9¾"	14,650
B4	4–4–0	R. Billinton	1899–02	51 10	180	19 × 26	6' 9"	17,730
B4X	4–4–0	*L. Billinton*	1922–24	58 1	180Su	20 × 26	6' 9"	19,645
C	0–6–0	Wainwright	1900–08	43 16	160	18½ × 26	5' 2"	19,520
C2	0–6–0	R. Billinton	1893–02	39 10	160	17½ × 26	5' 0"	18,050
C2X	0–6–0	*Marsh**	1908–40	45 5	170	17½ × 26	5' 0"	19,175
C3	0–6–0	Marsh	1906	47 10	170	17½ × 26	5' 0"	19,175
C14(‡)	0–4–0T	*Urie*	1913–23	25 15	150	(O)14 × 14	3' 0"	9,720
D	4–4–0	Wainwright	1901–07	50 0	175	19 × 26	6' 8"	17,450
D1	4–4–0	*Maunsell**	1921–27	52 4	180Su	19 × 26	6' 8"	17,950
D1	0–4–2T	Stroudley	1873–87	43 10	170	17 × 24	5' 6"	15,185

* Rebuilt from preceding class.
† Rebuilt from Stirling " B " Class, built 1898–99.
‡ Converted from Drummond 2–2–0T, built 1906–07.

ABBREVIATIONS—C.T., Crane Tank.
K.E.S.R., Kent & East Sussex Rly.
L.C.D.R., London, Chatham & Dover Rly.
P.D.S.W.J.R., Plymouth, Devonport & S.W. Junction Rly.
S.T., Saddle Tank.
W.T., Well Tank.

Principal Dimensions of Southern Region Locomotives—*continued*

Class	Wheels	Designer	Building Date	Weight of Loco. tons cwt.	Boiler Pressure lb. per sq. in.	Cylinders in.	Driving Wheels	Tractive Effort at 85% B.P.
								lb.
D3	0–4–4T	R. Billinton	1892–96	52 0	170	17½ × 26	5′ 6″	17,435
D15	4–4–0	Drummond	1912	61 11	180Su	20 × 26	6′ 7″	20,140
E	4–4–0	Wainwright ·	1905–09	52 5 53 10	180 160Su	19 × 26 20½ × 26	6′ 6″	18,410 19,050
E1	4–4–0	*Maunsell**	1919–20	53 9	180Su	19 × 26	6′ 6″	18,410
E1	0–6–0T	Stroudley	1874–91	44 3	170	17 × 24	4′ 6″	18,560
E1/R	0–6–2T	*Maunsell**	1927–28	50 5	170	17 × 24	4′ 6″	18,560
E2	0–6–0T	L. Billinton	1913–16	52 15 53 10	170	17½ × 26	4′ 6″	21,305
E3	0–6–2T	R. Billinton	1894–95	56 10	160 170	17½ × 26	4′ 6″	20,055 21,305
E4	0–6–2T	R. Billinton	1897–03	57 10 56 15	160 170	17½ × 26	5′ 0″	18,050 19,175
E4X	0–6–2T	*Marsh**	1909–11	59 5	170	17½ × 26	5′ 0″	19,175
E5	0–6–2T	R. Billinton	1902–04	60 0	160 175	17½ × 26	5′ 6″	16,410 17,945
E5X	0–6–2T	*Marsh**	1911	64 5	170	17½ × 26	5′ 6″	17,435
E6	0–6–2T	R. Billinton	1904–05	61 0	160 175	18 × 26	4′ 6″	21,215 23,205
E6X	0–6–2T	*Marsh**	1911	63 0	170	18 × 26	4′ 6″	22,540
G6	0–6–0T	Adams	1894–00	47 13	160	17½ × 24	4′10″	17,235
G16	4–8–0T	Urie	1921	95 2	180Su	(0) 22 × 28	5′ 1″	33,990
H	0–4–4T	Wainwright	1904–15	54 8	160	18 × 26	5′ 6″	17,360
H1	4–4–2	Marsh	1905–06	68 5	200Su	(0) 19 × 26	6′ 7½″	20,070
H2	4–4–2	Marsh	1911–12	68 5	200Su	(0) 21 × 26	6′ 7½″	24,520
H15	4–6–0	*Maunsell* (†) *Urie*(†)	1924–25 1915	80 11 82 1	175Su	21 × 28	6′ 0″	25,510

H15 continued.		Urie	1914	81	5	180Su	(0) 21 × 28	6′ 0″	26,240
		Maunsell*	1927	79	19	180Su	(0) 21 × 28	6′ 0″	26,240
		Maunsell	1924						
H16	4–6–2T	Urie	1921–22	96	8	180Su	(0) 21 × 28	5′ 7″	28,200
I1X	4–4–2T	*Maunsell* ‡	1925–32	71	18	180	17½ × 26	5′ 6″	18,460
I3	4–4–2T	Marsh	1907	75	10	180Su	19 × 26	6′ 9″	17,730
			1912–13	76	0	180Su	21 × 26	6′ 7½″	22,065
			1908–10	76	0	180Su	20 × 26	6′ 7½″	20,015
J	0–6–4T	Wainwright	1913	70	14	160Su	19½ × 26	5′ 6″	20,370
J1	4–6–2T	Marsh	1910	89	0	170Su	(0) 21 × 26	6′ 7½″	20,840
J2	4–6–2T	Marsh	1912	89	0	170Su	(0) 21 × 26	6′ 7½″	20,840
K	2–6–0	L. Billinton	1913–21	63	15	180Su	(0) 21 × 26	5′ 6″	26,580
K10	4–4–0	Drummond	1901–02	46	14	175	18½ × 26	5′ 7″	19,755
KES	0–8–0T	Hawthorn Leslie	1904	47	10	160	(0) 16 × 24	4′ 3″	16,385
L	4–4–0	Wainwright	1914	57	9	180Su	19½ × 26	6′ 8″	18,910
L1	4–4–0	Maunsell	1926	57	16	180Su	19½ × 26	6′ 8″	18,910
L11	4–4–0	Drummond	1903–07	50	11	175	18½ × 26	5′ 7″	19,755
L12	4–4–0	Drummond	1904–05	55	5	175Su	19 × 26	6′ 7″	17,675
Leader	0–6–6–0T	Bulleid	1949			280Su	(6) 12¼ × 15	5′ 1″	26,350
LN	4–6–0	Maunsell	1926–29	83	10	220Su	(4) 16½ × 26	6′ 7″	33,510
				84	16			6′ 3″	35,300
M7	0–4–4T	Drummond	1897–11	60	3	175	18½ × 26	5′ 7″	19,755
				60	4				
				62	0				
MN	4–6–2	Bulleid	1941–49	94	15	280Su	(3) 18 × 24	6′ 2″	37,515
N	2–6–0	Maunsell	1917–34	61	4	200Su	(0) 19 × 28	5′ 6″	26,035
N1	2–6–0	Maunsell	1922–30	64	5	200Su	(3) 16 × 28	5′ 6″	27,695

NOTES
* Rebuilt from preceding Class.
† Nos. 30330–335 rebuilt from Drummond 4-cyl. 4–6–0's built 1905–07.
‡ Rebuilt from Marsh I1 Class built 1906–07.

Principal Dimensions of Southern Region Locomotives—*continued*

Class	Wheels	Designer	Building Date	Weight of Loco. tons cwt.	Boiler Pressure lb. per sq. in.	Cylinders in.	Driving Wheels	Tractive Effort at 85% B.P.
N15	4-6-0	Maunsell	1925	80 19 79 18	200Su	(O) 20½ × 28	6′ 7″	25,320
		Urie	1918–23	80 7	180Su	(O)21 × 28 (O)22 × 28	6′ 7″	23,915 26,245
		Maunsell	1926–27	81 17	200Su	(O) 20½ × 28	6′ 7″	25,320
N15X	4-6-0	*Maunsell**	1934–36	73 2	180Su	(O) 21 × 28	6′ 9″	23,325
O1	0-6-0	*Wainwright†*	1903–27	41 1	150	18 × 26	5′ 1″ 5′ 2″	17,610 17,325
O2	0-4-4T	Adams	1889–95	46 18 48 8	160	17½ × 24	4′ 10″	17,235
P	0-6-0T	Wainwright	1909–10	28 10	160	12 × 18	3′ 9⅛″	7,810
Q	0-6-0	Maunsell	1938–39	49 10	200Su	19 × 26	5′ 1″	26,160
Q1	0-6-0	Bulleid	1942	51 5	230Su	19 × 26	5′ 1″	30,080
R	0-4-4T	Kirtley (L.C.D.R.)	1891–92	48 15	160	17½ × 24	5′ 6″	15,145
R1	0-4-4T	Kirtley	1900	52 3	160	17½ × 24	5′ 6″	15,145
R1	0-6-0T	*Wainwright‡*	1910–22	46 8 46 15	160	18 × 26	5′ 1″ 5′ 2″	18,780 18,480
S	0-6-0ST	*Maunsell§*	1917	53 10	160	18½ × 26	5′ 2″	19,520
S11	4-4-0	Drummond	1903	53 15	175Su	19 × 26	6′ 0″	19,390
S15	4-6-0	Urie	1920–21	79 16	180Su	(O) 21 × 28	5′ 7″	28,200
		Maunsell	1927–28 1936	80 14 79 15	200Su	(O) 20½ × 28	5′ 7″	29,855
	0-6-0T	Kirtley	1879–93	40 15	160	17½ × 24	4′ 6″	18,510

T1	0–4–4T	Adams	1888–96	57	2	160	18 × 26	5′ 7″	17,100
T9	4–4–0	Drummond	1899–1900	51 51 51	16 18 7	175Su	19 × 26	6′ 7″	17,675
T14	4–6–0	Drummond	1911	76	10	175Su	(4) 15 × 26	6′ 7″	22,030
U	2–6–0	Maunsell (‖)	1928–31 *	62 63	6 0	200Su	(O) 19 × 28	6′ 0″	23,865
U1	2–6–0	Maunsell (‖)	1928–31	65	6	200Su	(3) 16 × 28	6′ 0″	25,385
U.S.A.	0–6–0T	Vulcan Ironworks	1942–43	46	10	210	(O) 16½ × 24	4′ 6″	21,600
V	4–4–0	Maunsell	1930–35	67	2	200Su	(3) 16½ × 26	6′ 7″	25,135
W	2–6–4T	Maunsell	1931–36	90	14	200Su	(3) 16½ × 28	5′ 6″	29,450
WC & B.B.	4–6–2	Bulleid	1945–49	86	0	280Su	(3) 16⅜ × 24	6′ 2″	31,050
Z	0–8–0T	Maunsell	1929	71	12	180	(3) 16 × 28	4′ 8″	29,375
700	0–6–0	Drummond	1897	46	14	180Su	19 × 26	5′ 1″	23,540
756	0–6–0T	Hawthorn Leslie	1907	35	15	170	(O) 14 × 22	3′ 10″	13,545
757	0–6–2T	Hawthorn Leslie	1907	49	19	170	(O) 16 × 24	4′ 0″	18,495
1302	0–4–0CT	Neilson	1881	17	17	120	11 × 20	3′ 3″	6,330
0298	2–4–0WT	Beattie	1874–75	37	16	160	(O) 16½ × 20	5′ 7″	11,050
0395	0–6–0	Adams	1881–86	37 38	12 14	140 150	17½ × 26	5′ 1″	15,535 16,645
0458	0–4–0ST	Hawthorn Leslie	1890	21	2	120	(O) 12 × 20	3′ 2″	7,730
0415	4–4–2T	Adams	1882–5	55	2	160	(O) 17½ × 24	5′ 7″	14,920

NOTES

* Rebuilt from L. Billinton's " L " Class 4–6–4T built 1914–22.

† Rebuilt from Stirling " O " Class built 1878–99.

§ No. 3 1685 rebuilt from C Class.

‖ Class U includes 20 rebuilt " River " (K) Class 2–6–4T (built 1917–25) and Class U1 includes one rebuilt " River " (K1) Class (No. 31890 built 1925). All rebuilt thus 1928.

SOUTHERN REGION LOCO TENDERS

The numbers in the extreme left-hand column refer to those shown against the entry " tender type " in the list of dimensions at the head of each class in the locomotive lists.

Ref. in Text	No. of wheels	Water (galls.)	Wheel-base ft. in.	Weight full t. c.	Engine Classes fitted
(1)	6	2,100	12 0	28 5	OI
(2)	6	2.500	13 0	28 13	0395 in part
(4)	6	2,835	13 0	33 10	C2, C2X
(5)	6	2,985	13 0	35 15	C3 in part
(6)	6	3,000	12 0	34 2	BI
(7)	6	3,000	13 0	35 5	B4
(8)	6	3,112	13 0	37 5	C3 in part
(9)	6	3,300	13 0	33 4	0395 in part
(10)	6	3,300	13 0	38 5	C
(11)	6	3,300	13 0	39 0	DI
(12)	6	3,450	13 0	39 0	EI
(13)	6	3,450	13 0	39 2	D, E
(14)	6	3,450	13 0	40 6	L
(15)	6	3,500	13 0	39 5	HI, H2
(16)	6	3,500	13 0	39 5	N 31810-21/3-75 NI 31822
(17)	6	3,500	13 0	39 12	DI5 T9 30300/1/4/7/10/1/2/3/36 SII 30395/7 " 700 " 30316/26/39/46/50, 30687/8/94, 30699-701
(18)	6	3,500	14 0	39 12	KI0 30137/40/1 ; 30345/84/94 LII 30440/1 LI2 30416/7/9/21/2/4/5/30/1/3 T9 30281/2, 30704/26/9 " 700 " other than those listed under (17)
(19)	6	3,500	13 0	40 10	LI, Q, U 31790—809, UI 31890
(20)	6	3,500	13 0	40 14	KI0 30142/51, 30329/41/83/9/90

Class E5X 0-6-2T No. 32586 [W. *Beckerlegge*

Class E5 0-6-2T No. 32574 [W. *Beckerlegge*

Class E2 0-6-0T No. 32102 [W. *Gilburt*

Class A1X 0-6-0T No. 32644 [H. C. Casserley

Class E1 0-6-0T No. 32128 [H. C. Casserley

Class E1 R 0-6-2T No. 32124 [W. Beckerlegge

Class G6 0–6–0T No. 30266 [*C. C. B. Herbert*

Class B4 0–4–0T No. 30086 *Havre* [*P. Ransome-Wallis*

[A. F. Cook

Class C14 0–4–0T No. 30589

[S. C. Townroe

Class 0298 2–4–0T No. 30585

SOUTHERN REGION LOCO TENDERS—

Continued

Ref. in Text	No. of wheels	Water (galls.)	Wheel-base ft.	in.	Weight full t.	c.	Engine Classes fitted
(21)	6	3,500	13	0	41	5	N15 30793-806
(22)	6	3,600	13	0	39	5	B4X
(23)	6	3,700	13	0	38	0	QI
(24)	6	3,940	13	0	41	10	K
(25)	6	4,000	13	0	42	8	N (31400-14), N1 (other than 31822), U (other than 31790—809), U1 (other than 31890)
(26)	6	4,000	13	0	42	8	S15 30833-7
(27)	6	4,000	13	0	42	8	V
(28)	8*	4,000	14	6	44	17	L11 (other than those listed above and below) S15 30504-10 ; K10, L12, S11, T9 (other than those listed above)
(29)	8*	4,300	14	6	49	3	H15 30330-4 ; N15 30448-57
(30)	6	4,500	13	0	42	12	WC and BB (other than those listed below)
(31)	8*	4,500	14	6	48	12	H15 30335
(32)	8*	4,500	14	6	49	0	L11 30164/6, 30405/35/9
(33)	6	5,000	13	0	47	16	MN 35001-10
(34)	6	5,000	13	0	49	7	MN 35011-20
(35)	8	5,000	19	0	56	8	S15 30823-32, 30838-47
(36)	8	5,000	19	0	57	11	H15 30473-8, S15 30521-4; N15 30763-92; N15X
(37)	8	5,000	19	0	57	16	N15 30736-55; S15 30496-503, 30511-5
(38)	8	5,000	19	0	57	19	LN
(39)	8	5,200	19	0	57	14	H15 30482-90/1
(40)	6	5,500	13	0	47	5	BB 34071-90
(41)	8*	5,800	16	6	60	8	T14
(42)	6	6,000	13	0	52	7	MN 35021-30
(43)	6	Various	12	0	Various		O1‡

*Drummond

‡ Ex-LCDR " M " Class, water capacities average 2,510 gals., weights average 31 tons 0 cwt.

SOME S.R. LOCOMOTIVE HEAD SIGNALS

This list is not complete and gives only the principal one and two disc (or lamp) codes.

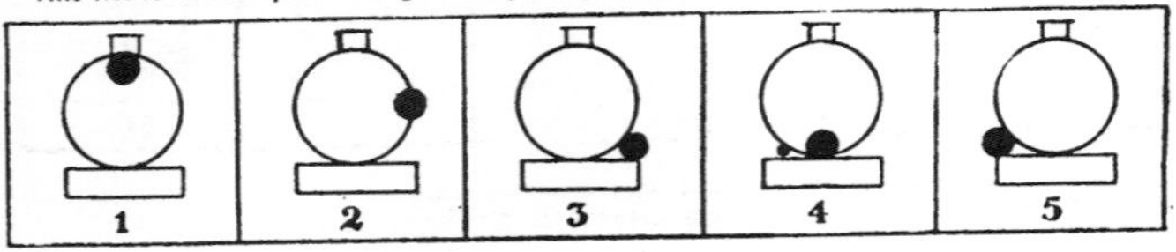

NO. 1

Victoria and Dover via Chatham
Victoria and Norwood Yard via Selhurst
Loughborough Sidings to Holborn
Ashford and Hastings
Reading and Margate via Redhill
Eastleigh and Bulford via Chandlers Ford and Andover
Southampton Terminus and Brockenhurst and Weymouth via Wimborne
Weymouth, Portland and Easton (Passenger Trains)
Plymouth Friary and Tavistock
Woking and Reading via Virginia Water West Curve
Exeter Central and Ilfracombe
Bodmin and Wadebridge
Petersfield and Midhurst
Exeter Central and Exmouth

NO. 2

Victoria or Clapham Junction and Holborn (L.L.)
London Bridge or Bricklayers' Arms and Portsmouth via Quarry line and Horsham
Via Mid Kent line and Beckenham Junction
Ashford and Eastbourne direct
Waterloo or Nine Elms and Southampton Terminus, direct (not boat trains)
Willesden and Feltham Yard via Gunnersbury
Waterloo or Nine Elms and Windsor via Twickenham
Southampton Central to Lymington
Yeovil Junction and Yeovil Town
Seaton Junction and Seaton
Barnstaple Junction and Torrington
Halwill and Bude

NO. 3

Victoria or Clapham Junction and Holborn
London Bridge or Bricklayers' Arms and Brighton via Quarry line
Tonbridge and Brighton via Eridge
Hastings via Mid Kent line, Oxted, Crowhurst Junction and Tonbridge
Dunton Green and Westerham
Ashford and Margate via Canterbury West
Lydd Branch
Canterbury West and Whitstable Harbour
Sandling Junction and Hythe
Folkestone Junction and Folkestone Harbour
Crowhurst and Bexhill
Swanley Junction and Gravesend West Street
Sittingbourne and Sheerness
Queenborough and Leysdown
Deal and Kearsney
Gravesend Central and Allhallows-on-Sea or Port Victoria
All stations to Feltham (except via Mortlake)

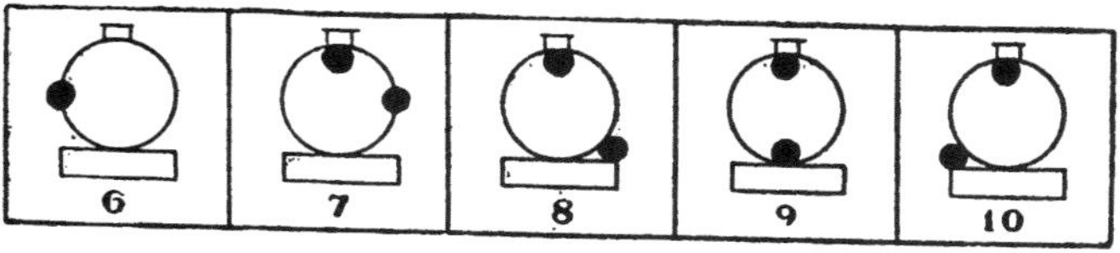

Weymouth and Portland and Easton (goods trains)
Bournemouth West and Brockenhurst via Wimborne

NO. 4

Victoria or Battersea Yard and Brighton via Redhill
Oxted and Eastbourne via Eridge
London Bridge and New Cross via Bricklayers' Arms Junction
Horsham and Brighton
Brookwood and Bisley Camp
Alton and Fareham
Bentley and Bordon
Salisbury and Bulford
Axminster and Lyme Regis
Tipton St. John's and Exmouth
Wareham and Swanage
Brockenhurst and Lymington Pier
Bere Alston and Callington

NO. 5

Victoria or Stewarts Lane and Clapham Junction
Oxted and Tunbridge Wells West via East Grinstead (H.L.)
Pulborough, Midhurst and Chichester
Havant and Hayling Island
London Bridge and Bricklayers' Arms
Tonbridge and Maidstone West
Ashford (Kent) and Dover via Minster and Deal
Elham Valley line
Stewarts Lane to Victoria
Southampton Docks and Nine Elms via main line (market goods, fruit or potato train)

NO. 6

London Bridge or Bricklayers' Arms and Dover or Ramsgate via East Croydon, Oxted and Tonbridge
Tonbridge and Hawkhurst
Battersea Yard and Kensington
Waterloo or Nine Elms and Reading via Twickenham
Willesden and Feltham Yard via Kew East Junction
Exeter Central and Sidmouth
Plymouth Friary and Turnchapel
Eastleigh or Southampton and Fawley
Bournemouth Central and Brockenhurst via Wimborne
Torrington and Halwill

NO. 7

Victoria or Battersea Yard and Portsmouth via Quarry line and Horsham
Via Maidstone East line to Victoria or Holborn
Waterloo or Nine Elms and Southampton Docks via Brentford, Chertsey and Woking

NO. 8

London Bridge or Bricklayers' Arms and Eastbourne or Hastings via Quarry line
Victoria or West London line and Ramsgate via Herne Hill or Catford Loop
London Bridge or Bricklayer's Arms and Hastings via Chislehurst and Tunbridge Wells Central

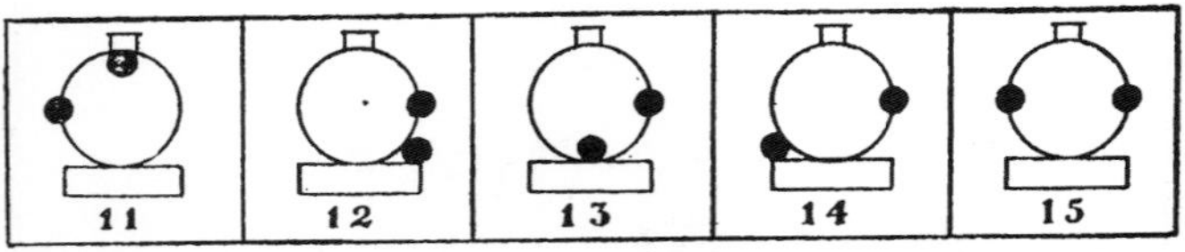

West London line to East Croydon via Crystal Palace (L.L.)
Special boat trains Waterloo and Southampton Docks via Northam
Special boat trains from Southampton Docks to Waterloo via Millbrook
Southampton and Andover via Redbridge

NO. 9

Victoria or Battersea Yard and Eastbourne or Hastings via Quarry line
London and Hither Green Sidings
Victoria and Folkestone Harbour or Dover Marine via Swanley, Otford and Tonbridge
Waterloo or Nine Elms and Plymouth
Bournemouth Central and Dorchester goods trains
Battersea Yard and Brent via New Kew Junction
Southampton Terminus and Portsmouth Harbour via Netley

NO. 10

London Bridge or Bricklayers' Arms and Portsmouth via Redhill and Horsham
Victoria or Battersea Yard and Norwood Yard via Crystal Palace (L.L.)
London Bridge and New Cross Gate to Eardley Sidings via Peckham Rye
Deptford Wharf and New Cross Gate
London Bridge or Bricklayers' Arms and Folkestone or Dover via Chislehurst, Tonbridge and Ashford
Dover and Margate via Deal and Minster Loop
Special boat trains Waterloo to Southampton Docks via Millbrook
Feltham to Wimbledon via Chertsey

NO. 11

Victoria or Battersea Yard and Portsmouth via Redhill and Horsham
Via Dartford Loop line
Victoria or Holborn and Hastings Branch via Orpington Loop and Tunbridge Wells Central
Bricklayers' Arms and Guildford via Leatherhead and Effingham Junction
Waterloo or Nine Elms and Southampton Terminus via Alton
Salisbury and Bournemouth West via Wimborne
Fareham and Gosport
Ballast trains to Meldon Quarry from Exeter Central and stations West thereof

NO. 12

Victoria or Battersea Yard and Portsmouth via Mitcham Junction
London Bridge or Bricklayers' Arms and Eastbourne or Hastings via Redhill
Victoria, Stewarts Lane or Holborn to North Kent lines via Nunhead line
Nine Elms and Feltham via Mortlake
Exeter Central to Nine Elms (market goods and fish)
Down main line goods terminating at Woking
Southampton Docks and Salisbury via Eastleigh

NO. 13

London Bridge or Bricklayers' Arms and Brighton via Redhill
Oxted and Brighton via East Grinstead (L.L.) and Lewes
Three Bridges and Tunbridge Wells West
West London line to Norwood Yard via Thornton Heath
Victoria or Holborn to Dover via Nunhead line and Maidstone East
Parcels and empty trains Waterloo to Clapham Junction (Kensington sidings)

Feltham Yard and Neasden via Kew East Junction
Portsmouth Harbour or Portsmouth and Southsea to Fratton Loco. Depot
Exeter Central and Exmouth Junction
Bournemouth West to Dorchester
Southampton and Salisbury via Redbridge

NO. 14

London Bridge and Portsmouth via Mitcham Junction
London Bridge, Oxted and Tunbridge Wells West via Hever
Oxted and Lewes or Seaford or Eastbourne via Haywards Heath and Keymer Junction (change to No. 5 or No. 21 code at Lewes)
London Bridge or Bricklayers' Arms and Dover via Chislehurst Loop and Maidstone East
Waterloo or Nine Elms and Brockenhurst and Bournemouth West via Sway

NO. 15

Via Bexley Heath line
Victoria, Stewarts Lane or Holborn via Nunhead line and Bexley Heath
Oxted and Brighton via Haywards Heath
Waterloo or Nine Elms and Reading via loop line
All trains terminating at Portsmouth and Southsea (trains from Salisbury to carry No. 17 to Eastleigh)
Exeter Central and Padstow
Light engines, Bournemouth Central or Bournemouth West to Bournemouth Central via triangle to turn.
Light engines Eastleigh Loco. to Portsmouth and Southsea
Light engines to Guildford Loco. via Woking (except via Staines)

NO. 16

London Bridge or Bricklayers' Arms and Portsmouth via West Croydon
Victoria or Battersea Yard and Eastbourne or Hastings via Redhill
Oxted and Brighton via Eridge
London Bridge or Bricklayers' Arms and Ramsgate via Tonbridge and Canterbury West
Waterloo or Nine Elms and Woking via Richmond and Chertsey
Milk and empty trains to Clapham Junction via Byfleet curve and Richmond

NO. 17

London Bridge or Bricklayers' Arms and Tonbridge or Reading via East Croydon and Redhill (also Tonbridge and Reading)
Brighton and Hove via Preston Park Spur
Three Bridges and Eridge
Victoria or Holborn and Folkestone or Dover via Orpington Loop, Tonbridge and Ashford
London Bridge or Bricklayers' Arms and Gillingham, Faversham, Ramsgate or Dover via Chislehurst Loop and Chatham
Waterloo or Nine Elms and Clapham Junction (empty trains and light engines)
Passenger trains Bournemouth Central and Weymouth

NO. 18

London Bridge or Bricklayers' Arms and Dover, Ramsgate or Hastings via Chislehurst, Swanley, Otford and Sevenoaks
Victoria, Oxted and Tunbridge Wells West via Hever
Holborn and Ramsgate via Herne Hill or Catford Loop
Light engines and trains requiring to run to up main loop, Clapham Junction, from stations westward
Southampton and Andover via Eastleigh
Light engines or engines with vehicles attached running round the triangle at Bournemouth West to turn

NO. 19

Victoria or Battersea Yard and Brighton via Quarry line
London Bridge or New Cross Gate and Norwood Yard
Tunbridge Wells West and Eastbourne
Victoria or Holborn and Ramsgate, Dover or Hastings via Nunhead line and Tonbridge
Horsham and Guildford
Waterloo or Nine Elms and Southampton Docks via East Putney
Salisbury and Portsmouth Harbour via Eastleigh
Portsmouth and Southsea to Salisbury via Eastleigh

NO. 20

Victoria, Stewarts Lane or Holborn to Ramsgate via Nunhead line, Chislehurst and Chatham
London Bridge or Bricklayers' Arms and North Kent line via Greenwich
Via Streatham Spur
Feltham Yard and Brent via Kew East Junction
Clapham Junction and Kensington
Portsmouth and Southsea to Salisbury via Redbridge
Salisbury and Portsmouth Harbour via Redbridge

NO. 21

Victoria and Newhaven Harbour
Victoria or Holborn to Ramsgate via Nunhead line and Maidstone East
Waterloo or Nine Elms and Portsmouth via Woking and Guildford
Light engines from all stations to Feltham Loco.
Light engines from all stations West of Basingstoke to Eastleigh Loco.

There are several three-disc codes in use though most of these are for race specials. The Plymouth-Brighton, Cardiff-Brighton and Bournemouth-Brighton through services are denoted by three-disc codes and Royal Specials utilize the standard British four-lamp head signal.

A book for the Youngsters!

The Adventures of

SAMMY THE SHUNTER

By Eileen Gibb

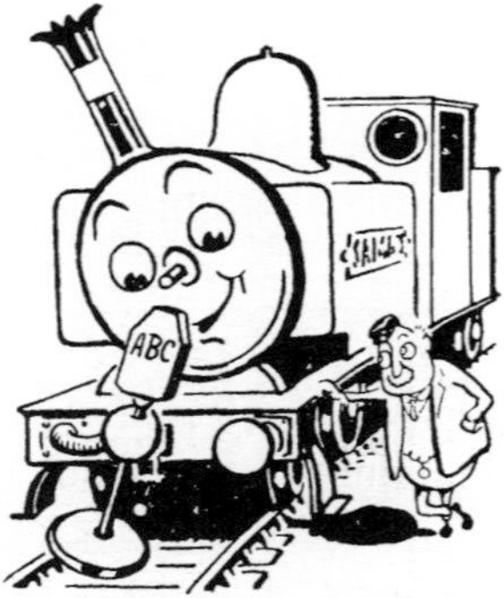

Hello children, this is Sammy!

Miss Gibb has written a series of charming little stories round the exploits of Sammy the shunting Engine, who did so want to be a main line express engine. The pictures have been drawn in full colour by Arthur Baldwin, the well-known humorous artist.

The stories and the illustrations will appeal to youngsters of all ages. No. 1 in the series is called "Sammy gets Streamlined" and will shortly be on sale at W. H. Smith and Sons bookstalls, Wymans and all leading booksellers.

1/6

THE ABC OF BRITISH RAILWAYS LOCOMOTIVES

PART 3—Nos. 40000-59999

LONDON,
Ian Allan Ltd

FOREWORD

THIS booklet lists all British Railways locomotives numbered between 40000 and 9999. This series of numbers includes all London Midland Region and Scottish (ex-L.M.S.) Region steam locos., i.e. steam locomotives of the former L.M.S.R. Under the general British Railways numbering scheme, the numbers of L.M.S.R. steam locomotives were increased by 40000, with certain exceptions which were to be completely renumbered. Renumbering is being carried out only as locomotives visit main works, and thus it may be some time before all locomotives bear the numbers shown in this book.

Former L.M.S.R. diesel and diesel-electric locomotives were to be renumbered, in common with all British Railways locomotives of similar propulsion, between 10000 and 29999, and details of them will be found in the ABC OF BRITISH RAILWAYS' LOCOMOTIVES Nos. 10000-39999.

THE BOILERS OF STANIER LOCOMOTIVES

THE early taper boilers of Sir William Stanier's design were domeless, with a smokebox regulator and a top feed toward the rear of the barrel. The superheaters were small, and the proportions of the boilers followed G.W.R. practice.

In the light of experience with these locos., successive developments were made in the boilers built from 1935 onward. The superheaters (sometimes in several stages) and the fireboxes were enlarged, the latter by sloping the back plate and increasing the length of grate ; domes were fitted, incorporating the regulator valve. In recent boilers the top feed casing has been moved much urther forward.

Earlier boilers have, in many cases, been fitted with domes and larger superheaters, and this, combined with the routine boiler changes which are made under the L.M.R. repair system, makes it impossible to tabulate the current condition of the locos. Furthermore, the variations of weight between different types of boiler fitted to each class produce variations in the loco. weights. The figures given in this book are therefore those applicable to recent locos. of the class.

The following gives an indication of the principal changes in certain classes :—

Class 3, 2–6–2 T

Nos. 40071–40144 were built domeless, and 40145–40209 with domes and larger fireboxes. The firebox distinction seems to be maintained.

Class 4, 2–6–4 T

Nos. 42500–36 were built domeless with 12-element superheaters, but many have now been fitted with domes. Nos. 42537–44 had larger barrels and fireboxes (but still with 25 sq. ft. grates) and 18 element superheaters. Nos. 42425–94 and 42545–42617 were built domed, with 18-element superheaters and 26.7 sq. ft. grates. From No. 42618 onward, and on all the Fairburn locos., the superheater was further increased to 21 elements.

Class 5, 4–6–0

Nos. 45000–69 were built domeless with 14-element superheaters. These boilers have now been rebuilt with domes and 24-element superheaters. Nos. 45070–45224 were also domeless, but with 21-element superheaters. These boilers are in course of rebuilding. Boilers are interchanged freely between locos. 45000–45224. From No. 45225 onward domes were fitted, and the superheaters increased to 24 elements. The grate area was also increased from the previous figure of 27.8 sq. ft. to 28.56 sq. ft. On Nos. 45472–99 the superheater was further increased to 28 elements, and this applies to all locos. below No. 45000. The larger firebox boilers are freely interchanged between locos. from No. 45225 onward, and some of the locos. in the earlier series have also been modified to take these boilers. This process will be continued as the original boilers wear out.

Class 5X, 4–6–0

Nos. 45552–45664 were built domeless, with 14-element superheaters and 29.5 sq. ft. of grate. From No. 45665 the superheater was increased to 21 elements, the grate to 31 sq. ft., and domes were fitted. Nos. 45702–42 had the superheater further increased to 24 elements. In this class there has been extensive rebuilding of boilers and interchange between locos. A number of the class still carry domeless boilers.

Class 8, 2–8–0

Nos. 48000–11 were domeless with 27.8 sq. ft. of grate, but all other locos. were built with domes and 28.65 sq. ft. grates. The whole class has 21-element superheaters. No. 48003 was soon modified to take the larger firebox, and other locos. of this batch will eventually follow suit.

THE CLASS 8 2-8-0 LOCOMOTIVES

THE Stanier Class 7 2-8-0 was introduced in 1935 and reclassified 8F in 1936. In 1935–9 Nos. 48000–26/96–48110 were built by the L.M.S. and 48027–95 by the Vulcan Foundry. Early in the war the Ministry of Supply ordered 240 locos. of similar design for overseas service from private builders : these were delivered in 1940–2, the actual total being 208. Prior to shipment overseas in 1941, a number of these locos. worked on the L.M.S. and G.W.R., and 53 of them carried L.M.S. numbers temporarily, 8226–63 (North British Loco. Co.) and 8286–8300 (Beyer Peacock).

When the remainder were shipped, No. 8293 was under repair following an accident, and it was permanently transferred to L.M.S. stock in 1943. In addition, 22 of the later M.o.S. locos., which had never received L.M.S. numbers, remained in England, and in 1943 became L.M.S. Nos. 8264–85.

When shipment of this class began in 1941 the need for locos. in the Middle East was so great that 51 of the original L.M.S. locos. were prepared for shipment. 43 actually left the country, and the remainder (Nos. 8024/69/78–80/5/8/93) were later returned to the L.M.S.

With a view to standardising the production of heavy freight locos. for home use, the M.o.S. ordered further Class 8 locos. from the other railway companies. These were built as follows in 1943–5 : Nos. 8400–79 by the G.W.R., Nos. 8500–59 by the L.N.E.R. and Nos. 8600–8704 by the S.R. The G.W. and L.N.E.-built locos. were loaned to the companies which built them until 1946–47, but were regarded as L.M.S. stock from the outset.

As the L.N.E.R. required further freight locos. for its own stock, the S.R. delivered 25 Class 8 locos. in 1944, and the L.N.E.R. shops built a further 43 in 1944–6. These locos. eventually became L.N.E.R. Nos. 3500–67, and in 1947–8 were loaned to the L.M.S., becoming Nos. 8705–72.

In the meantime construction had proceeded steadily in the L.M.S. shops, and between 1939 and 1945 Nos. 8111–75, 8301–99 and 8490–5 were built at Crewe and Horwich. In addition, concurrently with its M.o.S. deliveries, the N.B. Loco. Co. built 8176–8225.

The present stock of 624 locos. can be summarized thus :—

Built by L.M.S. or by private builders for L.M.S. ...	288
Built by other railways on L.M.S. account	245
Built by other railways on L.N.E.R. account	68
Built by private builders on M.o.S. account	23

In all 762 locos. have been built to this design. 40 of the W.D. locos. are being returned from the Middle East and will be added to L.M.R. stock when overhauled.

THE EX-L.N.W. 0-8-0 LOCOS

THE original L.N.W. 0-8-0 loco. was No. 2524, now 49011. This was a 2 cyl. simple built in 1892. All other locos. built by Webb were compounds, but those which survive have been converted to simple expansion. Locos. built by Whale and Bowen Cooke were all simple expansion, and commencing with those built in 1912, were superheated. All the locos. remaining in service now were built or rebuilt with superheaters and piston valves. Some of the rebuilds retained their original Joy valve gear, with the addition of rocking shafts to suit the piston valves. Locos. built (and many rebuilt) with piston valves had the valve gear arranged for direct drive.

The chronology of the locos. at present in service (except 49011) is as follows :—

Webb 3 cyl. compound, built 1893–1900, converted to simple by Whale (1904–9) and superheated later : All numbers between 48953 and 49002/4–10, 49011/4/7–39/41/3–51/3/6–59/61–4.

Webb 4 cyl. compound, built 1901-4, converted to simple by Whale, Bowen-Cooke, Beames and Hughes at dates bracketed, and then, or later, superheated : Nos. between 48901–5/7/8/11–7/20–52 (1923–7), 48893/5–9 (1923–5), 49065–76/85/90/9, 49100/20/2/32/3/42 (1906–10), 49145–51/3 (1910–17), 49265–7/92, 49304/19/24/31 (1917–8), 49335/7–46 (1918–20), 49347/8 (1908/7 respectively), 49350–59/61/4–71/3/5–9/81/2/5–94 (1921–3), 49425 (1922).

Of these locos. the following were converted to 2-8-0 (compound) by Whale in the years shown : 49266, 49319/90 (1904), 49267 (1905) ; 48895/8, 49340/3/5/51/3/67/93 (1906) ; 48896/7/9, 49359/65/72 (1907) ; 48893, 49373/86 (1908). They were converted to 2 cyl. 0-8-0 in 1917-25.

Whale-Bowen Cooke 2 cyl. simple, saturated, 160 lb. pressure, built 1910, later superheated (L.N.W. Class " G ") : 49077–84/7–9/91–4/6–8, 49101/2/4–9/12–7/9/21/3–7/9/30/4/5/7–41/3/4/54 (49154 was the first loco. of this type to be superheated in 1912, and classed " G 1 ").

Bowen Cooke 2 cyl. simple, superheated, 160 lb. pressure, L.N.W. Class " G1," built at dates shown : 49155–8/60–4/6–74/6–8/80/1/3/6–94/6/8/9, 49200 (1912), 49202–5/7–14/6–24 (1913), 49226/8–30/2/4/5/7–41/3–7/9/52–4 (1914), 49255/7/8/60–2/4 (1916), 49268–71/5–8 (1917), 49280–5/7–9/91/3/4/6/8/9, 49300–2/6–8/10–8/20–3/5–8/30/2–4 (1918).

Bowen Cooke 2 cyl. simple, superheated, 175 lb. pressure, L.N.W. Class " G2," built 1921/2 : 49395–49424/6–54.

From 1936,175 1b. boilers have been fitted to most of the locos. in Class G1. The locos. thus rebuilt are classified " G2A." All boilers built from 1924 have Belpaire fireboxes, but a number of locos. still retain round-top fireboxes.

CHIEF MECHANICAL ENGINEERS

BRITISH RAILWAYS (L. M. Region)

H. G. Ivatt ... 1948—

L.M.S.

George Hughes	1923—1925
Sir Henry Fowler ...	1925—1931
E. H. J. Lemon (Sir Ernest Lemon)	1931—1932
Sir William Stanier ...	1932—1944
Charles E. Fairburn ...	1944—1945
H. G. Ivatt	1945—1947

LOCOMOTIVE SUPERINTENDENTS AND C.M.E.'S—L.M.S. CONSTITUENT COMPANIES†

CALEDONIAN RAILWAY

Robert Sinclair (First loco engineer)‡	1847—1856
Benjamin Connor ...	1856—1876
George Brittain	1876—1882
Dugald Drummond ...	1882—1890
Hugh Smellie	1890
J. Lambie	1890—1895
J. F. McIntosh	1895—1914
William Pickersgill ...	1914—1923

FURNESS RAILWAY

R. Mason	1890—1897
W. F. Pettigrew ...	1897—1918
D. J. Rutherford	1918—1923

Previous to Mason, F.R. locomotives were designed by contract with "outside" builders.

GLASGOW AND SOUTH WESTERN RLY.

Patrick Stirling	1853—1866
James Stirling	1866—1877
Hugh Smellie	1877—1890
James Manson	1890—1912
Peter Drummond ...	1912—1918
R H. Whitelegg	1918—1923

HIGHLAND RAILWAY

William Stroudley (First loco engineer) ...	1866—1869
David Jones	1869—1896
Peter Drummond ...	1896—1911
F. G. Smith	1912—1915
C. Cumming	1915—1923

L. & Y.R.

Sir John Hawkshaw (Consultant),* Hurst and Jenkins successively to 1868

W. Hurst	1868—1876
W. Barton Wright ...	1876—1886
John A. F. Aspinall ...	1886—1899
H. A. Hoy...	1899—1904
George Hughes	1904—1922

L.N.W.R.

Francis Trevithick and J. E. McConnell, first loco engineers, 1846, with Alexander Allan largely responsible for design at Crewe.*

John Ramsbottom ...	1857—1871
Francis William Webb ...	1871—1903
George Whale	1903—1909
Charles John Bowen-Cooke	1909—1920
Capt. Hewitt Pearson Montague Beames ...	1920—1921
George Hughes	1922

The L. & Y. amalgamated with L.N.W.R. in 1921.

L.T. & S.R.

Thomas Whitelegg ...	1880—1910
Robert Harben Whitelegg	1910—1912

(LTSR absorbed by M.R., control of locos. transferred to Derby as from Aug., 1912.)

MARYPORT & CARLISLE

Hugh Smellie	1870—1878
J. Campbell	1878—
William Coulthard ...	* —1904
J. B. Adamson	1904—1923

MIDLAND RAILWAY

Matthew Kirtley (First loco engineer) ...	1844—1873
Samuel Waite Johnson ...	1873—1903
Richard Mountford Deeley	1903—1909
Henry Fowler	1909—1923

NORTH LONDON RAILWAY

(Worked by L. & N.W. by agreement dated Dec., 1908.)

William Adams	1853—1873
J. C. Park	1873—1893
Henry J. Pryce	1893—1908

* Date of actual entry into office not known.

† The status and title of Chief Mechanical Engineer were created by the L.Y.R. for J. A. F. Aspinall in 1886.

‡ Exclusive of previous service with amalgamated company.

LOCOMOTIVE SUPERINTENDENTS AND C.M.E.'S *(continued)*

NORTH STAFFORDSHIRE RAILWAY

L. Clare	1876—1882
L. Longbottom	1882—1902
J. H. Adams	1902—1915
J. A. Hookham	1915—1923

W. Angus was Loco. Supt. at Stoke prior to 1876. No earlier records can be traced.

WIRRAL

Eric G. Barker	1892—1902
T. B. Hunter	1903—1923

Barker of the Wirral Railway is noteworthy for originating the 4-4-4 tank type in this country (1896).

SOMERSET AND DORSET JOINT RAILWAY

Until leased by Mid. and L. & S.W. (as from 1st Nov., 1875) locomotives were bought from outside builders, principally George England of Hatcham Iron Works, S.E. After the above date, Derby and its various Loco. Supts. and CMEs have acted for S. & D.J., aided by a resident Loco. Supt. stationed at Highbridge works.

HISTORIC LOCOMOTIVES PRESERVED IN STORE

Type	Originating Company	Pre-grouping No.	L.M.S. No.	Name	Place of Preservation
2-4-0	M.R.	158A	(20002)	—	Derby
4-2-2	M.R.	118	(673)	—	Derby
2-2-2	L.N.W.	(49)	—	Columbine	York Museum.
2-2-2	L.N.W.	3020	—	Cornwall	Crewe
2-4-0	L.N.W.	(790)	5031	Hardwicke	Crewe
*0-4-0T	L.N.W.	—	—	Pet	Crewe
0-4-0	F.R.	3	—	Copperknob	Barrow
0-4-2	Liverpool & Manchester	—	—	Lion	Liverpool Lime St.
4-2-2	C.R.	123	(14010)	—	St. Rollox
4-6-0	H.R.	103	(17916)	—	St. Rollox

The un-bracketed numbers are the ones at present carried by the locos.

* 18" gauge works shunter.

NOTES ON THE USE OF THIS BOOK

1. At the head of each class will be found a list of any important sub-divisions of the class, usually in order of introduction. Each sub-division is given a reference mark, by which its relevant dimensions (if differing from those of other sub-divisions) and the locomotives it comprises (if known) may be identified.

2. The lists of dimensions at the head of each class show locomotives fitted with two inside cylinders unless otherwise stated, e.g. (O)= two outside cylinders.

3. Superheated locos. are denoted by the letters " Su " after the boiler pressure. " SS " denotes that some are superheated.

4. The date on which the first locomotive of a class was built is denoted by " Introduced." If the oldest loco. still running was built at a later date, that also is indicated.

5. Where locomotives have been renumbered other than by the addition of 40000 to their former L.M.S. numbers, the details of former L.M.S. numbers are given.

6. Tender weights have not been included in the lists of dimensions, owing to the numerous variations in weight within individual classes.

7. The numbers of locomotives in service have been checked to May 21, 1949.

SCOTTISH REGION (ex-L.M.S.)

MOTIVE POWER DEPOTS WITH CODES

Heavy type thus, **Inverness**, indicates a main district depot. In addition to depots shown, there are several sub-depots, the engines attached to which bear the code of the main district depot.

Depot	*Code*	*Depot*	*Code*
Inverness	60A	**St. Rollox**	65B
Aviemore	60B	Dawsholm	65D
Helmsdale	60C	Grangemouth	65F
Wick	60D	**Polmadie**	66A
Forres	60E	Motherwell	66B
Aberdeen	61B	Hamilton	66C
Keith	61C	Greenock	66D
Dundee	62B	**Corkerhill**	67A
Perth (South)	63A	Hurlford	67B
Stirling	63B	Ayr	67C
Forfar	63C	Adrossan	67D
Fort William	63D	**Carlisle Kingmoor**	68A
Oban	63E	Dumfries	68B
Edinburgh	64C	Stranraer	68C
Carstairs	64D	Beattock	68D

(For L.M.R. motive power depots, see page 74)

2-6-2T 3

Introduced 1930. Fowler design with parallel boiler.
*Introduced 1930. Condensing locos. for working to Moorgate, London.
Weight : { 70 tons 10 cwt. / 71 tons 16 cwt.*
Pressure : 200 lb Su.
Cyls. : (O) 17½" × 26".
Dr. Wheels : 5' 3". T.E. : 21,485 lb.
Walschaerts Valve Gear.

40001	40019	40037*	40054
40002	40020	40038*	40055
40003	40021*	40039*	40056
40004	40022*	40040*	40057
40005	40023*	40041	40058
40006	40024*	40042	40059
40007	40025*	40043	40060
40008	40026*	40044	40061
40009	40027*	40045	40062
40010	40028*	40046	40063
40011	40029*	40047	40064
40012	40030*	40048	40065
40013	40031*	40049	40066
40014	40032*	40050	40067
40015	40033*	40051	40068
40016	40034*	40052	40069
40017	40035*	40053	40070
40018	40036*		

Total 70

2-6-2T 3

Introduced 1935. Stanier taper boiler development of Fowler design (*above*).
*Introduced 1941. Rebuilt with larger boiler.
Weight : { 71 tons 5 cwt. / 72 tons 10 cwt.*
Pressure : 200 lb Su.
Cyls. : (O) 17½" × 26".
Dr. Wheels : 5' 3". T.E. : 21,485 lb.
Walschaerts Valve Gear.

40071	40080	40089	40098
40072	40081	40090	40099
40073	40082	40091	40100
40074	40083	40092	40101
40075	40084	40093	40102
40076	40085	40094	40103
40077	40086	40095	40104
40078	40087	40096	40105
40079	40088	40097	40106

40107	40133	40159	40185
40108	40134	40160	40186
40109	40135	40161	40187
40110	40136	40162	40188
40111	40137	40163*	40189
40112	40138	40164	40190
40113	40139	40165	40191
40114	40140	40166	40192
40115	40141	40167	40193
40116	40142	40168	40194
40117	40143	40169*	40195
40118	40144	40170	40196
40119	40145	40171	40197
40120	40146	40172	40198
40121	40147	40173	40199
40122	40148*	40174	40200
40123	40149	40175	40201
40124	40150	40176	40202
40125	40151	40177	40203*
40126	40152	40178	40204
40127	40153	40179	40205
40128	40154	40180	40206
40129	40155	40181	40207
40130	40156	40182	40208
40131	40157	40183	40209
40132	40158	40184	

Total 139

4-4-0 2P

*Introduced 1909. Fowler rebuild of Johnson locos. (introduced 1882).
Introduced 1912. Fowler rebuild of Johnson locos. with superheater and piston valves.
†Introduced 1914. Locos. built new to superheated design for S. & D.J.R. (taken into L.M.S.R. stock, 1930).
Weight : Loco. 53 tons 7 cwt.
Pressure : 160 lb. SS.
Cyls : { 18" × 26".* / 20½" × 26". Su.
Dr. Wheels : { 6' 6½".* / 7' 0½" Su.
T.E. : { 15,960 lb.* / 17,585 lb. Su.

40322†	40332	40359	40383*
40323†	40337	40362	40385*
40324†	40351	40364	40391*
40325†	40353	40370	40395
40326†	40356	40377	40396

40397	40443	40491	40527
40401	40444	40493	40528
40402	40446	40495	40529
40403	40447	40496	40530
40404	40448	40497	40531
40405	40450	40498	40532
40406	40452	40499	40533
40407	40453	40500	40534
40409	40454	40501	40535
40410	40455	40502	40536
40411	40456	40503	40537
40412	40458	40504	40538
40413	40459	40505	40539
40414	40461	40506	40540
40415	40462	40507	40541
40416	40463	40508	40542
40417	40464	40509	40543
40418	40468	40510	40544
40419	40470	40511	40546
40420	40471	40512	40547
40421	40472	40513	40548
40422	40477	40514	40549
40423	40478	40515	40550
40424	40479	40516	40551
40425	40480	40517	40552
40426	40482	40518	40553
40427	40483	40519	40554
40430	40484	40520	40556
40432	40485	40521	40557
40433	40486	40522	40558
40434	40487	40523	40559
40436	40488	40524	40560
40438	40489	40525	40561
40439	40490	40526	40562

Total 156

4-4-0 2P

Introduced 1928. Post-Grouping development of M.R. design, with modified dimensions and reduced boiler mountings.

*Introduced 1929. Locos. built for S. & D.J.R. (taken into L.M.S.R. stock, 1930).

†Fitted experimentally in 1933 with Dabeg feed-water heater.

Weight : Loco. 54 tons 1 cwt.
Pressure : 180 lb. Su.
Cyls. : 19″ × 26″.
Dr. Wheels : 6′ 9″. T.E. : 17,730 lb.

40563	40598	40632	40667
40564	40599	40633*†	40668
40565	40600	40634*	40669
40566	40601	40635*	40670
40567	40602	40636	40671
40568	40603	40637	40672
40569	40604	40638	40673
40570	40605	40640	40674
40571	40606	40641	40675
40572	40607	40642	40676
40573	40608	40643	40677
40574	40609	40644	40678
40575	40610	40645	40679
40576	40611	40646	40680
40577	40612	40647	40681
40578	40613	40648	40682
40579	40614	40649	40683
40580	40615	40650	40684
40581	40616	40651	40685
40582	40617	40652	40686
40583	40618	40653†	40687
40584	40619	40654	40688
40585	40620	40655	40689
40586	40621	40656	40690
40587	40622	40657	40691
40588	40623	40658	40692
40589	40624	40659	40693
40590	40625	40660	40694
40592	40626	40661	40695
40593	40627	40662	40696
40594	40628	40663	40697
40595	40629	40664	40698
40596	40630	40665	40699
40597	40631	40666	40700

Total 136

4-4-0 3P

Introduced 1901. Johnson M.R. design rebuilt by Fowler from 1916 with larger cyls., superheater, etc.

Weight : Loco. 55 tons 7 cwt.
Pressure : 175 lb. Su.
Cyls. : $20\frac{1}{2}$″ × 26″.
Dr. Wheels : 6′ 9″. T.E. : 20,065 lb.

40720	40729	40740	40747
40726	40734	40741	40758
40727	40735	40743	40762
40728	40739	40745	

Total 15

4-4-0 (3-Cyl. Compd.) 4P

*Introduced 1905. Development by Deeley of Johnson Midland compound, later superheated by Fowler.
†Introduced 1914. Fowler superheated rebuild of Johnson locos. (originally built 1902).
Remainder. Introduced 1924. Post-Grouping locos. with modified dimensions and (except 61045–64) reduced boiler mountings.
Weight : Loco. 61 tons 14 cwt.
Pressure : 200 lb Su.
Cyls : L.P. (2) 21″ × 26″.
H.P. (1) 19″ × 26″
Dr. Wheels : { 7′ 0″*†. / 6′ 9″.
T.E. (of L.P. cyls. at 80% boiler pressure) { 21,840 lb.*† / 22,650 lb.

40900	40929	41020†	41055
40901	40930	41021†	41056
40902	40931	41022†	41057
40903	40932	41023†	41058
40904	40933	41025†	41059
40905	40934	41028†	41060
40906	40935	41030†	41061
40907	40936	41031†	41062
40908	40937	41032†	41063
40909	40938	41034†	41064
40910	40939	41035†	41065
40911	41000*	41037†	41066
40912	41001*	41038†	41067
40913	41003*	41039†	41068
40914	41004*	41040†	41069
40915	41005†	41041†	41070
40916	41006†	41042†	41071
40917	41007†	41043†	41072
40918	41008†	41044†	41073
40919	41009†	41045	41074
40920	41010†	41046	41075
40921	41011†	41047	41076
40922	41012†	41048	41077
40923	41013†	41049	41078
40924	41014†	41050	41079
40925	41015†	41051	41080
40926	41016†	41052	41081
40927	41017†	41053	41082
40928	41019†	41054	41083

41084	41113	41142	41171
41085	41114	41143	41172
41086	41115	41144	41173
41087	41116	41145	41174
41088	41117	41146	41175
41089	41118	41147	41176
41090	41119	41148	41177
41091	41120	41149	41178
41092	41121	41150	41179
41093	41122	41151	41180
41094	41123	41152	41181
41095	41124	41153	41182
41096	41125	41154	41183
41097	41126	41155	41184
41098	41127	41156	41185
41099	41128	41157	41186
41100	41129	41158	41187
41101	41130	41159	41188
41102	41131	41160	41189
41103	41132	41161	41190
41104	41133	41162	41191
41105	41134	41163	41192
41106	41135	41164	41193
41107	41136	41165	41194
41108	41137	41166	41195
41109	41138	41167	41196
41110	41139	41168	41197
41111	41140	41169	41198
41112	41141	41170	41199

Total 232

2-6-2T 2

Introduced 1946. Ivatt taper boiler design.
Weight : 63 tons 5 cwt.
Pressure : 200 lb. Su.
Cyls. : (O) 16″ × 24″.
Dr. Wheels : 5′ 0″. T.E. : 17,410 lb.
Walschaerts Valve Gear.

41200	41208	41216	41224
41201	41209	41217	41225
41202	41210	41218	41226
41203	41211	41219	41227
41204	41212	41220	41228
41205	41213	41221	41229
41206	41214	41222	
41207	41215	41223	

Total 30

0-4-0ST 0F

Introduced 1890. Johnson Midland design.

†Introduced 1903. Larger Johnson Midland design.
Dr. Wheels : 3′ 10″.
Pressure : { 140 lb.* / 150 lb.†

	Weight tons	cwt.	Cyls. (O)	T.E.
41516*	23	3	13″ × 20″	8,745
41518†	32	3	15″ × 20″	11,640
41523†	32	3	15″ × 20″	12.475

Total 3

0-4-0T 0F

Introduced 1907. Deeley Midland design.
Weight : 32 tons 16 cwt.
Pressure : 160 lb.
Cyls. : (O) 15″ × 22″.
Dr. Wheels : 3′ 9⅝″. T.E. : 14,635 lb.
Walschaerts Valve Gear.

41528	41531	41534	41536
41529	41532	41535	41537
41530	41533		

Total 10

0-6-0T 1F

Introduced 1878. Johnson Midland design. Later rebuilt with Belpaire boilers.
Weight : 39 tons 11 cwt.
Pressure : { 150 lb.* / 140 lb.†
Cyls. : 17″ × 24″.
Dr. Wheels : 4′ 7″.
T.E. : { 16,080 lb.* / 15,005 lb.†

41660	41699	41725	41753
41661	41702	41726	41754
41664	41706	41727	41763
41666	41708	41734	41767
41671	41710	41739	41768
41672	41711	41745	41769
41682	41712	41747	41770
41686	41713	41748	41773
41690	41720	41749	41777
41695	41724	41752	41779
41780	41814	41847	41869
41781	41820	41852	41873
41793	41824	41853	41874
41794*	41826	41854	41875
41795	41829	41855	41878
41797	41833	41856	41879
41803	41835	41857	41885
41804	41838	41859	41889
41805	41839	41860	41890
41811	41844	41865	41895
41813	41846		

Total 82

0-4-4T 2P

Introduced : 1932. Stanier design.
Weight : 58 tons 1 cwt.
Pressure : 160 lb.
Cyls. : 18″ × 26″.
Dr. Wheels : 5′ 7″ T.E. : 17,100 lb.

41900	41903	41906	41908
41901	41904	41907	41909
41902	41905		

Total 10

4-4-2T 2P

Introduced 1900. L.T. & S. Whitelegg "51" Class.
Weight : 67 tons 15 cwt.
Pressure : 170 lb.
Cyls. : (O) 19″ × 26″.
Dr. Wheels : 6′ 6″. T.E. : 17,390 lb.

41911	41915	41919	41923
41912	41916	41920	41924
41913	41917	41921	41925
41914	41918	41922	41926

Total 16

4-4-2T 3P

*Introduced 1905. Rebuild of Whitelegg L.T. & S. "37" Class (originally introduced 1897).
†Introduced 1909. L.T. & S. Whitelegg "79" Class.
Remainder. Introduced 1923. Midland and L.M.S. development of L.T. & S. "79" Class.
Weight : { 71 tons 10 cwt.† / 71 tons 10 cwt. / 70 tons 15 cwt.*
Pressure : 170 lb.
Cyls. : (O) 19″ × 26″.
Dr. Wheels : 6′ 6″. T.E. : 17,390 lb.

Above : Class 3 2-6-2T No. 40010, fitted for auto working

[H. C. Casserley

Right : Class 3 2-6-2T No. 7 (now No. 40007) with outside steampipe and large chimney

[P. Ransome-Wallis

Below : Class 2 2-6-2T No. 41211, fitted for auto working

[J. P. Wilson

R. Tourret

Class 4P 4-4-0 No. 936 (now No. 40936) with high-sided tender

[J. P. Wilson

Class 2P 4-4-0 No. 40653, fitted with Dabeg feed-water heater

[H. C. Casserley

Class 3P 4-4-0 No. 40745

[H C. Casserley

Class 5 2-6-0 No. 42833

[P. Ransome-Wallis

Class 5 2-6-0 No. 2950 (now No. 42950)

[H. C. Casserley

Beyer-Garratt 2-6-6-2T No. 47972

Left : Class 7F 2-8-0 No. 13804 (now No. 53804)

[*W. S. Garth*

Below : Class 8F 2-8-0 No. 8602 (now No. 48602)

[*H. C. Casserley*

Left : The Lickey banker — 0-10-0 No. 22290 (now No. 58100)

[*H. C. Casserley*

[H. C. Casserley

Class 5 4-6-0 No. 45168, with top feed and dome combined

[E. D. Bruton

Class 5 4-6-0 No. 45442, with top feed immediately in front of the dome

[P. Ransome-Wallis

Class 5 4-6-0 No. 44998, with top feed almost midway between dome and chimney

[H. C. Casserley

" Jubilee " Class 5XP 4-6-0 No. 45656 *Cochrane*

[B. H. Carter

" Patriot " Class 5XP 4-6-0 No. 45506 *The Royal Pioneer Corps*

[P. Ransome-Wallis

" Royal Scot " Class 6P 4-6-0 No. 46134 *The Cheshire Regiment*

[E. Treacy

Rebuilt " Patriot " Class 6P 4-6-0 No. 45535 *Sir Herbert Walker, K.C.B*

[E. Treacy

Rebuilt " Royal Scot " 6P 4-6-0 No. 46127 *Old Contemptibles*

[P. Ransome-Wallis

Class 4 2-6-4T No. 42152

[H. C. Casserley

Class 4 (3-cyl.) 2-6-4T No. 2524 (now No. 42524)

[H. C. Casserley

Class 4 2-6-4T No. 42389

41928	41941	41954*	41967†
41929	41942	41955*	41968†
41930	41943	41956*	41969
41931	41944	41957*	41970
41932	41945	41958*	41971
41933	41946	41959*	41972
41934	41947	41960*	41973
41935	41948	41961*	41974
41936	41949	41962*	41975
41937	41950	41963*	41976
41938	41951	41964*	41977
41939	41952	41965†	41978
41940	41953*	41966†	

Total 51

0-6-2T 3F

Introduced 1903. Whitelegg L.T. & S. "69" Class (Nos. 41990–3 built 1912, taken directly into M.R. stock).
Weight : 64 tons 13 cwt.
Pressure : 170 lb.
Cyls. : 18″ × 26″.
Dr. Wheels : 5′ 3″. T.E. : 19,320 lb.

41980	41984	41988	41991
41981	41985	41989	41992
41982	41986	41990	41993
41983	41987		

Total 14

2-6-4T 4

*Introduced 1927. Fowler parallel boiler design.
†Introduced 1933. As earlier engines, but with side-window cabs and doors.
‡Introduced 1934. Stanier taper-boiler 3-cylinder design for L.T. & S. section.
§Introduced 1935. Stanier taper boiler 2-cylinder design.
¶Introduced 1945. Fairburn development of Stanier design with shorter wheelbase and detail alterations.

Weights: { 86 tons 5 cwt.*† / 92 tons 5 cwt.‡ / 87 tons 17 cwt.§ / 85 tons 5 cwt.¶ }
Pressure (all types) : 200 lb. Su.
Cyls. : { (O) 19″ × 26″*† / (3) 16″ × 26″‡ / (O) 19⅝″ × 26″§¶ }
Dr. Wheels (all types) : 5′ 9″.
T.E. : { 23,125 lb.*† / 24,600 lb‡ / 24,670 lb.§¶ }
Walschaerts valve gear.

¶Nos. 42107–42299 FAIRBURN LOCOS.

42107	42118	42129	42140
42108	42119	42130	42141
42109	42120	42131	42142
42110	42121	42132	42143
42111	42122	42133	42144
42112	42123	42134	42145
42113	42124	42135	42146
42114	42125	42136	42147
42115	42126	42137	42148
42116	42127	42138	42149
42117	42128	42139	42150

42151	42189	42227	42265
42152	42190	42228	42266
42153	42191	42229	42267
42154	42192	42230	42268
42155	42193	42231	42269
42156	42194	42232	42270
42157	42195	42233	42271
42158	42196	42234	42272
42159	42197	42235	42273
42160	42198	42236	42274
42161	42199	42237	42275
42162	42200	42238	42276
42163	42201	42239	42277
42164	42202	42240	42278
42165	42203	42241	42279
42166	42204	42242	42280
42167	42205	42243	42281
42168	42206	42244	42282
42169	42207	42245	42283
42170	42208	42246	42284
42171	42209	42247	42285
42172	42210	42248	42286
42173	42211	42249	42287
42174	42212	42250	42288
42175	42213	42251	42289
42176	42214	42252	42290
42177	42215	42253	42291
42178	42216	42254	42292
42179	42217	42255	42293
42180	42218	42256	42294
42181	42219	42257	42295
42182	42220	42258	42296
42183	42221	42259	42297
42184	42222	42260	42298
42185	42223	42261	42299
42186	42224	42262	
42187	42225	42263	
42188	42226	42264	

N.B.—Still being delivered in the 42107–46 series.

***Nos. 42300–94 FOWLER LOCOS.**

42300	42302	42304	42306
42301	42303	42305	42307

42308	42330	42352	42374
42309	42331	42353	42375
42310	42332	42354	42376
42311	42333	42355	42377
42312	42334	42356	42378
42313	42335	42357	42379
42314	42336	42358	42380
42315	42337	42359	42381
42316	42338	42360	42382
42317	42339	42361	42383
42318	42340	42362	42384
42319	42341	42363	42385
42320	42342	42364	42386
42321	42343	42365	42387
42322	42344	42366	42388
42323	42345	42367	42389
42324	42346	42368	42390
42325	42347	42369	42391
42326	42348	42370	42392
42327	42349	42371	42393
42328	42350	42372	42394
42329	42351	42373	

†Nos. 42395–42424 FOWLER LOCOS. WITH SIDE-WINDOW CAB.

42395	42403	42411	42418
42396	42404	42412	42419
42397	42405	42413	42420
42398	42406	42414	42421
42399	42407	42415	42422
42400	42408	42416	42423
42401	42409	42417	42424
42402	42410		

§Nos. 42425–94 STANIER 2-CYL LOCOS.

42425	42435	42445	42455
42426	42436	42446	42456
42427	42437	42447	42457
42428	42438	42448	42458
42429	42439	42449	42459
42430	42440	42450	42460
42431	42441	42451	42461
42432	42442	42452	42462
42433	42443	42453	42463
42434	42444	42454	42464

42465	42473	42481	42488
42466	42474	42482	42489
42467	42475	42483	42490
42468	42476	42484	42491
42469	42477	42485	42492
42470	42478	42486	42493
42471	42479	42487	42494
42472	42480		

‡Nos. 42500–36 STANIER 3-CYL. LOCOS.

42500	42510	42519	42528
42501	42511	42520	42529
42502	42512	42521	42530
42503	42513	42522	42531
42504	42514	42523	42532
42505	42515	42524	42533
42506	42516	42525	42534
42507	42517	42526	42535
42508	42518	42527	42536
42509			

§Nos. 42537–42672 STANIER 2-CYL. LOCOS.

42537	42559	42581	42603
42538	42560	42582	42604
42539	42561	42583	42605
42540	42562	42584	42606
42541	42563	42585	42607
42542	42564	42586	42608
42543	42565	42587	42609
42544	42566	42588	42610
42545	42567	42589	42611
42546	42568	42590	42612
42547	42569	42591	42613
42548	42570	42592	42614
42549	42571	42593	42615
42550	42572	42594	42616
42551	42573	42595	42617
42552	42574	42596	42618
42553	42575	42597	42619
42554	42576	42598	42620
42555	42577	42599	42621
42556	42578	42600	42622
42557	42579	42601	42623
42558	42580	42602	42624

42625	42637	42649	42661
42626	42638	42650	42662
42627	42639	42651	42663
42628	42640	42652	42664
42629	42641	42653	42665
42630	42642	42654	42666
42631	42643	42655	42667
42632	42644	42656	42668
42633	42645	42657	42669
42634	42646	42658	42670
42635	42647	42659	42671
42636	42648	42660	42672

¶**Nos. 42673–99 FAIRBURN LOCOS.**

42673	42680	42687	42694
42674	42681	42688	42695
42675	42682	42689	42696
42676	42683	42690	42697
42677	42684	42691	42698
42678	42685	42692	42699
42679	42686	42693	

2-6-0 5

Introduced 1926. Hughes design built under Fowler's direction. Walschaerts Valve Gear.

*Introduced 1931. Locos. rebuilt experimentally with Lentz R.C. poppet valves.

Weight : Loco. 66 tons 0 cwt.
Pressure : 180 lb. Su.
Cyls. : (O) 21″ × 26″.
Dr. Wheels : 5′ 6″. T.E. : 26,580 lb.

42700	42713	42726	42739	42752	42797	42842	42887
42701	42714	42727	42740	42753	42798	42843	42888
42702	42715	42728	42741	42754	42799	42844	42889
42703	42716	42729	42742	42755	42800	42845	42890
42704	42717	42730	42743	42756	42801	42846	42891
42705	42718	42731	42744	42757	42802	42847	42892
42706	42719	42732	42745	42758	42803	42848	42893
42707	42720	42733	42746	42759	42804	42849	42894
42708	42721	42734	42747	42760	42805	42850	42895
42709	42722	42735	42748	42761	42806	42851	42896
42710	42723	42736	42749	42762	42807	42852	42897
42711	42724	42737	42750	42763	42808	42853	42898
42712	42725	42738	42751	42764	42809	42854	42899
				42765	42810	42855	42900
				42766	42811	42856	42901
				42767	42812	42857	42902
				42768	42813	42858	42903
				42769	42814	42859	42904
				42770	42815	42860	42905
				42771	42816	42861	42906
				42772	42817	42862	42907
				42773	42818*	42863	42908
				42774	42819	42864	42909
				42775	42820	42865	42910
				42776	42821	42866	42911
				42777	42822*	42867	42912
				42778	42823	42868	42913
				42779	42824*	42869	42914
				42780	42825*	42870	42915
				42781	42826	42871	42916
				42782	42827	42872	42917
				42783	42828	42873	42918
				42784	42829*	42874	42919
				42785	42830	42875	42920
				42786	42831	42876	42921
				42787	42832	42877	42922
				42788	42833	42878	42923
				42789	42834	42879	42924
				42790	42835	42880	42925
				42791	42836	42881	42926
				42792	42837	42882	42927
				42793	42838	42883	42928
				42794	42839	42884	42929
				42795	42840	42885	42930
				42796	42841	42886	42931

42932	42936	42939	42942
42933	42937	42940	42943
42934	42938	42941	42944
42935			

Total 245

2-6-0 5

Introduced 1933. Stanier taper boiler design.
Weight : Loco. 69 tons 2 cwt.
Pressure : 225 lb. Su.
Cyls. : (O) 18″ × 28″.
Dr. Wheels : 5′ 6″. T.E. : 26,290 lb.
Walschaerts Valve Gear.

42945	42955	42965	42975
42946	42956	42966	42976
42947	42957	42967	42977
42948	42958	42968	42978
42949	42959	42969	42979
42950	42960	42970	42980
42951	42961	42971	42981
42952	42962	42972	42982
42953	42963	42973	42983
42954	42964	42974	42984

Total 40

2-6-0 4

Introduced 1947. Ivatt taper boiler design.
Weight : Loco. 59 tons 2 cwt.
Pressure : 225 lb. Su.
Cyls. : (O) 17½″ × 26″.
Dr. Wheels : 5′ 3″. T.E. : 24,170 lb.
Walschaerts Valve Gear.

43000	43010	43020	43030
43001	43011	43021	43031
43002	43012	43022	43032
43003	43013	43023	43033
43004	43014	43024	43034
43005	43015	43025	43035
43006	43016	43026	43036
43007	43017	43027	43037
43008	43018	43028	43038
43009	43019	43029	43039

N.B.—Still being delivered.

0-6-0 3F

Introduced 1885. Johnson Midland locos., rebuilt from 1920 by Fowler with Belpaire boilers.
Weight : Loco. 43 tons 17 cwt.
Pressure : 175 lb.
Cyls. : 18″ × 26″.
Dr. Wheels : 4′ 11″. T.E. : 21,240 lb.

43137	43180	43185	43188
43174	43181	43186	43189
43178	43183	43187	

Total 11

0-6-0 3F

Introduced 1885. Johnson Midland locos., rebuilt from 1916 by Fowler with Belpaire boilers.
*Introduced 1896. Locos. built for S. & D.J. (taken into L.M.S. stock 1930).
Weight : Loco. 43 tons 17 cwt.
Pressure : 175 lb.
Cyls. : 18″ × 26″.
Dr. Wheels : 5′ 3″. T.E. : 19,890 lb.

43191	43231	43259	43297
43192	43232	43260*	43298
43193	43233	43261	43299
43194*	43234	43263	43300
43200	43235	43266	43301
43201*	43237	43267	43305
43203	43239	43268	43306
43204*	43240	43271	43307
43205	43241	43273	43308
43207	43242	43274	43309
43208	43243	43275	43310
43210	43244	43277	43312
43211*	43245	43278	43313
43212	43246	43281	43314
43213	43247	43282	43315
43214	43248*	43283	43317
43216*	43249	43284	43318
43218*	43250	43286	43319
43219	43251	43287	43321
43222	43252	43290	43323
43223	43253	43292	43324
43224	43254	43293	43325
43225	43256	43294	43326
43226	43257	43295	43327
43228*	43258	43296	43329

43330	43408	43520	43618
43331	43410	43521	43619
43332	43411	43522	43620
43333	43419	43523	43621
43334	43427	43524	43622
43335	43428	43529	43623
43336	43429	43531	43624
43337	43431	43538	43627
43339	43433	43540	43629
43340	43435	43544	43630
43341	43436	43546	43631
43342	43440	43548	43633
43344	43441	43550	43634
43351	43443	43553	43636
43355	43444	43558	43637
43356	43446	43562	43638
43357	43448	43565	43639
43359	43449	43568	43644
43361	43453	43570	43645
43364	43454	43572	43650
43367	43456	43574	43651
43368	43457	43575	43652
43369	43459	43578	43653
43370	43462	43579	43656
43371	43463	43580	43657
43373	43464	43581	43658
43374	43468	43582	43660
43378	43469	43583	43661
43379	43474	43584	43662
43381	43476	43585	43664
43386	43482	43586	43665
43387	43484	43587	43667
43388	43490	43593	43668
43389	43491	43594	43669
43392	43494	43595	43673
43394	43496	43596	43674
43395	43497	43598	43675
43396	43499	43599	43676
43398	43502	43600	43678
43399	43506	43604	43679
43400	43507	43605	43680
43401	43509	43607	43681
43402	43510	43608	43682
43405	43514	43612	43683
43406	43515	43615	43684

43686	43717	43742	43759
43687	43721	43745	43760
43690	43723	43747	43762
43693	43724	43748	43763
43698	43727	43749	43765
43705	43728	43751	43766
43709	43729	43753	43767
43710	43731	43754	43770
43711	43734	43755	43771
43712	43735	43756	43772
43714	43737	43757	43773
43715			

Total 325

0-6-0 3F

Introduced 1906. Deeley Midland design, rebuilt by Fowler with Belpaire boiler.
Weight : Loco. 46 tons 3 cwt.
Pressure : 175 lb.
Cyls. : $18\frac{1}{2}'' \times 26''$.
Dr. Wheels : 5′ 3″. T.E. : 21,010 lb.

43775	43791	43806	43820
43776	43792	43807	43821
43777	43793	43808	43822
43778	43795	43809	43823
43779	43797	43810	43824
43781	43798	43811	43825
43782	43799	43812	43826
43784	43800	43813	43827
43785	43801	43814	43828
43786	43802	43815	43829
43787	43803	43817	43830
43789	43804	43818	43832
43790	43805	43819	43833

Total 52

0-6-0 4F

Introduced 1911. Fowler superheated Midland design.
Weight : 48 tons 15 cwt.
Pressure : 175 lb. Su.
Cyls. : $20'' \times 26''$.
Dr. Wheels : 5′ 3″. T.E. : 24,555 lb.

43835	43839	43843	43847
43836	43840	43844	43848
43837	43841	43845	43849
43838	43842	43846	43850

0-6-0 4F

Introduced 1924. Post-grouping development of Midland design with reduced boiler mountings.
*Introduced 1922. Locos. built for S.D. & J.R. to M.R. design (taken into L.M.S. stock, 1930).
Weight : Loco. 43 tons 15 cwt.
Pressure : 175 lb. Su.
Cyls. : 20″ × 26″.
Dr. Wheels : 5′ 3″. **T.E. : 24,555 lb.**

43851	43895	43939	43983
43852	43896	43940	43984
43853	43897	43941	43985
43854	43898	43942	43986
43855	43899	43943	43987
43856	43900	43944	43988
43857	43901	43945	43989
43858	43902	43946	43990
43859	43903	43947	43991
43860	43904	43948	43992
43861	43905	43949	43993
43862	43906	43950	43994
43863	43907	43951	43995
43864	43908	43952	43996
43865	43909	43953	43997
43866	43910	43954	43998
43867	43911	43955	43999
43868	43912	43956	44000
43869	43913	43957	44001
43870	43914	43958	44002
43871	43915	43959	44003
43872	43916	43960	44004
43873	43917	43961	44005
43874	43918	43962	44006
43875	43919	43963	44007
43876	43920	43964	44008
43877	43921	43965	44009
43878	43922	43966	44010
43879	43923	43967	44011
43880	43924	43968	44012
43881	43925	43969	44013
43882	43926	43970	44014
43883	43927	43971	44015
43884	43928	43972	44016
43885	43929	43973	44017
43886	43930	43974	44018
43887	43931	43975	44019
43888	43932	43976	44020
43889	43933	43977	44021
43890	43934	43978	44022
43891	43935	43979	44023
43892	43936	43980	44024
43893	43937	43981	44025
43894	43938	43982	44026

44027	44063	44099	44135
44028	44064	44100	44136
44029	44065	44101	44137
44030	44066	44102	44138
44031	44067	44103	44139
44032	44068	44104	44140
44033	44069	44105	44141
44034	44070	44106	44142
44035	44071	44107	44143
44036	44072	44108	44144
44037	44073	44109	44145
44038	44074	44110	44146
44039	44075	44111	44147
44040	44076	44112	44148
44041	44077	44113	44149
44042	44078	44114	44150
44043	44079	44115	44151
44044	44080	44116	44152
44045	44081	44117	44153
44046	44082	44118	44154
44047	44083	44119	44155
44048	44084	44120	44156
44049	44085	44121	44157
44050	44086	44122	44158
44051	44087	44123	44159
44052	44088	44124	44160
44053	44089	44125	44161
44054	44090	44126	44162
44055	44091	44127	44163
44056	44092	44128	44164
44057	44093	44129	44165
44058	44094	44130	44166
44059	44095	44131	44167
44060	44096	44132	44168
44061	44097	44133	44169
44062	44098	44134	44170

Total 192

44171	44217	44263	44309	44355	44401	44447	44493
44172	44218	44264	44310	44356	44402	44448	44494
44173	44219	44265	44311	44357	44403	44449	44495
44174	44220	44266	44312	44358	44404	44450	44496
44175	44221	44267	44313	44359	44405	44451	44497
44176	44222	44268	44314	44360	44406	44452	44498
44177	44223	44269	44315	44361	44407	44453	44499
44178	44224	44270	44316	44362	44408	44454	44500
44179	44225	44271	44317	44363	44409	44455	44501
44180	44226	44272	44318	44364	44410	44456	44502
44181	44227	44273	44319	44365	44411	44457	44503
44182	44228	44274	44320	44366	44412	44458	44504
44183	44229	44275	44321	44367	44413	44459	44505
44184	44230	44276	44322	44368	44414	44460	44506
44185	44231	44277	44323	44369	44415	44461	44507
44186	44232	44278	44324	44370	44416	44462	44508
44187	44233	44279	44325	44371	44417	44463	44509
44188	44234	44280	44326	44372	44418	44464	44510
44189	44235	44281	44327	44373	44419	44465	44511
44190	44236	44282	44328	44374	44420	44466	44512
44191	44237	44283	44329	44375	44421	44467	44513
44192	44238	44284	44330	44376	44422	44468	44514
44193	44239	44285	44331	44377	44423	44469	44515
44194	44240	44286	44332	44378	44424	44470	44516
44195	44241	44287	44333	44379	44425	44471	44517
44196	44242	44288	44334	44380	44426	44472	44518
44197	44243	44289	44335	44381	44427	44473	44519
44198	44244	44290	44336	44382	44428	44474	44520
44199	44245	44291	44337	44383	44429	44475	44521
44200	44246	44292	44338	44384	44430	44476	44522
44201	44247	44293	44339	44385	44431	44477	44523
44202	44248	44294	44340	44386	44432	44478	44524
44203	44249	44295	44341	44387	44433	44479	44525
44204	44250	44296	44342	44388	44434	44480	44526
44205	44251	44297	44343	44389	44435	44481	44527
44206	44252	44298	44344	44390	44436	44482	44528
44207	44253	44299	44345	44391	44437	44483	44529
44208	44254	44300	44346	44392	44438	44484	44530
44209	44255	44301	44347	44393	44439	44485	44531
44210	44256	44302	44348	44394	44440	44486	44532
44211	44257	44303	44349	44395	44441	44487	44533
44212	44258	44304	44350	44396	44442	44488	44534
44213	44259	44305	44351	44397	44443	44489	44535
44214	44260	44306	44352	44398	44444	44490	44536
44215	44261	44307	44353	44399	44445	44491	44537
44216	44262	44308	44354	44400	44446	44492	44538

44539	44548	44557*	44566	44575	44583	44591	44599
44540	44549	44558*	44567	44576	44584	44592	44600
44541	44550	44559*	44568	44577	44585	44593	44601
44542	44551	44560*	44569	44578	44586	44594	44602
44543	44552	44561*	44570	44579	44587	44595	44603
44544	44553	44562	44571	44580	44588	44596	44604
44545	44554	44563	44572	44581	44589	44597	44605
44546	44555	44564	44573	44582	44590	44598	44606
44547	44556	44565	44574				

Total 580

4-6-0 5

Introduced 1934. Stanier taper boiler design.

Experimental locos.

*Introduced 1947. Stephenson link motion (outside), roller bearings, double chimney.

†Introduced 1948. Caprotti Valve Gear.

‡Introduced 1948. Caprotti Valve Gear, roller bearings.

§Introduced 1948. Caprotti Valve Gear, roller bearings, double chimney

¶Introduced 1948. Roller bearings.

ϕIntroduced 1948. Roller bearings, double chimney.

Weights : Loco.
- 72 tons 2 cwt.
- 75 tons 6 cwt.*
- 74 tons 0 cwt.†
- 74 tons 0 cwt.‡
- 74 tons 0 cwt.§
- 75 tons 6 cwt.¶
- 75 tons 6 cwt.ϕ

Pressure : 225 lb. Su.
Cyls. : (O) 18½″ × 28″.
Dr. Wheels : 6′ 0″. T.E. : 25,455 lb.
Walschaerts Valve Gear, except where otherwise shown.

44658	44671	44684	44697
44659	44672	44685	44698
44660	44673	44686	44699
44661	44674	44687	44700
44662	44675	44688	44701
44663	44676	44689	44702
44664	44677	44690	44703
44665	44678	44691	44704
44666	44679	44692	44705
44667	44680	44693	44706
44668	44681	44694	44707
44669	44682	44695	44708
44670	44683	44696	44709

NOTE

To understand the system of reference marks used in this book, it is essential to read the notes on page 8.

44710	44755§	44800	44889
44711	44756§	44801	44846
44712	44757§	44802	44847
44713	44758¶	44803	44848
44714	44759¶	44804	44849
44715	44760¶	44805	44850
44716	44761¶	44806	44851
44717	44762¶	44807	44852
44718	44763¶	44808	44853
44719	44764¶	44809	44854
44720	44765ϕ	44810	44855
44721	44766ϕ	44811	44856
44722	44767*	44812	44857
44723	44768	44813	44858
44724	44769	44814	44859
44725	44770	44815	44860
44726	44771	44816	44861
44727	44772	44817	44862
44728	44773	44818	44863
44729	44774	44819	44864
44730	44775	44820	44865
44731	44776	44821	44866
44732	44777	44822	44867
44733	44778	44823	44868
44734	44779	44824	44869
44735	44780	44825	44870
44736	44781	44826	44871
44737	44782	44827	44872
44738†	44783	44828	44873
44739†	44784	44829	44874
44740†	44785	44830	44875
44741†	44786	44831	44876
44742†	44787	44832	44877
44743†	44788	44833	44878
44744†	44789	44834	44879
44745†	44790	44835	44880
44746†	44791	44836	44881
44747†	44792	44837	44882
44748‡	44793	44838	44883
44749‡	44794	44839	44884
44750‡	44795	44840	44885
44751‡	44796	44841	44886
44752‡	44797	44842	44887
44753‡	44798	44843	44888
44754‡	44799	44844	44889

44890	44936	44982	45028
44891	44937	44983	45029
44892	44938	44984	45030
44893	44939	44985	45031
44894	44940	44986	45032
44895	44941	44987	45033
44896	44942	44988	45034
44897	44943	44989	45035
44898	44944	44990	45036
44899	44945	44991	45037
44900	44946	44992	45038
44901	44947	44993	45039
44902	44948	44994	45040
44903	44949	44995	45041
44904	44950	44996	45042
44905	44951	44997	45043
44906	44952	44998	45044
44907	44953	44999	45045
44908	44954	45000	45046
44909	44955	45001	45047
44910	44956	45002	45048
44911	44957	45003	45049
44912	44958	45004	45050
44913	44959	45005	45051
44914	44960	45006	45052
44915	44961	45007	45053
44916	44962	45008	45054
44917	44963	45009	45055
44918	44964	45010	45056
44919	44965	45011	45057
44920	44966	45012	45058
44921	44967	45013	45059
44922	44968	45014	45060
44923	44969	45015	45061
44924	44970	45016	45062
44925	44971	45017	45063
44926	44972	45018	45064
44927	44973	45019	45065
44928	44974	45020	45066
44929	44975	45021	45067
44930	44976	45022	45068
44931	44977	45023	45069
44932	44978	45024	45070
44933	44979	45025	45071
44934	44980	45026	45072
44935	44981	45027	45073

45074	45114	45154[1]	45194
45075	45115	45155	45195
45076	45116	45156[1]	45196
45077	45117	45157[1]	45197
45078	45118	45158[1]	45198
45079	45119	45159	45199
45080	45120	45160	45200
45081	45121	45161	45201
45082	45122	45162	45202
45083	45123	45163	45203
45084	45124	45164	45204
45085	45125	45165	45205
45086	45126	45166	45206
45087	45127	45167	45207
45088	45128	45168	45208
45089	45129	45169	45209
45090	45130	45170	45210
45091	45131	45171	45211
45092	45132	45172	45212
45093	45133	45173	45213
45094	45134	45174	45214
45095	45135	45175	45215
45096	45136	45176	45216
45097	45137	45177	45217
45098	45138	45178	45218
45099	45139	45179	45219
45100	45140	45180	45220
45101	45141	45181	45221
45102	45142	45182	45222
45103	45143	45183	45223
45104	45144	45184	45224
45105	45145	45185	45225
45106	45146	45186	45226
45107	45147	45187	45227
45108	45148	45188	45228
45109	45149	45189	45229
45110	45150	45190	45230
45111	45151	45191	45231
45112	45152	45192	45232
45113	45153	45193	45233

[1] NAMES :

45154 Lanarkshire Yeomanry.
45156 Ayrshire Yeomanry.
45157 The Glasgow Highlander.
45158 Glasgow Yeomanry.

45234	45280	45326	45372
45235	45281	45327	45373
45236	45282	45328	45374
45237	45283	45329	45375
45238	45284	45330	45376
45239	45285	45331	45377
45240	45286	45332	45378
45241	45287	45333	45379
45242	45288	45334	45380
45243	45289	45335	45381
45244	45290	45336	45382
45245	45291	45337	45383
45246	45292	45338	45384
45247	45293	45339	45385
45248	45294	45340	45386
45249	45295	45341	45387
45250	45296	45342	45388
45251	45297	45343	45389
45252	45298	45344	45390
45253	45299	45345	45391
45254	45300	45346	45392
45255	45301	45347	45393
45256	45302	45348	45394
45257	45303	45349	45395
45258	45304	45350	45396
45259	45305	45351	45397
45260	45306	45352	45398
45261	45307	45353	45399
45262	45308	45354	45400
45263	45309	45355	45401
45264	45310	45356	45402
45265	45311	45357	45403
45266	45312	45258	45404
45267	45313	45359	45405
45268	45314	45360	45406
45269	45315	45361·	45407
45270	45316	45362	45408
45271	45317	45363	45409
45272	45318	45364	45410
45273	45319	45365	45411
45274	45320	45366	45412
45275	45321	45367	45413
45276	45322	45368	45414
45277	45323	45369	45415
45278	45324	45370	45416
45279	45325	45371	45417

45418	45439	45460	45481
45419	45440	45461	45482
45420	45441	45462	45483
45421	45442	45463	45484
45422	45443	45464	45485
45423	45444	45465	45486
45424	45445	45466	45487
45425	45446	45467	45488
45426	45447	45468	45489
45427	45448	45469	45490
45428	45449	45470	45491
45429	45450	45471	45492
45430	45451	45472	45493
45431	45452	45473	45494
45432	45453	45474	45495
45433	45454	45475	45496
45434	45455	45476	45497
45435	45456	45477	45498
45436	45457	45478	45499
45437	45458	45479	
45438	45459	45480	

(Still being delivered in 44658 series.)

"Patriot" Class

4-6-0 5XP & 6P

***5XP** Introduced 1930. Fowler 3-cyl. rebuild of L.N.W. "Claughton" Class (introduced 1912), retaining original wheels and other details.

Remainder. Introduced 1933. New locos. to Fowler design (45502–41 were officially considered as rebuilds).

†**6P** Introduced 1946. Ivatt rebuild of Fowler locos. with large taper boiler, new cylinders and double chimney.

Weight : Loco. { 80 tons 15 cwt. (5XP). 82 tons 0 cwt. (6P).

Pressure : { 200 lb. Su. (5XP). 250 lb. Su. (6P).

Cyls. : { (3) 18″ × 26″ (5XP). (3) 17″ × 26″ (6P).

Dr. Wheels : 6′ 9″.

T.E. : { 26,520 lb (5XP). 29,570 lb. (6P).

Walschaerts Valve Gear.

45500*Patriot
45501*St. Dunstan's
45502 Royal Naval Division
45503 The Royal Leicestershire Regt.
45504 Royal Signals
45505 The Royal Army Ordnance Corps
45506 The Royal Pioneer Corps
45507 Royal Tank Corps
45508
45509
45510
45511 Isle of Man
45512†Bunsen
45513
45514†Holyhead
45515 Caernarvon
45516 The Bedfordshire and [Hertfordshire Regt.
45517
45518 Bradshaw
45519 Lady Godiva
45520 Llandudno
45521†Rhyl
45522†Prestatyn
45523†Bangor
45524 Blackpool
45525†Colwyn Bay
45526†Morecambe and Heysham
45527†Southport
45528†
45529†Stephenson
45530†Sir Frank Ree
45531†Sir Frederick Harrison
45532†Illustrious
45533 Lord Rathmore
45534†E. Tootal Broadhurst
45535†Sir Herbert Walker, K.C.B.
45536†Private W. Wood, V.C.
45537 Private E. Sykes, V.C.
45538 Giggleswick
45539 E. C. Trench
45540†Sir Robert Turnbull
45541 Duke of Sutherland
45542
45543 Home Guard
45544
45545†Planet
45546 Fleetwood
45547
45548 Lytham St. Annes
45549
45550
45551

Total 52

"Jubilee" Class

4-6-0 5XP & 6P

5XP Introduced 1934. Stanier taper boiler development of the "Patriot" class.
***6P** Introduced 1942. Rebuilt with larger boiler and double chimney.
Weight : Loco. : { 79 tons 11 cwt. / 82 tons 0 cwt.* }
Pressure : { 225 lb. Su. / 250 lb. Su. }
Cyls. : 17" × 26".
Dr. Wheels : 6' 9".
T.E. : { 26,610 lb. / 29,570 lb.* }
Walschaerts Valve Gear.

45552 Silver Jubilee
45553 Canada
45554 Ontario
45555 Quebec
45556 Nova Scotia
45557 New Brunswick
45558 Manitoba
45559 British Columbia
45560 Prince Edward Island
45561 Saskatchewan
45562 Alberta
45563 Australia
45564 New South Wales
45565 Victoria
45566 Queensland
45567 South Australia
45568 Western Australia
45569 Tasmania
45570 New Zealand

45571 South Africa
45572 Eire
45573 Newfoundland
45574 India
45575 Madras
45576 Bombay
45577 Bengal
45578 United Provinces
45579 Punjab
45580 Burma
45581 Bihar and Orissa
45582 Central Provinces
45583 Assam
45584 North West Frontier
45585 Hyderabad
45586 Mysore
45587 Baroda
45588 Kashmir
45589 Gwalior
45590 Travancore
45591 Udaipur
45592 Indore
45593 Kolhapur
45594 Bhopal
45595 Southern Rhodesia
45596 Bahamas
45597 Barbados
45598 Basutoland
45599 Bechuanaland
45600 Bermuda
45601 British Guiana
45602 British Honduras
45603 Solomon Islands
45604 Ceylon
45605 Cyprus
45606 Falkland Islands
45607 Fiji
45608 Gibraltar
45609 Gilbert and Ellice Islands
45610 Gold Coast
45611 Hong Kong
45612 Jamaica
45613 Kenya
45614 Leeward Islands
45615 Malay States
45616 Malta G.C.
45617 Mauritius
45618 New Hebrides
45619 Nigeria
45620 North Borneo
45621 Northern Rhodesia
45622 Nyasaland
45623 Palestine
45624 St. Helena
45625 Sarawak
45626 Seychelles
45627 Sierra Leone
45628 Somaliland
45629 Straits Settlements
45630 Swaziland
45631 Tanganyika
45632 Tonga
45633 Aden
45634 Trinidad
45635 Tobago
45636 Uganda
45637 Windward Islands
45638 Zanzibar
45639 Raleigh
45640 Frobisher
45641 Sandwich
45642 Boscawen
45643 Rodney
45644 Howe
45645 Collingwood
45646 Napier
45647 Sturdee
45648 Wemyss
45649 Hawkins
45650 Blake
45651 Shovell
45652 Hawke
45653 Barham
45654 Hood
45655 Keith
45656 Cochrane
45657 Tyrwhitt
45658 Keyes
45659 Drake
45660 Rooke

45661 Vernon
45662 Kempenfelt
45663 Jervis
45664 Nelson
45665 Lord Rutherford of [Nelson
45666 Cornwallis
45667 Jellicoe
45668 Madden
45669 Fisher
45670 Howard of Effingham
45671 Prince Rupert
45672 Anson
45673 Keppel
45674 Duncan
45675 Hardy
45676 Codrington
45677 Beatty
45678 De Robeck
45679 Armada
45680 Camperdown
45681 Aboukir
45682 Trafalgar
45683 Hogue
45684 Jutland
45685 Barfleur
45686 St. Vincent
45687 Neptune
45688 Polyphemus
45689 Ajax
45690 Leander
45691 Orion
45692 Cyclops
45693 Agamemnon
45694 Bellerophon
45695 Minotaur
45696 Arethusa
45697 Achilles
45698 Mars
45699 Galatea
45700 Britannia
45701 Conqueror
45702 Colossus
45703 Thunderer
45704 Leviathan
45705 Seahorse
45706 Express
45707 Valiant
45708 Resolution
45709 Implacable
45710 Irresistible
45711 Courageous
45712 Victory
45713 Renown
45714 Revenge
45715 Invincible
45716 Swiftsure
45717 Dauntless
45718 Dreadnought
45719 Glorious
45720 Indomitable
45721 Impregnable
45722 Defence
45723 Fearless
45724 Warspite
45725 Repulse
45726 Vindictive
45727 Inflexible
45728 Defiance
45729 Furious
45730 Ocean
45731 Perseverance
45732 Sanspareil
45733 Novelty
45734 Meteor
45735*Comet
45736*Phoenix
45737 Atlas
45738 Samson
45739 Ulster
45740 Munster
45741 Leinster
45742 Connaught

Total 191

For full details of
BRITISH RAILWAYS CLASS
"WD" 2-8-0s
running on the L.M. Region,
see the
A.B.C. OF BRITISH RAILWAYS LOCOMOTIVES PT. IV. Nos. 60000–90999

"Royal Scot" Class

4-6-0 **6P**

Introduced 1927. Fowler parallel boiler design.

*Introduced 1935. Stanier taper boiler rebuild with simple cyls. of experimental high pressure loco. No. 6399 *Fury*.

†Introduced 1943. Stanier rebuild of Fowler locos. with taper boiler, new cyls. and double chimney.

Weight: Loco. { 84 tons 18 cwt. / 84 tons 1 cwt.* / 83 tons† }

Pressure: 250 lb. Su.

Cyls.: (3) 18″×26″.

Dr. Wheels: 6′ 9″. T.E.: 33,150 lb.

Walschaerts Valve Gear.

46100 Royal Scot
46101†Royal Scots Grey
46102 Black Watch
46103†Royal Scots Fusilier
46104†Scottish Borderer
46105†Cameron Highlander
46106 Gordon Highlander
64107 Argyll and Sutherland Highlander
46108†Seaforth Highlander
46109†Royal Engineer
46110 Grenadier Guardsman
46111†Royal Fusilier
46112†Sherwood Forester
46113 Cameronian
46114†Coldstream Guardsman
46115†Scots Guardsman
46116†Irish Guardsman
46117†Welsh Guardsman
46118†Royal Welch Fusilier
46119†Lancashire Fusilier
46120†Royal Inniskilling Fusilier
46121†Highland Light Infantry, City of Glasgow Regiment
46122†Royal Ulster Rifleman
46123†Royal Irish Fusilier
46124†London Scottish
46125†3rd Carabinier
46126†Royal Army Service Corps
46127†Old Contemptibles
46128†The Lovat Scouts
46129†The Scottish Horse
46130 The West Yorkshire Regiment
46131†The Royal Warwickshire Regiment
46132†The King's Regiment Liverpool
46133†The Green Howards
46134 The Cheshire Regiment
46135†The East Lancashire Regiment
46136 The Border Regiment
46137 The Prince of Wales's Volunteers (South Lancashire)
46138†The London Irish Rifleman
46139†The Welch Regiment
46140 The King's Royal Rifle Corps
46141 The North Staffordshire Regiment
46142 The York and Lancaster Regiment
46143†The South Staffordshire Regiment
46144†Honourable Artillery Company
46145†The Duke of Wellington's Regt. (West Riding)
46146†The Rifle Brigade
46147†The Northamptonshire Regiment
46148 The Manchester Regiment
46149†The Middlesex Regiment
46150†The Life Guardsman
46151 The Royal Horse Guardsman
46152†The King's Dragoon Guardsman
46153 The Royal Dragoon

Above : Class 4 4-6-0 No. 57954

Right : " Clan " Class 4-6-0 No. 54767 *Clan Mackinnon*

[Photos : C. C. B. Herbert

Below : Class 4 4-6-0 No. 54653

[W. P. Smith

Above : The " Prince of Wales " Class was one of the last three remaining L.N.W.R. express types still represented in early 1949 ; now only one " Precursor " survives. Here is a " Prince " in its heyday with the up " Irish Mail " near Colwyn Bay

[*H. Gordon Tidey*

Below : The modern successor. Class 7P Pacific No. 46225 *Duchess of Gloucester* near Clifton with a Perth-Euston Express

[*E. Treacy*

46225

NORTH OF THE BORDER

Right : A Dornoch branch train near The Mound, on the east coast of Ross and Cromarty. Ex-Highland Railway 0-4-4T No. 15053 (now No. 55053) in charge

[P. Ransome-Wallis

Above : Class 3F 0-6-0 No. 17640 (now No. 57640) at the head of a freight near Hillington, Renfrew

Right : Demoted to freight duty, McIntosh "Dunalastair IV" 4-4-0 No. 54439 is seen at work near Uddingston, Lanark

[Photos : E. R. Wethersett

E. Treacy

The Turbomotive in action. She heads the pre-war 5.25 p.m. Liverpool-London express past Wavertree

[H. C. Casserley

One of the first Stanier Pacifics. No. 46201 *Princess Elizabeth* rounds a bend at Berkhamsted with an up Liverpool express

Left : Class 3F 0-6-0 No. 52427

[H. C. Casserley

Below : Class 2F 0-6-0 No. 57243 (built by Drummond)

[C. C. B. Herbert

[P. Ransome-Wallis

Class 3F 0-6-0T No. 17423 (now No. 57423), built by McIntosh

46154†The Hussar
46155 The Lancer
46156 The South Wales Borderer
46157†The Royal Artilleryman
46158 The Loyal Regiment
46159†The Royal Air Force
46160†Queen Victoria's Rifleman
46161†King's Own
46162†Queen's Westminster Rifleman
46163 Civil Service Rifleman
46164 The Artists' Rifleman
46165 The Ranger (12th London Regt.)
46166†London Rifle Brigade
46167†The Hertfordshire Regiment
46168†The Girl Guide
46169†The Boy Scout
46170*British Legion **Total 71**

"Princess Royal" Class

4-6-2 **7P**

*Introduced 1933. Stanier taper boiler design.

†Introduced 1935. Experimental turbine-driven locomotive ("Turbomotive"). (*NOTE : Cyl. and T.E. figures given below do not apply to this locomotive.*)

Remainder. Introduced 1935. Development of original design with alterations to valve gear, boiler and other details.

Weight : Loco. { 110 tons 11 cwt.† / 104 tons 10 cwt. (remainder).
Pressure : 250 lb. Su.
Cyls. : (4) 16¼"×28".
Dr. Wheels : 6′ 6″. T.E. : 40,285 lb.

Walschaerts Valve Gear and rocking shafts.

46200*The Princess Royal
46201*Princess Elizabeth
46202†
46203 Princess Margaret Rose
46204 Princess Louise
46205 Princess Victoria
46206 Princess Marie Louise
46207 Princess Arthur of Connaught
46208 Princess Helena Victoria
46209 Princess Beatrice
46210 Lady Patricia
46211 Queen Maud
46212 Duchess of Kent
Total 13

"Princess Coronation" Class

4-6-2 **7P**

Introduced 1938. Enlargement of "Princess Royal" class. All except Nos. 46230–4/9–55 originally streamlined (introduced 1937. Streamlining removed from 1946).

*Introduced 1947. Ivatt development with roller bearings and detail alterations.

Weight : { 105 tons 5 cwt. / 106 tons 8 cwt.*

Pressure : 250 lb. Su.

Cyls. : (4) 16½"×28".

Dr. Wheels : 6′ 9″. T.E. : 40,000 lb.
Walschaerts Valve Gear and rocking shafts.

46220 Coronation
46221 Queen Elizabeth
46222 Queen Mary
46223 Princess Alice
46224 Princess Alexandra
46225 Duchess of Gloucester
46226 Duchess of Norfolk
46227 Duchess of Devonshire
46228 Duchess of Rutland
46229 Duchess of Hamilton

46230 Duchess of Buccleuch
46231 Duchess of Atholl
46232 Duchess of Montrose
46233 Duchess of Sutherland
46234 Duchess of Abercorn
46235 City of Birmingham
46236 City of Bradford
46237 City of Bristol
46238 City of Carlisle
46239 City of Chester
46240 City of Coventry
46241 City of Edinburgh
46242 City of Glasgow
46243 City of Lancaster
46244 King George VI
46245 City of London
46246 City of Manchester
46247 City of Liverpool
46248 City of Leeds
46249 City of Sheffield
46250 City of Lichfield
46251 City of Nottingham
46252 City of Leicester
46253 City of St. Albans
46254 City of Stoke-on-Trent
46255 City of Hereford
46256*Sir William A. Stanier, F.R.S.
46257*City of Salford

Total 38

2-6-0 — 2

Introduced 1946. Ivatt taper boiler design.
Weight : Loco. 47 tons 2 cwt.
Pressure : 200 lb. Su.
Cyls. : (O) 16" × 24".
Dr. Wheels : 5′ 0″. T.E. : 17,410 lb.
Walschaerts Valve Gear.

46400	46409	46418	46427
46401	46410	46419	46428
46402	46411	46420	46429
46403	46412	46421	46430
46404	46413	46422	46431
46405	46414	46423	46432
46406	46415	46424	46433
46407	46416	46425	46434
46408	46417	46426	

Total 35

2-4-2T — 1P

Introduced 1890. Webb L.N.W. design.
Weight : 50 tons 10 cwt.
Pressure : 150 lb.
Cyls. : 17" × 24".
Dr. Wheels : 5′ 8½″. T.E. : 12,910 lb.

46601	46637	46669	46712
46603	46639	46676	46727
46604	46643	46680	46742
46616	46654	46683	46749
46620	46656	46687	46757
46628	46658	46688	
46632	46663	46701	
46635	46666	46710	

Total 29

2-4-2T — 2P

Introduced 1889. Aspinall L. & Y. design, sold to Wirral Rly., 1921 (loco. built 1890). The number 50638 in the present class was left allotted to this engine.
Weight : 55 tons 19 cwt.
Pressure : 180 lb.
Cyls. : 17½" × 26".
Dr. Wheels : 5' 8". T.E. : 18,360 lb.

46762 **Total 1**

0-6-2T — 2

Introduced 1898. Webb L.N.W. "18" Passenger tank."
Weight : 52 tons 6 cwt.
Pressure : 150 lb.
Cyls. : 18" × 24".
Dr. Wheels : 5' 2½". T.E. : 15,865 lb.

46876	46900	46912	46924
46899	46906	46922	

Total 7

0-4-0ST — 0F

Introduced 1932. Kitson design prepared to Stanier's requirements.
Weight : 33 tons 0 cwt.
Pressure : 160 lb.
Cyls. : (O) 15½" × 30".
Dr. Wheels : 3' 10". T.E. : 14,205 lb.

47000	47002	47003	47004
47001			

Total 5

0-6-0T — 2F

Introduced 1928. Fowler short-wheelbase dock tanks.
Weight : 43 tons 12 cwt.
Pressure : 160 lb.
Cyls. : (O) 17" × 22".
Dr. Wheels : 3' 11". T.E. : 18,400 lb.
Walschaerts Valve Gear.

47160	47163	47166	47168
47161	47164	47167	47169
47162	47165		

Total 10

0-4-0T — Sentinel

Geared Sentinel locos.

*Introduced 1929. Single-speed locos. for S.D. & J. (taken into L.M.S. stock 1930).
†Introduced 1930. Two-speed locos. for L.M.S.
‡Introduced 1932. Single-speed loco. for L.M.S.
Weight : 27 tons 15 cwt.* / 20 tons 17 cwt.† / 18 tons 18 cwt.‡
Pressure : 275 lb. Su.
Cyls. : (4)6¾" × 9".* / 6¾" × 9"†‡
Dr. Wheels : 3' 1½"* / 2' 6"†‡
T.E. : 15,500 lb.* / 11,800 lb.†‡

47180†	47182†	47184‡	47191*
47181†	47183†	47190*	

Total 7

0-6-0T — 3F

Introduced 1899. Johnson large Midland design, rebuilt with Belpaire boiler from 1919; fitted with condensers for London area.
*Introduced 1899. Non-condensing.
Weight : 48 tons 15 cwt.
Pressure : 160 lb.
Cyls. : 18" × 26".
Dr. Wheels : 4' 7". T.E. : 20,835 lb.

47200	47215	47230*	47245
47201	47216	47231*	47246*
47202	47217	47232*	47247
47203	47218	47233*	47248*
47204	47219	47234*	47249
47205	47220	47235*	47250*
47206	47221	47236*	47251
47207	47222	47237*	47252*
47208	47223	47238*	47253*
47209	47224	47239*	47254*
47210	47225	47240	47255*
47211	47226	47241	47256*
47212	47227	47242	47257*
47213	47228	47243	47258*
47214	47229	47244	47259*

Total 60

0-6-0T 3F

Introduced 1924. Post-grouping development of Midland design with detail alterations.

*Introduced 1929. Locos. built for S. & D.J. (taken into L.M.S. stock 1930).

Weight : 49 tons 10 cwt.
Pressure : 160 lb.
Cyls. : 18″ × 26″.
Dr. Wheels : 4′ 7″. T.E. : 20,835 lb.

47260	47296	47332	47368
47261	47297	47333	47369
47262	47298	47334	47370
47263	47299	47335	47371
47264	47300	47336	47372
47265	47301	47337	47373
47266	47302	47338	47374
47267	47303	47339	47375
47268	47304	47340	47376
47269	47305	47341	47377
47270	47306	47342	47378
47271	47307	47343	47379
47272	47308	47344	47380
47273	47309	47345	47381
47274	47310*	47346	47382
47275	47311*	47347	47383
47276	47312*	47348	47384
47277	47313*	47349	47385
47278	47314*	47350	47386
47279	47315*	47351	47387
47280	47316*	47352	47388
47281	47317	47353	47389
47282	47318	47354	47390
47283	47319	47355	47391
47284	47320	47356	47392
47285	47321	47357	47393
47286	47322	47358	47394
47287	47323	47359	47395
47288	47324	47360	47396
47289	47325	47361	47397
47290	47326	47362	47398
47291	47327	47363	47399
47292	47328	47364	47400
47293	47329	47365	47401
47294	47330	47366	47402
47295	47331	47367	47403

47404	47449	47495	47540
47405	47450	47496	47541
47406	47451	47497	47542
47407	47452	47498	47543
47408	47453	47499	47544
47409	47454	47500	47545
47410	47455	47501	47546
47411	47457	47502	47547
47412	47458	47503	47548
47413	47459	47504	47549
47414	47460	47505	47550
47415	47461	47506	47551
47416	47462	47507	47552
47417	47463	47508	47554
47418	47464	47509	47555
47419	47465	47510	47556
47420	47466	47511	47557
47421	47467	47512	47558
47422	47468	47513	47559
47423	47469	47514	47560
47424	47470	47515	47561
47425	47471	47516	47562
47426	47472	47517	47563
47427	47473	47518	47564
47428	47474	47519	47565
47429	47475	47520	47566
47430	47476	47521	47567
47431	47477	47522	47568
47432	47478	47523	47569
47433	47479	47524	47570
47434	47480	47525	47571
47435	47481	47526	47572
47436	47482	47527	47573
47437	47483	47528	47574
47438	47484	47529	47575
47439	47485	47530	47576
47440	47486	47531	47577
47441	47487	47532	47578
47442	47488	47533	47579
47443	47489	47534	47580
47444	47490	47535	47581
47445	47491	47536	47582
47446	47492	47537	47583
47447	47493	47538	47584
47448	47494	47539	47585

47586	47610	47635	47658
47587	47611	47636	47659
47588	47612	47637	47660
47589	47614	47638	47661
47590	47615	47639	47662
47591	47616	47640	47664
47592	47618	47641	47665
47593	47619	47642	47666
47594	47620	47643	47667
47595	47621	47644	47668
47596	47622	47645	47669
47597	47623	47646	47670
47598	47624	47647	47671
47599	47625	47648	47672
47600	47626	47649	47673
47601	47627	47650	47674
47602	47628	47651	47675
47603	47629	47652	47676
47604	47630	47653	47677
47605	47631	47654	47678
47606	47632	47655	47679
47607	47633	47656	47680
47608	47634	47657	47681
47609			

Total 417

0-4-2ST 1F

Introduced 1896. Webb L.N.W. Bissel truck design (oldest survivor built 1901).
Weight : 34 tons 17 cwt.
Pressure : 150 lb.
Cyls. : 17″ × 24″.
Dr. Wheels : 4′ 5½″. T.E. : 16,530 lb.

47862 47865 **Total 2**

0-8-2T 6F

Introduced 1911. Bowen Cooke L.N.W. design (tank version of " G " 0-8-0).
Weight : 72 tons 10 cwt.
Pressure : 170 lb.
Cyls. : 20½″ × 24″.
Dr. Wheels : 4′ 5½″. T.E. : 27,240 lb.

47877	47884	47885	47896
47881			

Total 5

0-8-4T 7F

Introduced 1923. Beames L.N.W. design, built after grouping (tank version of G2 0-8-0).
Weight : 88 tons 0 cwt.
Pressure : 185 lb. Su.
Cyls. : 20½″ × 24″.
Dr. Wheels : 4′ 5½″. T.E. : 29,815 lb.

47931	47933	47937	47939
47932	47936		

Total 7

2-6-6-2T Beyer-Garratt

*Introduced 1927. Original design with fixed coal bunker.
Remainder introduced 1930. Development with detail alterations, later fitted with revolving coal bunkers. No. 47997 fitted 1927 with fixed bunker.
Weight : { 148 tons 15 cwt.* / 155 tons 10 cwt.
Pressure : 190 lb. Su.
Cyls. : (4) 18½″ × 26″.
Dr. Wheels : 5′ 3″. T.E. : 45,620 lb.
Walschaerts Valve Gear.

47967	47976	47984	47992
47968	47977	47985	47993
47969	47978	47986	47994
47970	47979	47987	47995
47971	47980	47988	47996
47972	47981	47989	47997
47973	47982	47990	47998*
47974	47983	47991	47999*
47975			

Total 33

2-8-0 8F

(See note p. 4)

Introduced 1935. Stanier taper boiler design.
Weight : Loco. 72 tons 2 cwt.
Pressure : 225 lb. Su.
Cyls. : (O) 18½″ × 28″.
Dr. Wheels : 4′ 8½″. T.E. : 32,440 lb.
Walschaerts Valve Gear.

48000	48005	48010	48027
48001	48006	48011	48029
48002	48007	48017	48033
48003	48008	48024	48035
48004	48009	48026	48036

48037	48108	48153	48198	48281	48340	48385	48430
48050	48109	48154	48199	48282	48341	48386	48431
48053	48110	48155	48200	48283	48342	48387	48432
48054	48111	48156	48201	48284	48343	48388	48433
48055	48112	48157	48202	48285	48344	48389	48434
48056	48113	48158	48203	48293	48345	48390	48435
48057	48114	48159	48204	48301	48346	48391	48436
48060	48115	48160	48205	48302	48347	48392	48437
48062	48116	48161	48206	48303	48348	48393	48438
48063	48117	48162	48207	48304	48349	48394	48439
48064	48118	48163	48208	48305	48350	48395	48440
48065	48119	48164	48209	48306	48351	48396	48441
48067	48120	48165	48210	48307	48352	48397	48442
48069	48121	48166	48211	48308	48353	48398	48443
48070	48122	48167	48212	48309	48354	48399	48444
48073	48123	48168	48213	48310	48355	48400	48445
48074	48124	48169	48214	48311	48356	48401	48446
48075	48125	48170	48215	48312	48357	48402	48447
48076	48126	48171	46216	48313	48358	48403	48448
48078	48127	48172	48217	48314	48359	48404	48449
48079	48128	48173	48218	48315	48360	48405	48450
48080	48129	48174	48219	48316	48361	48406	48451
48081	48130	48175	48220	48317	48362	48407	48452
48082	48131	48176	48221	48318	48363	48408	48453
48083	48132	48177	48222	48319	48364	48409	48454
48084	48133	48178	48223	48320	48365	48410	48455
48085	48134	48179	48224	48321	48366	48411	48456
48088	48135	48180	48225	48322	48367	48412	48457
48089	48136	48181	48264	48323	48368	48413	48458
48090	48137	48182	48265	48324	48369	48414	48459
48092	48138	48183	48266	48325	48370	48415	48460
48093	48139	48184	48267	48326	48371	48416	48461
48095	48140	48185	48268	48327	48372	48417	48462
48096	48141	48186	48269	48328	48373	48418	48463
48097	48142	48187	48270	48329	48374	48419	48464
48098	48143	48188	48271	48330	48375	48420	48465
48099	48144	48189	48272	48331	48376	48421	48466
48100	48145	48190	48273	48332	48377	48422	48467
48101	48146	48191	48274	48333	48378	48423	48468
48102	48147	48192	48275	48334	48379	48424	48469
48103	48148	48193	48276	48335	48380	48425	48470
48104	48149	48194	48277	48336	48381	48426	48471
48105	48150	48195	48278	48337	48382	48427	48472
48106	48151	48196	48279	48338	48383	48428	48473
48107	48152	48197	48280	48339	48384	48429	48474

48475	48535	48620	48665
48476	48536	48621	48666
48477	48537	48622	48667
48478	48538	48623	48668
48479	48539	48624	48669
48490	48540	48625	48670
48491	48541	48626	48671
48492	48542	48627	48672
48493	48543	48628	48673
48494	48544	48629	48674
48495	48545	48630	48675
48500	48546	48631	48676
48502	48547	48632	48677
48503	48548	48633	48678
48504	48549	48634	48679
48505	48550	48635	48680
48506	48551	48636	48681
48507	48552	48637	48682
48508	48553	48638	48683
48509	48554	48639	48684
48510	48555	48640	48685
48511	48556	48641	48686
48512	48557	48642	48687
48513	48558	48643	48688
48514	48559	48644	48689
48515	48600	48645	48690
48516	48601	48646	48691
48517	48602	48647	48692
48518	48603	48648	48693
48519	48604	48649	48694
48520	48605	48650	48695
48521	48606	48651	48696
48522	48607	48652	48697
48523	48608	48653	48698
48524	48609	48654	48699
48525	48610	48655	48700
48526	48611	48656	48701
48527	48612	48657	48702
48528	48613	48658	48703
48529	48614	48659	48704
48530	48615	48660	48705
48531	48616	48661	48706
48532	48617	48662	48707
48533	48618	48663	48708
48534	48619	48664	48709

48710	48726	48742	48758
48711	48727	48743	48759
48712	48728	48744	48760
48713	48729	48745	48761
48714	48730	48746	48762
48715	48731	48747	48763
48716	48732	48748	48764
48717	48733	48749	48765
48718	48734	48750	48766
48719	48735	48751	48767
48720	48736	48752	48768
48721	48737	48753	48769
48722	48738	48754	48770
48723	48739	48755	48771
48724	48740	48756	48772
48725	48741	48757	

Total 624

4-6-0 4F

Introduced 1906. Whale. L.N.W. " 19″ Goods " (survivor built 1908).
Weight : Loco. 63 tons 0 cwt.
Pressure : 175 lb.
Cyls. : 19″ × 26″.
Dr. Wheels : 5′ 2½″. T.E. : 22,340 lb

48824

Total 1

0-8-0 6F & 7F

(see note p. 5)

G1 Class 6F

*Introduced 1912. Bowen Cooke L.N.W. superheated design, developed from earlier saturated design (many rebuilt from earlier Webb, Whale and Bowen Cooke compound and simple designs introduced 1892 onwards). Many later rebuilt with Belpaire boilers.

G2 Class 7F

†Introduced 1921. Development of G1 with higher pressure boiler. Many later rebuilt with Belpaire. boilers.

G2a Class 7F

Remainder. Introduced 1936. G1 locos. rebuilt with G2 Belpaire boilers.

Weights : Loco. { 60 tons 15 cwt. (G1)
62 tons 0 cwt. (G2, G2a).

Pressure : { 160 lb. Su. (G1).
175 lb. Su. (G2, G2a).

Cyls. : $20\frac{1}{2}'' \times 24''$.

Dr. Wheels : 4′ $5\frac{1}{2}''$.

T.E. : { 25,640 lb. (G1).
28,045 lb. (G2, G2a).

Nos. 48893–49394 CLASSES G1* AND G2a.

48893	48941	49026	49066
48895	48942	49027	49067*
48896	48943	49028	49068
48897	48944	49029	49069
48898	48945	49030*	49070
48899	48948	49031	49071*
48901	48950	49032*	49072
48902*	48951	49033	49073
48903	48952	49034	49074
48904*	48953	49035	49075*
48905	48954	49036	49076*
48907	48964	49037	49077
48908*	48966	49039	49078
48911*	49002	49041	49079
48914	49004	49043*	49080
48915	49005	49044	49081
48917	49006	49045	49082
48920	49007	49046	49083*
48921	49008	49047	49084
48922	49009	49048	49085*
48925	49010	49049	49087
48926	49011*	49050	49088
48927	49014	49051	49089*
48929*	49017*	49053*	49090
48930	49018	49057	49091*
48931*	49019	49058*	49092*
48932	49020	49059*	49093
48933	49021	49061	49094
48934	49022	49062	49096
48935*	49023	49063	49097
48936	49024	49064	49098*
48940	49025	49065	49099

49100*	49153	49210	49268
49101	49154	49211*	49269*
49102*	49155	49212	49270
49104	49156*	49213*	49271
49105	49157	49214	49275
49106	49158	49216	49276
49107*	49160	49217	49277
49108	49161	49218	49278
49109	49162*	49219	49279*
49112	49163	49220	49280
49113	49164	49221*	49281
49114	49167	49222*	49282
49115	49168	49223	49283*
49116	49169	49224	49284
49117	49170	49226	49285*
49119	49171*	49228	49287
49120	49172	49229	49288
49121	49173	49230	49289
49122	49174	49232*	49291
49123	49176	49234	49292
49124*	49177	49235	49293
49125	49178	49237	49294
49126	49180	49238	49296
49127	49181	49239	49298
49129	49183*	49240	49299
49130	49186	49241*	49300
49132	49187*	49243	49301
49133*	49188	49244	49302
49134	49189	49245	49304
49135*	49190*	49246	49306
49137	49191	49247	49307
49138	49192	49249	49308
49139	49193*	49252	49310
49140*	49194*	49253	49311
49141	49196	49254	49312
49142	49198	49255*	49313
49143	49199	49257	49314
49144	49200	49258	49315
49145	49202	49260	49316
49146	49203	49261*	49317
49147	49204*	49262	49318
49148	49205	49264	49319
49149	49207	49265	49320*
49150	49208*	49266	49321
49151*	49209	49267	49322

49323	49341	49357	49377
49324*	49342	49358	49378
49325	49343	49359*	49379
49326*	49344	49361	49381
49327	49345	49364*	49382
49328	49346*	49365	49385
49330	49347	49366	49386
49331	49348	49367	49387
49332*	49350	49368	49388
49333	49351	49369	49389
49334*	49352	49370*	49390
49335	49353*	49371*	49391
49337	49354	49373	49392
49339	49355	49375	49393
49340	49356	49376	49394

Nos. 49395–49454† CLASS G2.

49395	49410	49425	49440
49396	49411	49426	49441
49397	49412	49427	49442
49398	49413	49428	49443
49399	49414	49429	49444
49400	49415	49430	49445
49401	49416	49431	49446
49402	49417	49432	49447
49403	49418	49433	49448
49404	49419	49434	49449
49405	49420	49435	49450
49406	49421	49436	49451
49407	49422	49437	49452
49408	49423	49438	49453
49409	49424	49439	49454

Totals G2 60 G1 66 G2a 302

NOTE.

To understand the system of reference marks used in this book it is essential to read the notes on page 8.

0-8-0 7F

Introduced 1929. Fowler design, developed from L.N.W. G2.
Weight : Loco. 60 tons 15 cwt.
Pressure : 200 lb. Su.
Cyls. : 19½" × 26".
Dr. Wheels : 4' 8½". T.E. : 29,745 lb.
Walschaerts Valve Gear.

49500	49547	49590	49636
49501	49548	49591	49637
49502	49550	49592	49638
49503	49552	49593	49639
49505	49553	49594	49640
49506	49554	49595	49641
49508	49555	49596	49642
49509	49556	49598	49643
49510	49557	49599	49645
49511	49558	49600	49647
49513	49560	49602	49648
49514	49561	49603	49649
49515	49563	49604	49650
49516	49564	49605	49651
49519	49566	49606	49652
49520	49567	49608	49653
49523	49568	49609	49654
49524	49569	49610	49655
49526	49570	49611	49656
49528	49571	49612	49657
49529	49572	49613	49658
49530	49573	49614	49659
49531	49574	49615	49660
49532	49575	49617	49661
49533	49576	49618	49662
49534	49578	49619	49663
49535	49579	49620	49664
49536	49580	49621	49665
49537	49581	49622	49666
49538	49582	49623	49667
49539	49583	49624	49668
49540	49584	49625	49670
49541	49585	49627	49671
49543	49586	49628	49672
49544	49587	49631	49673
49545	49588	49634	49674
49546	49589	49635	

Total 147

4-6-0 — 5P

*Introduced 1921. Hughes superheated L. & Y. Class 8. Cylinder diameter later reduced (oldest survivor built 1923).
†Introduced 1924. Locos. with longer wheelbase, larger fireboxes and parts originally made for 4-6-4T.
Weight : Loco. { 79 tons 1 cwt.* / 77 tons 18 cwt.†
Pressure : 180 lb. Su.
Cyls. : { (4) 15¾″ × 26″*. / (4) 16½″ × 26″†.
Dr. Wheels : 6′ 3″.
T.E. : { 26,315 lb.* / 28,880 lb.†
Walschaerts Valve Gear and rocking shafts.

50442* | 50448* | 50455†

Total 3

2-4-2T — 2P & 3P

2P Introduced 1889. Aspinall L. & Y. Class 5 with 2 tons coal capacity.
*Introduced 1892. Locos. with smaller cylinders.
†Introduced 1898. Locos. with longer tanks and 4 tons coal capacity.
‡Introduced 1905. Hughes locos. built with Belpaire boiler and extended smokebox.
ϕIntroduced 1910. Loco. rebuilt with Belpaire boiler.
Weight : { 55 tons 19 cwt. / 55 tons 19 cwt.* / 59 tons 3 cwt.†‡
Pressure : 180 lb.
Cyls. : { 17½″ × 26″* / 17½″ × 26″†‡ / 18″ × 26″†‡
Dr. Wheels : 5′ 8″.
T.E. : { 18,360 lb.* / 18,360 lb. / 18,955 lb.†‡

3P §Introduced 1911. Hughes L. & Y. Class 6 (superheated development of Class 5).
¶Introduced 1914. Locos. rebuilt from Class 5.
|| Loco. as ¶ but with reduced cylinder diameters.
Weight : { 66 tons 9 cwt.§ / 60 tons 5 cwt.¶
Pressure : 180 lb. Su.
Cyls. : { 19½″ × 26″||. / 20½″ × 26″ (remainder)
T.E. : { 22,445 lb||. / 24,585 lb. (remainder)
Dr. Wheels : 5′ 8″.

50621	50676ϕ	50749	50840†
50622	50678*	50750	50842†
50623	50681	50752*	50844†
50625	50686	50755	50849†ϕ
50630	50687	50757	50850†
50633	50689	50762	50852†
50634*	50692ϕ	50764	50855*†
50636	50695	50765	50859†
50639	50697	50766*	50865*†
50640	50703	50777	50869†
50642	50705	50778	50872‡
50643*	50711	50781	50873‡
50644	50712	50788	50880‡
50646	50714*	50793	50886‡
50647	50715*	50795*	50887‡
50648	50720	50798	50889‡
50650ϕ	50721	50799*	50891¶
50651ϕ	50725	50802	50892‡
50652*ϕ	50731	50804*	50893¶
50653*	50732	50806	50898‡
50655	50735	50807*	50909§
50656*	50736ϕ	50812	50925¶||
50660	50738	50815*ϕ	50951¶
50665*	50743	50818	50953¶||
50671	50746	50829†ϕ	
50675*	50748	50831†	

Totals 2P 96
3P 6

0-4-0ST — 0F

Introduced 1891. Aspinall L. & Y. Class 21.
Weight : 21 tons 5 cwt.
Pressure : 160 lb.
Cyls. : (O) 13″ × 18″.
Dr. Wheels : 3′ 0⅝″. T.E. : 11,335 lb.

51202	51217	51230	51240
51204	51218	51231	51241
51206	51221	51232	51244
51207	51222	51234	51246
51212	51227	51235	51253
51216	51229	51237	

Total 23

0-6-0ST 2F

Introduced 1891. Aspinall rebuild of L. & Y. Barton Wright Class 23 0-6-0. Originally introduced 1876.
Weight : 43 tons 17 cwt.
Pressure : 140 lb. Cyls. : $17\frac{1}{2}'' \times 26''$.
Dr. Wheels : 4′ 6″. T.E. : 17,545 lb.

51307	51397	51453	51492
51313	51400	51457	51496
51316	51404	51458	51497
51319	51408	51460	51498
51321	51410	51462	51499
51323	51412	51464	51500
51336	51413	51470	51503
51338	51415	51471	51504
51343	51419	51472	51506
51345	51423	51474	51510
51348	51424	51475	51511
51353	51425	51477	51512
51358	51429	51479	51513
51361	51432	51481	51514
51371	51436	51482	51516
51375	51439	51484	51519
51376	51441	51486	51521
51379	51444	51488	51524
51381	51445	51489	51526
51390	51446	51490	51530
51396	51447	51491	

Total 83

0-6-0T 1F

Introduced 1897. Aspinall L. & Y. Class 24 dock tanks.
Weight : 50 tons 0 cwt.
Pressure : 140 lb.
Cyls. : (O) $17'' \times 24''$.
Dr. Wheels : 4′ 0″. T.E. : 15,285 lb.

51535	51537	51544	51546
51536			

Total 5

0-6-0 2F

Introduced 1887. Barton Wright L. & Y. Class 25.
Weight : Loco. 39 tons 1 cwt.
Pressure : 140 lb.
Cyls. : $17\frac{1}{2}'' \times 26''$.
Dr. Wheels : 4′ 6″. T.E. : 17,545 lb.

52016	52024	52041	52051
52019	52030	52043	52053
52021	52031	52044	52056
52022	52034	52045	52059
52023	52037	52047	52064

Total 20

0-6-0 3F

Introduced 1889. Aspinall L. & Y. Class 27.

†Introduced 1911. Rebuilt with Belpaire boiler and extended smokebox.

*Introduced 1913. Pettigrew Furness Rly. design.

Weight : Loco. 42 tons 3 cwt.
42 tons 13 cwt.*
43 tons 11 cwt.†
Pressure : 180 lb.
170 lb.*
Cyl. : $18'' \times 26''$.
Dr. Wheels : 5′ 1″.
4′ $7\frac{1}{2}''$.*
T.E. : 21,130 lb.
21,935 lb.*

52088†	52132	52175	52229
52089	52133	52176	52230
52091†	52135	52177	52231
52092	52136	52179	52232
52093	52137	52181	52233
52094	52138	52182	52235
52095	52139	52183	52236
52098	52140†	52184	52237
52099	52141	52186	52238
52100	52143	52189	52239
52102	52150	52191	52240
52104	52154†	52192	52243
52105	52156	52194	52244
52107	52157	52196	52245
52108	52159	52197	52246
52110†	52160	52201†	52248
52111	52161†	52203	52250†
52112	52162	52207	52252
52118	52163	52208	52253†
52119	52164	52212	52255
52120	52165	52215	52258
52121	52166	52216	52260
52123	52167	52217	52262
52124	52169	52218	52266†
52125	52171	52219	52268
52126	52172	52220	52269
52129	52174	52225	52270

52271	52338	52400†	52448†
52272	52341	52403	52449
52273†	52343	52404	52450
52275	52345	52405	52452
52278	52348	52407	52453
52279	52349	52408	52454
52280	52350	52410	52455
52284	52351	52411	52456
52285	52353	52412	52458
52288	52355	52413	52459
52289	52356	52414	52460
52290	52357	52415	52461
52293	52358	52416	52464
52294	52360	52418	52465
52296	52362	52427	52466
52299	52363	52428†	52494*
52300	52365	52429	52499*
52304	52366	52430	52501*
52305	52368	52431†	52508*
52309	52369	52432	52509*
52311	52376	52433	52510*
52312†	52378	52435	52515
52317	52379†	52437	52517
52319†	52381	52438†	52518
52321	52382	52439	52521
52322	52386	52440	52522
52326	52387	52441	52523
52328	52388	52442	52524
52330†	52389	52443	52525
52331	52390	52444†	52526
53333	52393	52445	52527
52334	52397	52446	52529
52336	52399	52447	

Totals : L. & Y. 232 F.R. 6

0-6-0 3F

*Introduced 1912. Hughes L. & Y. Class 28, superheated development of Class 27.
Remainder. Introduced 1913. Rebuilds of Class 27.
Weight : Loco. 46 tons 10 cwt.
Pressure : 180 lb. Su.
Cyls. : 20½" × 26".
Dr. Wheels : 5′ 1". T.E. : 27,405 lb.

52541*	52561	52581	52607
52542*	52569	52582	52608
52549*	52572	52583	52609
52551*	52575	52587	52615
52554*	52576	52588	52616
52557	52578	52590	52619
52558	52579	52592	
52559	52580	52598	

Total 30

0-8-0 6F

*Introduced 1900. Aspinall L. & Y. Class 30 (survivor built 1903).
Introduced 1910. Hughes Class 30 with larger boiler (some rebuilt from Aspinall design).
Weight : Loco. { 53 tons 16 cwt.* / 63 tons.
Pressure : 180 lb.
Cyls. : 20" × 26".
Dr. Wheels : 4′ 6". T.E. : 29,465 lb.

52727*	52806	52825	52831
52782	52822	52827	52839

Total 8

0-8-0 7F

Introduced 1912. L. & Y. Cl. 31. Superheated development of Class 30.
*Introduced 1915. Rebuild of Class 30 (survivor rebuilt 1921).
Weight : Loco. 66 tons 4 cwt.
Pressure : 180 lb. Su.
Cyls. : 21½" × 26".
Dr. Wheels : 4′ 6". T.E. : 34,055 lb.

52856	52886	52913	52956
52857	52906	52916	52962
52870	52910	52945	52971*

Total 13

2-8-0 7F

Introduced 1914. Fowler design for S. & D.J. with 4′ 9" boiler (some rebuilt from 1925 series).
*Introduced 1925. Fowler design with 5′ 3" boiler (all taken into L.M.S. stock, 1930).
Weight : Loco. { 64 tons 15 cwt. / 68 tons 11 cwt.*
Pressure : 190 lb. Su.
Cyls. : (O) 21" × 28".
Dr. Wheels : 4′ 8½". T.E. : 35,295 lb.
Walschaerts Valve Gear.

53800	53803	53806*	53809
53801	53804	53807*	53810
53802	53805	53808*	

Total 11

4-4-0 "Loch" Class 2P

Introduced 1896. Jones Highland design, later rebuilt with C.R. boiler.
Weight: Loco. 54 tons 10 cwt.
Pressure: 180 lb.
Cyls.: (O) 19" × 24".
Dr. Wheels: 6' 3½". T.E.: 17,560 lb.

54385 Loch Tay

Total 1

4-4-0 "Ben" Class 2P

Introduced 1898. Drummond Highland "Small Ben," later rebuilt with C.R. boiler.
Weight: Loco. 46 tons 17 cwt.
Pressure: 180 lb.
Cyls.: 18¼" × 26".
Dr. Wheels: 6' 0". T.E.: 18,400 lb.

54398 Ben Alder
54399 Ben Wyvis
54404 Ben Clebrig
54409 Ben Alisky
54410 Ben Dearg

Total 5

4-4-0 3P

Introduced 1910. McIntosh Caledonian "Dunalastair IV Superheater" or "139" class.
*Introduced 1915. Superheated rebuild of McIntosh Caledonian "Dunalastair IV" or "140" class (originally introduced 1904).
Weight: Loco. 61 tons 5 cwt.
Pressure: 180 lb. Su.
Cyls.: 20¼" × 26".
Dr. Wheels: 6' 6". T.E.: 20,915 lb.

54438	54445	54451	54456
54439	54446	54452	54457
54440	54447	54453	54458
54441	54448	54454	54459
54443	54449	54455	54460
54444	54450		

Total 22

4-4-0 3P

Introduced 1916. Pickersgill Caledonian "113" and "928" classes.
Weight: Loco. 61 tons 5 cwt.
Pressure: 180 lb. Su.
Cyls.: 20" × 26".
Dr. Wheels: 6' 6". T.E.: 20,400 lb.

54461	54465	54469	54473
54462	54466	54470	54474
54463	54467	54471	54475
54464	54468	54472	54476

Total 16

4-4-0 3P

Introduced 1920. Pickersgill Caledonian "72" class.
Weight: Loco. 61 tons 5 cwt.
Pressure: 180 lb. Su.
Cyls.: 20½" × 26".
Dr. Wheels: 6' 6". T.E.: 21,435 lb.

54477	54485	54493	54501
54478	54486	54494	54502
54479	54487	54495	54503
54480	54488	54496	54504
54481	54489	54497	54505
54482	54490	54498	54506
54483	54491	54499	54507
54484	54492	54500	54508

Total 32

4-6-0 4

Introduced 1925. Post-Grouping development of Caledonian "60" Class.
Weight: Loco. 74 tons 15 cwt.
Pressure: 180 lb. Su.
Cyls.: (O) 20½" × 26".
Dr. Wheels: 6' 1". T.E.: 22,900 lb.

54630	54636	54640	54647
54634	54638	54642	54648
54635	54639	54645	54649

Total 12

4-6-0 4

Introduced 1916. Pickersgill Caledonian "60" Class.
Weight: Loco. 75 tons 0 cwt.
Pressure: 180 lb. Su.
Cyls.: (O) 20" × 26".
Dr. Wheels: 6' 1". T.E.: 21,795 lb.

54650	54651	54653	54654

Total 4

4-6-0 "Clan" Class 4

Introduced 1919. Cumming Highland "Clan" Class (survivor built 1921).
Weight : Loco. 62 tons 5 cwt.
Pressure : 175 lb. Su.
Cyls. : (O) 21" × 26".
Dr. Wheels : 6' 0". T.E. : 23,688 lb.
Walschaerts Valve Gear.

54767 Clan Mackinnon

Total 1

0-4-4T 1P

Introduced 1905. Drummond Highland design.
Weight : 35 tons 15 cwt.
Pressure : 150 lb.
Cyls. : 14" × 20".
Dr. Wheels : 4' 6". T.E. : 9,255 lb.

55051 | 55053

Total 2

0-4-4T 2P

*Introduced 1895. McIntosh Caledonian "19" class, with railed coal bunkers.
Remainder. Introduced 1897. McIntosh "92" class, developed from "29" class with larger tanks and highsided coal bunkers (both classes originally fitted for condensing on Glasgow underground system).
Weight : { 53 tons 16 cwt.* / 53 tons 19 cwt.
Pressure : 180 lb.
Cyls. : 18" × 26".
Dr. Wheels : 5' 9". T.E. : 18,680 lb.

55119*	55126	55136	55142
55121*	55127	55138	55143
55122*	55129	55139	55144
55123*	55132	55140	55145
55124*	55134	55141	55146
55125	55135		

Total 22

0-4-4T 2P

Introduced 1900. McIntosh Caledonian "439" or "Standard Passenger" class.
*Introduced 1915. Pickersgill locos. with detail alterations.
Weight : { 53 tons 19 cwt. / 57 tons 12 cwt.*
Pressure : 180 lb.
Cyls. : 18" × 26".
Dr. Wheels : 5' 9". T.E. : 18,680 lb.

55159	55179	55200	55219
55160	55181	55201	55220
55161	55182	55202	55221
55162	55183	55203	55222
55164	55184	55204	55223
55165	55185	55206	55224
55166	55186	55207	55225
55167	55187	55208	55226
55168	55188	55209	55227*
55169	55189	55210	55228*
55170	55191	55211	55229*
55171	55192	55212	55230*
55172	55193	55213	55231*
55173	55194	55214	55232*
55174	55195	55215	55233*
55175	55196	55216	55234*
55176	55197	55217	55235*
55177	55198	55218	55236*
55178	55199		

Total 74

0-4-4T 2P

Introduced 1922. Pickersgill Caledonian "431" class (developed from "439" class) with cast-iron front buffer beam for banking.
Weight : 57 tons 17 cwt.
Pressure : 180 lb.
Cyls. : 18½" × 26".
Dr. Wheels : 5' 9". T.E. : 19,200 lb.

55237 | 55238 | 55239 | 55240

Total 4

0-4-4T 2P

Introduced 1925. Post-Grouping development of Caledonian "439" class.
Weight : 59 tons 12 cwt.
Pressure : 180 lb.
Cyls. : 18½" × 26".
Dr. Wheels : 5' 9". T.E. : 19,200 lb.

55260	55263	55266	55268
55261	55264	55267	55269
55262	55265		

Total 10

4-6-2T 4P

Introduced 1917. Pickersgill Caledonian "944" class.
Weight : 91 tons 13 cwt.
Pressure: 180 lb. Su. Cyls.: (O) 19½″ × 26″.
Dr. Wheels : 5′ 9″. T.E. : 21,920 lb.

55350	55353	55356	55360
55352	55354	55359	55361

Total 8

0-4-0ST 0F

Introduced 1885. Drummond and McIntosh Caledonian "Pugs."
Weight : 27 tons 7 cwt.
Pressure : 160 lb. Cyls. : (O) 14″ × 20″.
Dr. Wheels : 3′ 8″. T.E. : 12,115 lb.

56010	56026	56030	56035
56011	56027	56031	56038
56020	56028	56032	56039
56025	56029		

Total 14

0-6-0T 2F

Introduced 1911. McIntosh Caledonian dock shunters, "498" class.
Weight : 47 tons 15 cwt.
Pressure : 160 lb. Cyls. : (O) 17″ × 22″.
Dr. Wheels : 4′ 0″. T.E. : 18,015 lb.

56151	56157	56163	56169
56152	56158	56164	56170
56153	56159	56165	56171
56154	56160	56166	56172
56155	56161	56167	56173
56156	56162	56168	

Total 23

0-6-0T 3F

Introduced 1895. McIntosh Caledonian "29" and "782" classes (56231–9 originally condensing).
Weight : 47 tons 15 cwt.
Pressure : 160 lb. Cyls. : 18″ × 26″.
Dr. Wheels : 4′ 6″. T.E. : 21,215 lb.

56230	56236	56242	56248
56231	56237	56243	56249
56232	56238	56244	56250
56233	56239	56245	56251
56234	56240	56246	56252
56235	56241	56247	56253

56254	56286	56316	56346
56255	56287	56317	56347
56256	56288	56318	56348
56257	56289	56319	56349
56258	56290	56320	56350
56259	56291	56321	56352
56260	56292	56322	56353
56261	56293	56323	56354
56262	56294	56324	56355
56263	56295	56325	56356
56264	56296	56326	56357
56265	56297	56327	56358
56266	56298	56328	56359
56267	56299	56329	56360
56268	56300	56330	56361
56269	56301	56331	56362
56271	56302	56332	56363
56272	56303	56333	56364
56273	56304	56334	56365
56274	56305	56335	56366
56275	56306	56336	56367
56276	56307	56337	56368
56277	56308	56338	56369
56278	56309	56339	56370
56279	56310	56340	56371
56280	56311	56341	56372
56281	56312	56342	56373
56282	56313	56343	56374
56283	56314	56344	56375
56284	56315	56345	56376
56285			

Total 145

0-6-0 2F

Introduced 1883. Drummond Caledonian "Standard Goods"; later additions by Lambie and McIntosh.
*Rebuilt with L.M.S. boilers.
Weight : Loco. { 41 tons 6 cwt. / 42 tons 4 cwt.*
Pressure : 180 lb.
Cyls. : 18″ × 26″.
Dr. Wheels : 5′ 0″. T.E. : 21,480 lb.

57230	57235	57239	57243
57232	57236	57240	57244
57233	57237	57241	57245
57234	57238	57242	57246

57247	57299	57354	57407
57249	57300	57355	57409
57250	57302	57356	57410
57251	57303	57357	57411
57252	57306	57358	57412
57253	57307	57359	57413
57254	57309	57360	57414
57255	57310	57361	57415
57256	57311	57362	57416
57257	57312	57363	57417
57258	57314	57364	57418
57259	57315	57365	57419
57260	57316	57366	57420
57261	57317	57367	57423
57262	57318	57368	57424
57263	57319	57369	57425
57264	57320	57370	57426
57265	57321	57372	57427
57266	57322	57373	57429
57267	57323	57375	57430
57268	57324	57377	57431
57269	57325	57378	57432
57270	57326	57379	57433
57271	57328	57381	57434
57272	57329	57383	57435
57273	57331	57384	57436
57274	57332	57385	57437
57275	57334	57386	57438
57276	57335	57387	57439
57277	57336	57388	57440
57278	57337	57389	57441
57279	57338	57390	57443
57280	57339	57391	57444
57282	57340	57392	57445
57283	57341	57394	57446
57284	57342	57395	57447
57285	57344	57396	57448
57287	57345	57397	57449
57288	57346	57398	57450
57289	57347	57399	57451
57291	57348	57400	57452
57292	57349	57401	57453
57294	57350	57402	57454
57295	57351	57403	57455
57296	57352	57404	57456
57298	57353	57405	57457

57458	57462	57465	57470
57459	57463	57467	57472
57460	57464	57468	57473
57461			

Total 213

0-6-0 3F

Introduced 1899. McIntosh Caledonian "812" and "652" classes.
Weight: Loco. 45 tons 14 cwt.
Pressure: 180 lb.
Cyls.: 18½" × 26".
Dr. Wheels: 5′ 0″. T.E.: 22,690 lb.

57550	57573	57596	57621
57552	57575	57597	57622
57553	57576	57599	57623
57554	57577	57600	57625
57555	57579	57601	57626
57556	57580	57602	57627
57557	57581	57603	57628
57558	57582	57604	57630
57559	57583	57605	57631
57560	57584	57607	57632
57561	57585	57608	57633
57562	57586	57609	57634
57563	57587	57611	57635
57564	57588	57612	57637
57565	57589	57613	57638
57566	57590	57614	57640
57568	57591	57615	57642
57569	57592	57617	57643
57570	57593	57618	57644
57571	57594	57619	57645
57572	57595	57620	

Total 83

0-6-0 3F

Introduced 1918. Pickersgill Caledonian "294" class (superheated) and "670" classes.
Weight: Loco. 50 tons 13 cwt.
Pressure: 180 lb. Su.
Cyls.: 18½" × 26".
Dr. Wheels: 5′ 0″. T.E.: 22,690 lb.

57650	57655	57665	57670
57651	57658	57666	57671
57652	57659	57667	57672
57653	57661	57668	57673
57654	57663	57669	57674

[F. F. Moss

Class 4F 2-6-0 No. 43019

[H. C. Casserley

Class 7F 0-8-0 No. 9615 (now No. 49615)

[W. S. Garth

Class 2F 2-6-0 No. 6419 (now No. 46419)

[H. C. Casserley

Class 1F 2-4-0 No. 20216 (now No. 58022)

[F. F. Moss

Class 2F 0-6-0 No. 22353 (now No. 58112)

[H. C. Casserley

Class 2F 0-6-0 No. 58246

[R. M. Casserley

Class 2F 0-6-0 No. 58203

[H. C. Casserley

Class 3F 0-6-0 No. 43506

[H. C. Casserley

Class 4F 0-6-0 No. 44402

[W. Beckerlegge

Class 1P 2-4-2T No. 46637

[H. C. Casserley

Class 3F 0-6-2T No. 1987 (now No. 41987)

[H. C. Casserley

Class 2P 0-4-4T No. 41909

[P. Ransome-Wallis

Class 2P 4-4-0 No. 14398 *Ben Alder* (now No. 54398)

[P. Ransome-Wallis

Class 3P 2-4-2T No. 50891

[H. C. Casserley

Class 1P 0-4-4T No. 58091

Above : Class 2F 0-6-2T No. 58916

[J. Gain

Left: Class 3F 0-6-0T No. 7205 (now No. 47205)

[W. Beckerlegge

Below: Class 1F 0-6-0T No. 41710

[H. C. Casserley

Above: Class 1F 0-6-0T No. 11537 (now No. 51537)

[P. Ransome-Wallis

Right: Class 3P 4-4-2T No. 41960

[H. C. Casserley

Below: Class 2F 0-6-0T No. 58853

[H. C. Casserley

Left : Class 2F 0-6-0ST No. 11491 (now No. 51491)

[*D. S. Giles*

Right : Class 0F 0-4-0ST No. 1509 (now No. 41509)

[*R. S. M. McNaught*

Left : 0-4-2ST Crane Engine No. 27217 (now No. 58865)

[*H. C. Casserley*

Right : "Sentinel" Class 0-4-0T No. 7180 (now No. 47180)

[*D. S. Giles*

57679	57684	57688	57690
57681	57686	57689	57691
57682			

Total 29

0-6-0 3F

Introduced 1900. Drummond Highland design, later rebuilt with Caledonian boilers.
Weight : Loco. 43 tons 10 cwt.
Pressure : 175 lb.
Cyls. : 18½" × 26".
Dr. Wheels : 5' 0". T.E. : 21,470 lb.

57693	57695	57698	57702
57694	57697		

Total 6

4-6-0 4

Introduced 1918. Cumming Highland "Clan Goods" Class.
Weight : Loco. 56 tons 9 cwt.
Pressure : 175 lb. Su.
Cyls. : (O) 20½" × 26".
Dr. Wheels : 5' 3". T.E. : 25,800 lb.
Walschaerts Valve Gear.

57950	57954	57955	57956
57951			

Total 5

"Precursor" Class

4-4-0 3P

Introduced 1913. Superheated rebuild of Whale L.N.W. "Precursor" class (introduced 1904, survivor rebuilt 1915).
Weight : Loco. 59 tons 17 cwt.
Pressure : 180 lb. Su.
Cyls. : 20½" × 26".
Dr. Wheels : 6' 9". T.E. : 20,640 lb.

(Former L.M.S. number in brackets)

58010 (25297) Sirocco

Total 1

2-4-0 1P

(Former L.M.S. numbers in brackets)

Introduced 1876. Johnson Midland "1" Class, rebuilt with Belpaire boiler, 1926.
Weight : 40 tons 10 cwt.
Pressure : 140 lb.
Cyls. : 18" × 24".
Dr. Wheels : 6' 3". T.E. : 12,340 lb.

58020 (20155)

Introduced 1879. Johnson Midland "207" Class, rebuilt with Belpaire boiler, 1926.
Weight : 40 tons 16 cwt.
Pressure : 140 lb.
Cyls. : 18" × 26".
Dr. Wheels : 6' 9". T.E. : 12,375 lb.

58022 (20216)

Total 2

0-4-4T 1P

Introduced 1875. Johnson Midland design later rebuilt with Belpaire boiler.
Weight : 53 tons 4 cwt.
Pressure : 140 lb.
Cyls. : 18" × 24".
Dr. Wheels : 5' 7". T.E. : 13,810 lb.

(Former L.M.S. numbers in brackets)

58031	(1246)	58035	(1252)
58032	(1247)	58036	(1255)
58033	(1249)	58038	(1261)
58034	(1251)		

Total 7

0-4-4T 1P

Introduced 1881. Johnson Midland design later rebuilt with Belpaire boiler.
*Locos. with increased boiler pressure.
Weight : 53 tons 4 cwt.
Pressure : { 140 lb. / 150 lb.* }
Cyls. : 18" × 24". T.E. : { 14,460 lb. / 15,490 lb.* }
Dr. Wheels : 5' 4".

(Former L.M.S. numbers in brackets)

Nos. 58040–59 LOCOS. WITH 140 lb. PRESSURE.

58040	(1273)	58049	(1322)
58041	(1275)	58050	(1324)
58042	(1278)	58051	(1330)
58043	(1287)	58052	(1337)
58045	(1295)	58053	(1340)
58046	(1298)	58054	(1341)
58047	(1303)	58056	(1344)
58048	(1315)	58058	(1350)

Nos. 58060–91 LOCOS. WITH 150 lb. PRESSURE.

58059	(1353)	58075	(1390)
58060	(1357)	58076	(1396)
58061	(1358)	58077	(1397)
58062	(1360)	58079	(1406)
58063	(1365)	58080	(1411)
58064	(1366)	58082	(1416)
58065	(1367)	58083	(1420)
58066	(1368)	58084	(1421)
58067	(1370)	58085	(1422)
58068	(1371)	58086	(1423)
58069	(1373)	58087	(1424)
58070	(1375)	58088	(1425)
58071	(1377)	58089	(1426)
58072	(1379)	58090	(1429)
58073	(1382)	58091	(1430)

Total 46

2-4-0T 1P

Introduced 1877. Webb L.N.W. design.
Weight : 38 tons 4 cwt.
Pressure : 150 lb.
Cyls. : 17″×20″.
Dr. Wheels : 4′ 8½″. T.E. : 13,045 lb.

(Former L.M.S. number in brackets)

58092 (26428)

Total 1

0-10-0

Introduced 1919. Fowler Midland banker for Lickey incline.
Weight : Loco. 73 tons 13 cwt.
Pressure : 180 lb. Su.
Cyls. (4) : 16¾″×28″.
Dr. Wheels : 4′ 7½″. T.E. : 43,315 lb.
Walschaerts Valve Gear.

(Former L.M.S. number in brackets)

58100 (22290)

Total 1

0-6-0 2F

*Introduced 1868. Kirtley Midland double-framed design with round top boiler (Survivor built 1870).
Remainder. Rebuilt with Belpaire boiler.
Weight : Loco. 37 tons 12 cwt.
Pressure : 160 lb.
Cyls. : 18″×24″.
Dr. Wheels : 5′ 3″. T.E. : 16,785 lb.

(Former L.M.S. numbers in brackets)

58110 (22630)*	58112 (22853)
58111 (22846)	

0-6-0 2F

*Introduced 1875. Johnson Midland 4′ 11″ design, with round top boiler.
†Introduced 1917. Rebuilt with Belpaire boiler.
‡Introduced 1878. Johnson Midland 5′ 3″ design, with round top boiler.
§Introduced 1917. Rebuilt with Belpaire boiler.
Weight : Loco. Various.
37 tons 12 cwt. to 40 tons 3 cwt.
Pressure : 160 lb.
Cyls. : 18″×26″.
Dr. Wheels : { 4′ 11″*, 4′ 11″†, 5′ 3″‡, 5′ 3″§ }
T.E. : { 19,420 lb.*, 19,420 lb.†, 18,185 lb.‡, 18,185 lb.§ }

(Former L.M.S. numbers in brackets)

58114† (22900)	58118† (22907)
58115† (22901)	58119† (22911)
58116† (22902)	58120† (22912)
58117† (22904)	58121† (22913)

58122† (22915)
58123† (22918)
58124† (22920)
58125† (22921)
58126† (22924)
58127† (22926)
58128† (22929)
58129† (22931)
58130† (22932)
58131† (22933)
58132† (22934)
58133† (22935)
58134† (22940)
58135† (22944)
58136† (22945)
58137† (22946)
58138† (22947)
58139† (22950)
58140† (22951)
58142† (22954)
58143† (22955)
58144† (22958)
58145† (22959)
58146† (22963)
58147† (22965)
58148† (22967)
58149† (22968)
58151† (22970)
58152† (22971)
58153† (22974)
58154† (22975)
58155† (22976)
58156† (22977)
58157† (22978)
58158† (22982)
58159† (22983)
58160† (22984)
58161† (2987)
58162† (2988)
58163† (2989)
58164† (2990)
58165† (2992)
58166† (2993)
58167† (2994)
58168† (2995)
58169† (2996)
58170† (2997)
58171† (2998)
58172† (2999)
58173† (23000)
58174† (23001)
58175† (23002)
58176† (23003)
58177† (23005)
58178† (23006)
58179† (23007)
58180† (23008)
58181† (23009)
58182† (23010)
58183† (23011)
58184† (23012)
58185† (23013)
58186† (23014)
58187† (23018)
58188§ (3023)
58189§ (3027)
58190§ (3031)
58191§ (3035)
58192§ (3037)
58193§ (3038)
58194§ (3039)
58195§ (3042)
58196§ (3044)
58197§ (3045)
58198§ (3047)
58199§ (3048)
58200§ (3049)
58201§ (3051)
58202§ (3052)
58203§ (3054)
58204§ (3058)
58206§ (3062)
58207§ (3064)
58208§ (3066)
58209§ (3071)
58211§ (3074)
58212§ (3078)
58213§ (3084)
58214§ (3090)
58215§ (3094)
58216§ (3095)
58217§ (3096)
58218§ (3098)
58219§ (3099)
58220§ (3101)
58221§ (3103)
58224§ (3113)
58225§ (3118)
58226§ (3119)
58228§ (3127)
58229* (3130)
58230† (3134)
58231† (3138)
58232† (3140)
58233† (3144)
58234† (3149)
58235† (3150)
58236* (3151)
58237† (3154)
58238† (3156)
58239† (3157)
58240* (3161)
58241† (3164)
58242† (3166)
58243† (3168)
58244† (3171)
58245† (3173)
58246* (3175)
58247* (3176)
58248† (3177)
58249§ (3190)
58251‡ (3229)
58252§ (3262)
58253§ (3264)
58254§ (3270)
58257§ (3372)
58258§ (3377)
58259§ (3385)
58260§ (3420)
58261§ (3423)
58262‡ (3425)
58264§ (3445)
58265§ (3451)
58267§ (3477)
58268§ (3479)
58269§ (3485)
58271§ (3492)
58272§ (3493)
58273§ (3503)
58274‡ (3508)
58275§ (3511)
58276§ (3512)
58277§ (3516)
58278§ (3517)
58279§ (3525)
58280§ (3526)
58281§ (3527)
58282§ (3533)
58283§ (3536)
58285§ (3539)
58286§ (3543)
58287§ (3545)
58288§ (3551)
58289§ (3559)
58290§ (3561)
58291§ (3564)
58293§ (3571)
58294§ (3592)
58295§ (3603)
58296§ (3617)
58298§ (3648)
58299§ (3655)
58300§ (3688)
58302§ (3691)
58303§ (3696)
58304§ (3703)
58305§ (3707)
58306§ (3725)
58307§ (3726)
58308§ (3738)
58309§ (3739)
58310§ (3764)

Total 181

0-6-0 2F

Introduced 1873. Webb L.N.W. "Coal Engines."
Weight: Loco. 32 tons 0 cwt.
Pressure: 150 lb.
Cyls.: 17" × 24".
Dr. Wheels: 4' 5½". T.E.: 16,530 lb.
(Former L.M.S. numbers in brackets)

58321	(28091)	58338	(28199)
58322	(28093)	58340	(28205)
58323	(28100)	58341	(28216)
58326	(28106)	58343	(28227)
58327	(28107)	58346	(28239)
58328	(28115)	58347	(28245)
58329	(28116)	58348	(28246)
58330	(28128)	58349	(28247)
58332	(28141)	58350	(28251)
58333	(28152)	58351	(28253)
58334	(28158)	58352	(28256)
58335	(28166)	58354	(28263)
58336	(28172)	58360	(28312)

Total 26

0-6-0 2F

Introduced 1887. Webb L.N.W. "18" Goods ("Cauliflowers") many later rebuilt with Belpaire boilers.
Weight. Loco. 36 tons 10 cwt.
Pressure: 150 lb.
Cyls.: 18" × 24".
Dr. Wheels: 5' 2½". T.E.: 15,865 lb.
(Former L.M.S. numbers in brackets)

58362	(28318)	58380	(28443)
58363	(28333)	58381	(28450)
58364	(28335)	58382	(28451)
58365	(28337)	58383	(28457)
58367	(28339)	58384	(28458)
58368	(28345)	58388	(28487)
58369	(28370)	58389	(28492)
58371	(28385)	58393	(28507)
58373	(28403)	58394	(28509)
58375	(28408)	58396	(28512)
58376	(28417)	58397	(28513)
58377	(28428)	58398	(28515)
58378	(28430)	58399	(28521)
58379	(28442)	58400	(28525)
58404	(28531)	58419	(28583)
58406	(28543)	58420	(28585)
58409	(28548)	58421	(28589)
58410	(28549)	58422	(28592)
58411	(28551)	58424	(28598)
58412	(28553)	58426	(28611)
58413	(28555)	58427	(28616)
58415	(28559)	58429	(28619)
58417	(28575)	58430	(28622)
58418	(28580)		

Total 47

0-6-0T 2F

Introduced 1879. Park North London design (oldest survivor built 1881).
Weight: 45 tons 10 cwt.
Pressure: 160 lb.
Cyls.: (O) 17" × 24".
Dr. Wheels: 4' 4". T.E.: 18,140 lb.
(Former L.M.S. numbers in brackers)

58850	(27505)	58857	(27517)
58851	(27509)	58858	(27520)
58852	(27510)	58859	(27522)
58853	(27512)	58860	(27527)
58854	(27513)	58861	(27528)
58855	(27514)	58862	(27530)
58856	(27515)	58863	(27532)

Total 14

0-4-2ST Crane Engine

Introduced 1872. Rebuild with crane of North London Sharp-Stewart 0-4-0T of 1858.
Weight: 32 tons 6 cwt.
Pressure: 120 lb.
Cyls.: 13" × 17".
Dr. Wheels: 3' 10". T.E.: 6,370 lb.
(Former L.M.S. number in brackets)

58865 (27217) **Total 1**

0-6-2T 2F

Introduced 1882. Webb L.N.W. "Coal Tanks."
Weight: 43 tons 15 cwt.
Pressure: 150 lb.
Cyls.: 17" × 24".
Dr. Wheels: 4' 5½". T.E.: 16,530 lb.
(Former L.M.S. numbers in brackets)

58880–Service Locomotives.

58880	(27553)	58895	(27654)	58912	(7751)	58925	(7794)
58881	(27561)	58897	(27674)	58913	(7752)	58926	(7799)
58882	(27562)	58899	(7692)	58915	(7757)	58927	(7802)
58883	(27580)	58900	(7699)	58916	(7759)	58928	(7803)
58887	(27596)	58902	(7710)	58917	(7765)	58929	(7808)
58888	(27602)	58903	(7711)	58919	(7773)	58932	(7822)
58889	(27603)	58904	(7720)	58921	(7782)	58933	(7829)
58890	(27619)	58908	(7737)	58923	(7789)	58934	(7830)
58891	(27621)	58910	(7741)	58924	(7791)	58935	(7833)
58892	(27625)	58911	(7746)				

Total 38

FORMER L.M.S. SERVICE LOCOMOTIVES

0-4-0ST 0F

Introduced 1890. Johnson Midland design.
Weight : 23 tons 3 cwt.
Pressure : 140 lb.
Cyls. : 20" × 13".
Dr. Wheels : 3' 10". T.E. : 8,745 lb.

41509 Derby Loco. Works

(*see p. 12 for remainder of class*)

0-6-0ST 2F

Introduced 1870. Webb version of Ramsbottom "Special Tank" (oldest survivor built 1875).
Weight : 34 tons 10 cwt.
Pressure : 140 lb.
Cyls. : 17" × 24".
Dr. Wheels : 4' 5½". T.E. : 17,005 lb.

3323 (L.N.W. No) Crewe Loco. Works
C.D.3 Wolverton Carriage Works
C.D.6 ,, ,, ,,
C.D.7 ,, ,, ,,
C.D.8 "Earlestown" Wolverton Carriage Works

0-6-0ST 2F

Introduced 1891. Aspinall rebuild of L. & Y. Barton Wright class 23 0-6-0 tender loco. (introduced 1876).
Weight : 43 tons 17 cwt.
Pressure : 140 lb.
Cyls. : 17½" × 26".
Dr. Wheels : 4' 6". T.E. 17,545 lb.

51304, 51305, 51324, 51368, 51394 — Horwich Loco. Works

(*see p. 54 for remainder of class*)

0-4-0 Diesel

Introduced 1936. Fowler diesel.
Weight : 21 tons 5 cwt.

E.D. No. 2 Beeston Sleeper Depot

0-4-0 Battery

Introduced 1914.
Weight : 18 tons.
Midland design, for West India Docks.

41550

Unnumbered

Introduced 1917. North Staffordshire design, now used at Oakamoor (Electrical Engineer's dept.).
Weight : 17 tons.

LONDON MIDLAND REGION (ex. L.M.S.)

MOTIVE POWER DEPOTS WITH CODES

Heavy type thus, **Rugby,** indicates a main district depot. In addition to depots shown, there are several sub-depots, the engines attached to which bear the code of the main district depot.

Depot	*Code*
Willesden	1A
Camden	1B
Watford	1C
Rugby	2A
Nuneaton	2D
Warwick	2E
Coventry	2F
Bletchley	2B
Northampton	2C
Bescot	3A
Bushbury	3B
Walsall	3C
Aston	3D
Monument Lane	3E
Shrewsbury	4A
Swansea	4B
Upper Bank	4C
Abergavenny	4D
Tredegar	4E
Crewe North	5A
Crewe South	5B
Stafford	5C
Stoke	5D
Alsager	5E
Uttoxeter	5F
Chester	6A
Mold Junction	6B
Birkenhead	6C
Llandudno Junc.	7A
Bangor	7B
Holyhead	7C
Rhyl	7D
Edge Hill	8A
Warrington	8B
Speke Junction	8C
Widnes	8D
Longsight	9A
Stockport	9B
Macclesfield	9C
Buxton	9D
Springs Branch	10A
Preston	10B
Patricroft	10C
Plodder Lane	10D
Sutton Oak	10E
Carnforth	11A

Depot	*Code*
Barrow	11B
Oxenholme	11D
Tebay	11E
Carlisle (Upperby)	12B
Penrith	12C
Workington	12D
Moor Row	12E
Cricklewood	14A
Kentish Town	14B
St. Albans	14C
Wellingboro'	15A
Kettering	15B
Leicester	15C
Bedford	15D
Nottingham	16A
Peterborough	16B
Kirkby	16C
Mansfield	16D
Derby	17A
Burton	17B
Coalville	17C
Rowsley	17D
Toton	18A
Westhouses	18B
Hasland	18C
Staveley	18D
Sheffield	19A
Millhouses	19B
Ganklow	19C
Trafford Park	19G
Heaton Mersey	19D
Belle Vue	19E
Brunswick*	
Glazebrook*	
Northwich*	
Southport*	
Walton*	
Warrington*	
Widnes†	
Wigan†	
Leeds	20A
Stourton	20B
Royston	20C
Normanton	20D
Manningham	20E
Skipton	20F

Depot	*Code*
Hellifield	20G
Lancaster	20H
Saltley	21A
Bournville	21B
Bromsgrove	21C
Stratford-on-Avon	21D
Bristol	22A
Gloucester	22B
Bath	22C
Templecombe	22D
Highbridge	22E
Bank Hall	23A
Aintree	23B
Southport	23C
Wigan (C)	23D
Accrington	24A
Rose Grove	24B
Lostock Hall	24C
Lower Darwen	24D
Blackpool	24E
Fleetwood	24F
Wakefield	25A
Huddersfield	25B
Goole	25C
Mirfield	25D
Sowerby Bridge	25E
Low Moor	25F
Farnley Junction	25G
Newton Heath	26A
Agecroft	26B
Bolton	26C
Bury	26D
Bacup	26E
Lees	26F

The following sheds, although having L.M.R. engines on loan, are now administered by the Eastern Region.

Plaistow	13A
Devons Road	13B
Tilbury	13C
Shoeburyness	13D
Upminster	13E

* Ex-Cheshire Lines Committee, Eastern Region.

† Ex-Eastern Region.

PRINCIPAL DIMENSIONS

TENDER ENGINES

Page	Power Classification	Class	Designer	Original Owning Co.	Building or Re-building Date	Boiler Pressure	Cylinders	Driving Wheels	Weight Engine in Working Order	Tractive Effort at 85% B.P.
						lb. per sq. in.			T. Cwt.	lb.
4-6-2										
45	7P	" Princess Coronation " ...	Stanier	L.M.S.	1937	250 Su	(4) $16\frac{1}{2} \times 28$	6′ 9″	{ 106–8 / 105–5	40,000
45	7P	" Princess Royal " ...	Stanier	L.M.S.	1933	250 Su	(4) $16\frac{1}{4} \times 28$	6′ 6″	104–10	40,285
45	7P	" Turbomotive "	Stanier	L.M.S.	1935	250 Su	—	6′ 6″	110–11	—
4-6-0										
36	6P	Taper Boilered " Scot " ...	Fowler (1928) Reb. Stainer ...	L.M.S.	1935	250 Su	(3) 18×26	6′ 9″	84–1	33,150
36	6P	Rebuilt " Scot "	Fowler (1927) Reb. Stanier ...	L.M.S.	1943	250 Su	(3) 18×26	6′ 9″	83–0	33,150
36	6P	" Royal Scot "	Fowler	L.M.S.	1927	250 Su	(3) 18×26	6′ 9″	84–18	33,150
33	6P	Rebuilt " Jubilee " ...	Stanier Reb. ...	L.M.S.	1942	250 Su	(3) 17×26	6′ 9″	82–0	29,570
32	6P	Rebuilt " Patriot " ...	Fowler (1930) Reb. Ivatt ...	L.M.S.	1946	250 Su	(3) 17×26	6′ 9″	82–0	29,570
33	5XP	" Jubilee	Stanier	L.M.S.	1934	225 Su	(3) 17×26	6′ 9″	79–11	26,610
32	5XP	" Patriot "	Fowler	L.M.S.	1930	200 Su	(3) 18×26	6′ 9″	80–15	26,520
30	5	....	Stanier	L.M S.	1934	225 Su	O $18\frac{1}{2} \times 28$	6′ 0″	72–2*	25,455
53	5P	" Class 8 "	Hughes	L. & Y.	1921	180 Su	(4) $15\frac{3}{4} \times 26$	6′ 3″	79–1	26,315
54	5P	....	Hughes	L.M.S.	1924	180 Su	(4) $16\frac{1}{2} \times 26$	6′ 3″	77–18	28,880
51	4F	" 19-inch Goods " ...	Whale	L.N.W.	1906	175	19×26	5′ $2\frac{1}{2}$″	63–0	22,340
51	4	....	Pickersgill... ...	L.M.S.	1925	180 Su	O $20\frac{1}{2} \times 26$	6′ 1″	74–15	22,900
57	4	" 60 " Class	Pickersgill... ...	Cal.	1916	180 Su	O 20×26	6′ 1″	75–0	21,795
57	4	" Clan "	Cumming	High.	1919	175 Su	O 21×26	5′ 0″	62–5	23,690
69	4	" Clan Goods "	Cumming	High.	1918	175 Su	O $20\frac{1}{2} \times 26$	5′ 3″	56–9	25,800

* For weights of experimental locos see p. 30.

Page	Power Classification	Class	Designer	Original Owning Co.	Building or Re-building Date	Boiler Pressure	Cylinders	Driving Wheels	Weight Engine in Working Order	Tractive Effort at 85% B.P.
						lb. per sq. in.			T. Cwt.	lb.
4-4-0										
11	4P	Compound	Fowler	L.M.S.	1924	200 Su	(1) 19 × 26 (2) 21 × 26	6′ 9″	61–14	22,650
11	4P	Compound	Deeley	Mid.	1905	200 Su	(1) 19 × 26 (2) 21 × 26	7′ 0″	61–14	21,840
69	3P	" Precursor "	Whale (1904) ... Reb. Bowen Cooke	L.N.W.	1913	180 Su	20½ × 26	6′ 9″	59–17	20,640
10	3P	....	Johnson (1901) ... Reb. Fowler	Mid.	1916	175 Su	20½ × 26	6′ 9″	55–7	20,065
57	3P	" 72 "	Pickersgill... ...	Cal.	1920	180 Su	20¼ × 26	6′ 6″	61–5	21,435
57	3P	" 113 " & " 928 " ...	Pickersgill... ...	Cal.	1916	180 Su	20 × 26	6′ 6″	61–5	20,400
57	3P	" Dunalastair IV " ... Suphtr.	McIntosh	Cal.	1910	180 Su	20¼ × 26	6′ 6″	59–0	20,915
57	3P	" Dunalastair IV " ... Suphtr. Reb.	McIntosh (1907) ... (Reb.)	Cal.	1915	180 Su	20¼ × 26	6′ 6″	59–0	20,915
10	2P	....	Fowler	L.M.S.	1928	180 Su	19 × 26	6′ 9″	54–1	17,730
10	2P	....	Fowler	S. & D.J.	1930	180 Su	19 × 26	6′ 9″	54–1	17,730
9	2P	....	Fowler	S. & D.J.	1914	160 Su	20½ × 26	7′ 0½″	53–7	17,585
9	2P	....	Johnson (1891) ... Reb. Fowler	Mid.	1912	160 Su	20½ × 26	7′ 0½″	53–7	17,585
9	2P	....	Johnson (1882) ... Reb. Fowler	Mid.	1910	160	18 × 26	6′ 6½″	53–7	17,585
57	2P	" Ben "	P. Drummond ...	High.	1898	180	18¼ × 26	6′ 0″	46–17	18,400
57	2P	" Loch "	Jones	High.	1896	180	O 19 × 24	6′ 3½″	54–10	17,560

2-8-0											
49	8F	....	Stanier	L.M.S.	1935	225 Su	O	18½ × 28	4′ 8½″	72–2	32,440
56	7F	....	Fowler	S. & D.J.	1914 / 1925	190 Su	O	21 × 28	4′ 8½″	64–15 / 68–11	35,295
2-6-0											
25	5	....	Stanier	L.M.S.	1933	225 Su	O	18 × 28	5′ 6″	69–2	26,290
24	5	....	Hughes/Fowler ...	L.M.S.	1926	180 Su	O	21 × 26	5′ 6″	66–0	26,580
25	4	....	Ivatt	L.M.S.	1947	225 Su	O	17½ × 26	5′ 3″	59–2	24,170
46	2	....	Ivatt	L.M.S.	1946	200 Su	O	16 × 24	5′ 0″	47–2	17,410
2-4-0											
69	1P	....	Johnson	Mid.	1879	140		18 × 26	6′ 9″	40–16	12,375
69	1P	....	Johnson	Mid.	1876	140		18 × 24	6′ 3″	40–10	12,340
0-10-0											
70		" Lickey Banker "............	Fowler	Mid.	1919	180 Su		(4)16¾ × 28	4′ 7½″	73–13	43,315
0-8-0											
53	7F	....	Fowler	L.M.S.	1929	200 Su		19½ × 26	4′ 8½″	60–15	29,745
52	7F	G2a	See notes on page 5			175 Su		20½ × 24	4′ 5½″	62–0	28,045
51	7F	G2	See notes on page 5			175 Su		20½ × 24	4′ 5½″	62–0	28,045
51	6F	G1	See notes on page 5			160 Su		20½ × 24	4′ 5½″	60–5	25,640
56	7F	" Class 31 "	Hughes	L. & Y.	1912	180 Su		21½ × 26	4′ 6″	66–4	34,055
56	6F	" Class 30 "	Aspinall	L. & Y.	1901	180		20 × 26	4′ 6″	53–16	29,465
56	6F	" Class 30," Large boiler...	Hughes	L. & Y.	1910	180		20 × 26	4′ 6″	63–0	29,465
0-6-0											
27	4F	....	Fowler	L.M.S.	1924	175 Su		20 × 26	5′ 3″	48–15	24,555
27	4F	....	Fowler	S. & D.J.	1922	175 Su		20 × 26	5′ 3″	48–15	24,555
26	4F	....	Fowler	Mid.	1911	175 Su		20 × 26	5′ 3″	48–15	24,555

Page	Power Classi-fication	Class	Designer	Original Owning Co.	Building or Re-building Date	Boiler Press-ure	Cylinders	Driving Wheels	Weight Engine in Working Order	Tractive Effort at 85% B.P.
						lb. per sq. in.			T. Cwt.	lb.
0-6-0—*continued*										
56	3F	" Class 28 "	Hughes	L. & Y.	1912	180 Su	20½ × 26	5′ 1″	46–10	27,405
55	3F	" Class 27 "	Aspinall	L. & Y.	1889	180	18 × 26	5′ 1″	42–3	21,130
26	3F	....	Deeley ... ... Reb. Fowler	Mid.	1906	175	18½ × 26	5′ 3″	46–3	21,010
25	3F	....	Johnson (1885) ... Reb. Deeley	Mid.	1916	175	18 × 26	5′ 3″	43–17	19,890
25	3F	....	Johnson (1885) ... Reb. Fowler	Mid.	1920	175	18 × 26	4′ 11″	43–17	21,240
25	3F	....	Johnson .. ... Reb. Fowler	S. & D.J.	1896	175	18 × 26	5′ 3″	43–17	19,890
55	3F	....	Pettigrew ...	Fur.	1913	170	18 × 26	4′ 7½″	42–13	21,935
60	3F	" 294 " & " 670 " classes...	Pickersgill... ...	Cal.	1918	180 Su	18¼ × 26	5′ 0″	50–13	22,690
60	3F	" 812 " & " 652 " classes...	McIntosh	Cal.	1899	180	18¼ × 26	5′ 0″	45–14	22,690
69	3F	....	P. Drummond ...	High.	1900	175	18¼ × 26	5′ 0″	43–10	21,470
72	2F	" Cauliflower "	Webb	L.N.W.	1887	150	18 × 24	5′ 2½″	36–10	15,865
72	2F	" Coal Engines " ...	Webb	L.N.W.	1873	150	17 × 24	4′ 5½″	32–0	16,530
55	2F	" Class 25 "	Barton Wright ...	L. & Y.	1887	140	17½ × 26	4′ 6″	39–1	17,545
70	2F	....	Johnson	Mid.	1878	160	18 × 26	5′ 3″	Various from	18,185
70	2F	....	Johnson	Mid.	1875	160	18 × 26	4′ 11″	40t. 3c. to	19,420
70	2F	....	Kirtley	Mid.	1868	160	18 × 24	5′ 3″	37t. 12c.	16,785
59	2F	....	D. Drummond ...	Cal.	1883	180	18 × 26	5′ 0″	41–6 / 42–4	21,480

TANK ENGINES

Page	Power Classi-fication	Class	Designer	Original Owning Co.	Building or Re-building Date	Boiler Press-ure	Cylinders	Driving Wheels	Weight Engine in Working Order	Tractive Effort at 85% B.P.
4-6-2T										
59	4P	" 944 " class	Pickersgill... ...	Cal.	1917	180 Su	O 19½ × 26	5′ 9″	91–13	21,920
4-4-2T										
12	3P	" 79 " class	Whitelegg ...	L.T. & S., Mid. & L.M.S.	1909	170	O 19 × 26	6′ 6″	71–10	17,390
12	3P	" 37 " class	Whitelegg (Reb.)	L.T. & S.	1897	170	O 19 × 26	6′ 6″	70–15	17,390
12	2P	" 51 " class	Whitelegg ...	L.T. & S.	1900	170	O 19 × 26	6′ 6″	67–15	17,390

2-6-4T										
22	4	....	Fairburn	L.M.S.	1945	200 Su	O 19$\frac{5}{8}$ × 26	5′ 9″	85–5	24,670
22	4	....	Stanier	L.M.S.	1935	200 Su	O 19$\frac{5}{8}$ × 26	5′ 9″	87–17	24,670
22	4	....	Stanier	L.M.S.	1934	200 Su	(3) 16 × 26	5′ 9″	92–5	24,600
22	4	....	Fowler	L.M.S.	1927	200 Su	O 19 × 26	5′ 9″	86–5	23,125
2-6-2T										
9	3	....	Stanier (Reb.) ...	L.M.S.	1941	200 Su	O 17$\frac{1}{2}$ × 26	5′ 3″	72–10	21,485
9	3	....	Stanier	L.M.S.	1935	200 Su	O 17$\frac{1}{2}$ × 26	5′ 3″	71–5	21,485
9	3	....	Fowler	L.M.S.	1930	200 Su	O 17$\frac{1}{2}$ × 26	5′ 3″	70–10*	21,485
11	2	....	Ivatt...	L.M.S.	1946	200 Su	O 16 × 24	5′ 0″	63–5	17,410
2-4-2T										
54	3P	"Class 6"	Hughes	L. & Y.	1911	180 Su	{ 20$\frac{1}{2}$ × 26 / 19$\frac{1}{2}$ × 26 }	{ 5′ 8″ / 5′ 8″ }	{ 66–9 / 6[illegible]–5 }	{ 24,585 / 22,245 }
54	2P	"Class 5"	Aspinall	L. & Y.	1889	180	18 × 26	5′ 8″	55–19	18,955
54	2P	"Class 5"	Aspinall	L. & Y.	1892	180	17$\frac{1}{2}$ × 26	5′ 8″	55–19	18,360
54	2P	....	Aspinall	L. & Y.	1898	180	18 × 26	5′ 8″	57–0	18,955
47	2P	"Class 5"	Aspinall	Wirral	1890	180	17$\frac{1}{2}$ × 26	5′ 8″	55–19	18,360
46	1P	....	Webb	L.N.W.	1890	150	17 × 24	5′ 8$\frac{1}{2}$″	50–10	12,910
2-4-0T										
70	1P	....	Webb	L.N.W.	1877	150	17 × 20	4′ 8$\frac{1}{2}$″	38–4	13,045
2-6-6-2T										
49		"Garratt"	Fowler and Beyer Peacock	L.M.S.	{ 1927 / 1930 }	190 Su	(4) 18$\frac{1}{2}$ × 26	5′ 3″	{ 148–15 / 155–10 }	45,620
0-8-4T										
49	7F	....	Beames	L.N.W.	1923	185 Su	20$\frac{1}{2}$ × 24	4′ 5$\frac{1}{2}$″	88–0	29,815
0-8-2T										
49	6F	....	Bowen Cooke ...	L.N.W.	1911	170	20$\frac{1}{2}$ × 24	4′ 5$\frac{1}{2}$″	72–10	27,240

*—71t. 16c. for Locos with condensing apparatus.

Page	Power Classification	Class	Designer	Original Owning Co.	Building or Re-building Date	Boiler Pressure	Cylinders	Driving Wheels	Weight Engine in Working Order	Tractive Effort at 85% B.P.
						lb. per sq. in.			T. Cwt.	lb.
0-6-2T										
21	3F	....	Whitelegg ...	L.T. & S.	1903	170	18 × 26	5′ 3″	64–13	19,320
47	2	....	Webb	L.N.W.	1898	150	18 × 24	5′ 2½″	52–6	15,865
72	2F	....	Webb	L.N.W.	1882	150	17 × 24	4′ 5½″	43–15	16,530
0-6-0T										
48	3F	....	Fowler	L.M.S.	1924	160	18 × 26	4′ 7″	49–10	20,835
48	3F	....	Fowler	S. & D.J.	1929	160	18 × 26	4′ 7″	49–10	20,835
47	3F	....	Johnson	Mid.	1899	160	18 × 26	4′ 7″	48–15	20,835
59	3F	"29" & "782" classes ...	McIntosh	Cal.	1895	160	18 × 26	4′ 6″	47–15	21,235
47	2F	Dock Tanks	Fowler	L.M.S.	1928	160	O 17 × 22	3′ 11″	43–12	18,400
72	2F	....	Park	N.L.	1879	160	O 17 × 24	4′ 4″	45–10	18,140
59	2F	Dock Tanks, "498" class	McIntosh	Cal.	1912	160	O 17 × 22	4′ 0″	47–15	18,015
55	1F	....	Aspinall	L. & Y.	1897	140	O 17 × 24	4′ 0″	50–0	15,285
12	1F	....	Johnson	Mid.	1878	{150	17 × 24	4′ 7″	39–11	16,080
						{140	17 × 24	4′ 7″	39–11	15,005
0-6-0ST										
55	2F	"Class 23" Rebuilt ...	Barton Wright* (1876) ... ... (Reb.) Aspinall	L. & Y.	1891	140	17½ × 26	4′ 6″	43–17	17,545
73	2F	"Special Tanks"	Ramsbottom/Webb	L.N.W.	1870	140	17 × 24	4′ 5½″	34–10	17,005
0-4-4T										
12	2P	....	Stanier	L.M.S.	1932	160	18 × 26	5′ 7″	58–1	17,100
58	2P	....	Pickersgill... ...	L.M.S.	1925	180	18¼ × 26	5′ 9″	59–12	19,200
58	2P	"431" class	Pickersgill... ...	Cal.	1922	180	18¼ × 26	5′ 9″	57–17	19 200
58	2P	"439" class	{McIntosh	Cal.	1900}	180	18 × 26	5′ 9″	{53–19	18,680
			{Pickersgill ...	Cal.	1915}				{57–12	
58	2P	"19" class	McIntosh	Cal.	1895	180	18 × 26	5′ 9″	53–16	18,680
58	2P	"29" class	McIntosh	Cal.	1897	180	18 × 26	5′ 9″	53–19	18,680

*—Originally 0–6–0 Tender Locos.

69	1P	....	Johnson	Mid.	1881	150		18 × 24	5′ 4″	53–4	15,490
						140		18 × 24	5′ 4″	53–4	14,460
69	1P	....	Johnson	Mid.	1875	140		18 × 24	5′ 7″	53–4	13,810
58	1P	....	P. Drummond ...	High.	1905	150		14 × 20	4′ 6″	35–15	9,255
0-4-2ST											
49	1F	....	Webb	L.N.W.	1896	150		17 × 24	4′ 5½″	34–17	16,530
72	Engine Crane	....	Sharp-Stewart (1858) (Reb.) Park	*N.L.	1872	120		13 × 17	3′ 10″	32–6	6,370
0-4-0T											
12	0F	....	Deeley	Mid.	1907	160	O	15 × 22	3′ 9¾″	32–16	14,635
47		Sentinel (47190-1)... ...	....	S. & D.J.	1929	275 Su	(4)	6¾ × 9	3′ 1½″	27–15	15,500
47		Sentinel (47180/1/2/3) ...	....	L.M.S.	1930	275 Su		6¾ × 9	2′ 6″	20–17	11,800
47		Sentinel (47184)	....	L.M.S.	1932	275 Su		6¾ × 9	2′ 6″	18–18	11,800
0-4-0ST											
47	0F	....	Stanier	L.M.S.	1932	160	O	15½ × 20	3′ 10″	33–0	14,205
54	0F	" Class 21 "	Aspinall	L. & Y.	1891	160	O	13 × 18	3′ 0⅜″	21–5	11,335
12	0F	....	Johnson	Mid.	1903	150	O	15 × 20	3′ 10″	32–3	12,475
						140					11,640
12	0F	....	Johnson	Mid.	1890	140	O	13 × 20	3′ 10″	23–3	8,745
59	0F	" Pugs "	D. Drummond ...	Cal.	1885	160	O	14 × 20	3′ 8″	27–7	12,115

NOTES

Tractive effort calculated to nearest 5 lb. O (in Cylinders column)—Outside cylinders. *Originally 0-4-0T

THE ABC OF BRITISH RAILWAYS LOCOMOTIVES

EDITED BY A. F. COOK

PART 4 - Nos. 60001-90774

LONDON:

Ian Allan Ltd

FOREWORD

THIS booklet lists all British Railways locomotives numbered between 60000 and 90774. This series of numbers includes all Eastern, North Eastern and Scottish (ex-L.N.E.R.) Region steam locomotives, i.e. steam locomotives of the former L.N.E.R., and ex-Ministry of Supply 2-8-0 locos. Under the general British Railways renumbering scheme, the numbers of L.N.E.R. steam locomotives were increased by 60000, with the exception of Classes W1 and L1. Renumbering of the ex-M.o.S. 2-8-0 locomotives is now taking place (*see page 64*), and a further scheme involves Class B7 (*see page 20*). Renumbering is being carried out only as locomotives visit main works for repairs, and thus it will be some time before all locomotives bear the numbers shown in this book.

Former L.N.E.R. electric and diesel electric locomotives have been renumbered in the 20000 and 15000 series, and details of them will be found in " ABC of British Railways Locomotives " Part 2 (Nos. 10000-39999).

BRITISH RAILWAYS, EASTERN & NORTH EASTERN REGION

Chief Mechanical Engineer

A. H. Peppercorn 1948

LOCOMOTIVE SUPERINTENDENTS AND CHIEF MECHANICAL ENGINEERS OF THE L.N.E.R.

Sir Nigel Gresley	1923—1941
E. Thompson ..	1941—1946
A. H. Peppercorn	1946—1947

Great Northern Railway

A. Sturrock ..	1850—1866
P. Stirling ..	1866—1895
H. A. Ivatt ..	1896—1911
H. N. Gresley ..	1911—1922

North Eastern Railway

E. Fletcher ..	1854—1883
A. McDonnell*..	1883—1884
T. W. Worsdell ..	1885—1890
W. Worsdell ..	1890—1910
Sir Vincent Raven	1910—1922

Great Eastern Railway

R. Sinclair ..	1862—1866
S. W. Johnson ..	1866—1873
W. Adams ..	1873—1878
M. Bromley ..	1878—1881
T. W. Worsdell ..	1881—1885
J. Holden ..	1885—1907
S. D. Holden ..	1908—1912
A. J. Hill ..	1912—1922

Lancashire, Derbyshire and East Coast Railway

R. A. Thom ..	1902—1907

Manchester, Sheffield and Lincolnshire Railway

Richard Peacock	—1854
W. G. Craig ..	1854—1859
Charles Sacré ..	1859—1886
T. Parker ..	1886—1893
H. Pollitt ..	1893—1897

Great Central Railway

H. Pollitt ..	1897—1900
J. G. Robinson ..	1900—1922

Hull and Barnsley Railway

M. Stirling ..	1885—1922

Midland and Great Northern Joint Railway

W. Marriott ..	1884—1924

North British Railway

T. Wheatley† ..	1867—1874
D. Drummond ..	1875—1882
M. Holmes ..	1882—1903
W. P. Reid ..	1903—1919
W. Chalmers ..	1919—1922

* Between McDonnell and T. W. Worsdell there was an interval during which the office was covered by a locomotive committee.

† Previous to whom, the records are indeterminate.

ROUTE AVAILABILITY OF LOCOMOTIVES

Restrictions on the working of locomotives over the routes of the former L.N.E.R. are denoted by Route Availability numbers. In general a locomotive is not permitted to work over a line of lower R.A. number than itself. The scheme is as follows :

R.A.1 : J15, J62, J63, J65, J71, Y1, Y3, Y6, Y7, Y8, Y10, Y11, Z4.

R.A.2 : E4, J24, J67/1, J70, J72, J77, J93, Y9, Z5.

R.A.3 : B12/1, D3, D41, F2 (modified for Eastern Section), F3, F4, F5, J3, J4, J10, J21, J25, J36, J66, J67/2, J68, J69, J88, J92, N9, N10.

R.A.4 : A6, B12/3, D2, D31, D40, F6, G5, J1, J5, J17, J26, J55, J83, N4, N5/2, N8, N13, N14, Q5, V4.

R.A.5 : A5, A8, B1, B2, B4, B5, B6, B17/1, B17/4, C12, C13, C14, D1, D9, D15, D16, F2, J2, J6, J11, J19, J20, J27, J52, J73, J94, K2, L2, M2, N1, N5/3, N7.

R.A.6 : C15, C16, D10, D11, D20, D29, D30, D32, D33, D34, J35, J39, J50, K1, K4, N2, N15, O1, O2, O3, O4, O7, Q6, V1, Y4.

R.A.7 : A7, B7, B16/1, B17/5, C1, C4, L1, L3, Q7, U1, V3.

R.A.8 : B16/2, B16/3, D49, J37, J38, K3, K5, Q1, S1, T1.

R.A.9 : A1, A2, A3, A4, V2, W1.

POWER CLASSIFICATION

Ex-L.N.E.R. locomotives are classified for haulage purposes under the ex-L.M.S. system as follows :

7P : A1, A3, A4, W1.

4P : B4, B12, B17, D49, A5.

3P : D10, D11, D29, D30, D32, D33, D34.

2P : D9, D16, D31, D40, D41, C1, C4, C12, C13, C14, C15, G5.

1P : D1, D2, D3, F2, F4.

7MT : A2, A2/2, A2/3.

6MT : A2/1, B7, K1, K3, K4, K5, V2.

5MT : B1, V4.

4MT : K2, L1, N14, N15, V1, V3.

3MT : B5, N2, N7.

2MT : J1, J2, N1, N4, N5.

8F : O1, O2, O3, W.D. 2-8-0 and 2-10-0.
7F : O4, S1.
6F : J38.
5F : Q4, L3, Q1.
4F : J37, J39, J50, J94.
3F : J5, J6, J11, J24, J35, J52, J55, J68, J69.
2F : J3, J4, J10, J21, J36, J66, J67, J72, J83.
0F : J62, J63, J88, Y9, Z4, Z5.
Unclassified : U1, Y1, Y3.

SOME POINTS OF INTEREST

Classification of L.N.E.R. Locomotives

The L.N.E.R. locomotive classification scheme was based on that used on the former G.N.R. Each wheel arrangement was allotted a letter, and the classes of that arrangement were numbered in groups according to the pre-grouping ownership, in the order G.N., G.C., G.E., N.E., N.B., G.N.S. L.N.E.R. classes were at first usually added at the end of the list, but the new standard locomotives have been given the lowest number in most groups. Types 0-8-2T (R) and 2-2-4 (X) have now disappeared. Many classes are sub-divided into " parts," denoted thus : " D16/3." This division is not entirely consistent, as some classes with comparatively wide variations, such as " A4," are not sub-divided, but others, such as " O4," have some divisions dependent only on details such as brakes and whether or not the tender has a water scoop. In these lists, sub-divisions are denoted by " parts " where these exist, but elsewhere it is to be assumed that any variations between the locomotives in the class are not covered by the classification (e.g. " A4 ").

Boiler Interchangeability

There are several types of boiler which are common to more than one ex-L.N.E.R. class. In some cases boilers are frequently interchanged between the classes, a locomotive under repair receiving the first boiler of that type which is available. In other cases the boilers are identical from the manufacturing standpoint, but the fittings vary on the different classes, and interchanges are not normally made. Groups of classes with similar boilers include : A2/1 and V2 ; A5 and D9 ; A6, A8 (except for superheater) and T1 ; B1, B2, B17/6, O1, O2/4 and O4/8 ; B4, C4, O4 and S1 ; B5, B9 and Q4 (sup.) ; B12/1 and J20 ; B16 and Q7 ; C12, J4, J50 and J55 ; C13 and C14 ; C15, C16 (except for superheater), J36, N14 and N15 ; D1, D2 (sup.), J2, J6 and N2 (with recent boiler) ; D2 (sat.), J1, J5 and N1 (this group differs only from the preceding in being saturated) ; D10, D11 and L3 ; D16/3 and J19 ; D29, D30, D32, D33 and D34 ; D40 (sat.) and D41 ; D49, J38/2 and J39 ; E4, F3 and J15 ; F2, J10, N4 and N5 ; F5 and F6 ; G5 and J24 ; J21, J25, N8, N9 and N10 ; J35 and J37 ; J62 and J63 ; J65, J66 and J67 ; J68 and J69 ; J71 and J72 ; O2 and O3.

Boilers of Ex-N.E.R. Locomotives

Although several ex-N.E.R. classes have boilers very similar in dimensions to standard L.N.E.R. classes (e.g. B16 and B1), it is not possible for the standard boilers to be fitted to the N.E. locomotives as the latter have their frames ½″ closer together than L.N.E.R. standard. Most of the N.E. boilers had the dome on the centre of the barrel, whereas most of the L.N.E.R. boilers have the dome to the rear of the barrel, a bracket for stays being attached near the centre of the barrel. Since 1937 new boilers with domes to the rear and standard stays have been built for the more modern N.E. classes, including A8, B16, J26 and J27.

Ex-North Eastern 0-6-0 Locomotives

Of the remaining ex-N.E. 0-6-0 locomotives, classes J21, J25, J26 and J27 have the same length and wheelbase, the two former having 4′ 3″ diameter boilers and the two latter 5′ 6″. The fireboxes of J26 and J27 are also larger, and the boilers originally fitted to J26 had shallower fireboxes than those of J27. J21 and J25 have identical boilers. J24 has a 4′ 3″ boiler shorter than that of J25, and the wheelbase is also shorter. For 22 years up to the introduction of J38, J26 and J27 were the only 0-6-0s in the country with boilers as large in diameter as 5′ 6″.

Ex-G.E.R. Locomotives

F3 was the tank version of E4, and is larger than the other G.E. 2-4-2Ts, F4, F5 and F6 (the " Worsdell Gobblers "). The first F4s were built in 1886-8 and many more were built from 1903. F5 is a rebuild of F4 with higher pressure boiler, and F6 were the locomotives built new with the higher boiler pressure.

Of the G.E. 0-6-0Ts, although the boilers are all of the same dimensions, J65 are much smaller locomotives than the rest. The other classes are generally similar, except that J68 and J69 have larger tanks and higher pressure. J69 are rebuilds from J67, and J68 new locomotives. J69 and many of J68 were originally passenger locomotives for the London suburban area.

Ex-G.N.R. Locomotives

The standard 0-6-0 and 4-4-0 of the early Ivatt period became L.N.E.R. J4 and D4. They had identical 4′ 4″ diameter boilers, cylinders and other details. D2 was developed from D4, with a 4′ 8″ boiler and longer firebox ; the corresponding larger 0-6-0 was J5. Later all class D4 and most of J4 were rebuilt with 4′ 8″ boilers, but with fireboxes of the same length as before, becoming D3 and J3. J1 was a large-wheeled version of J5. Towards the end of the Ivatt regime, superheated developments of these classes, with piston valves, were introduced, D1 (from D2), J2 (from J1) and J6 (from J5). The tank version of J1 was N1 and the tank version of J2 was N2. As built N2 had Gresley twin-tube superheaters instead of the Robinson pattern of the other classes, but these locomotives are now receiving the Robinson apparatus.

NOTES ON THE USE OF THIS BOOK

In the lists of locomotives which follow :

1. Many of the classes listed are sub-divided, the sub-divisions being denoted in some cases by " Parts " shown thus : D16/3. At the head of each class will be found a list of such sub-divisions, if any, usually arranged in order of introduction. Each part is given there a reference mark by which its relevant dimensions, if differing from other parts, and the locos in the list it comprises, may be identified. Any other differences between locomotives are also indicated, with reference marks, below the details of the class's introduction. For further remarks on the classification of ex-L.N.E.R. locos, see the note on p. 5.

2. The lists of dimensions at the head of each class show locomotives fitted with two inside cylinders, Stephenson gear and slide valves, unless otherwise stated, e.g. (O) = two outside cylinders, P.V. = piston valves.

3. The following method is used to denote superheated locomotives, the letters being inserted, where applicable, after the boiler pressure details : Su = All engines superheated.
SS = Some engines superheated.

4. The date on which the first locomotive of a class was built is denoted by " Introduced." If the oldest locomotive still running was built at a later date, that also is indicated.

5. The numbers of locomotives in service have been checked to May 31st, 1949.

6. S denotes Service (Departmental) locomotive. This reference letter is introduced only for the reader's guidance and is not borne by the locomotive concerned.

NUMERICAL LIST OF ENGINES

4-6-2 Class A4

Introduced 1935. Gresley streamlined design.
*† Inside cylinder reduced to 17".
†‡ Non-corridor tender (remainder corridor).
§ Kylchap blast pipe and double chimney.
Weights: Loco. 102 tons 19 cwt.
Tender { 64 tons 19 cwt. / 60 tons 7 cwt.†
Pressure: 250 lb. Su.
Cyls. { (3) 18½" × 26". / (2) 18½" × 26". (1) 17" × 26"*
Driving Wheels: 6' 8"
T.E. { 35455 lb. / 33616 lb.*
Walschaerts gear and derived motion P.V.

60001‡ Sir Ronald Matthews
60002‡ Sir Murrough Wilson
60003* Andrew K. McCosh
60004‡ William Whitelaw
60005‡§ Sir Charles Newton
60006 Sir Ralph Wedgwood
60007 Sir Nigel Gresley
60008 Dwight D. Eisenhower
60009 Union of South Africa
60010 Dominion of Canada
60011 Dominion of India
60012* Commonwealth of Australia
60013 Dominion of New [Zealand
60014* Silver Link
60015 Quicksilver
60016 Silver King
60017 Silver Fox
60018‡ Sparrow Hawk
60019‡ Bittern
60020† Guillemot
60021‡ Wild Swan
60022§ Mallard
60023‡ Golden Eagle
60024 Kingfisher
60025 Falcon
60026 Miles Beevor
60027 Merlin
60028 Walter K. Whigham
60029 Woodcock
60030‡ Golden Fleece
60031* Golden Plover
60032‡ Gannet
60033§ Seagull
60034§ Lord Faringdon

Total 34

4-6-2 Class A3

A3 Introduced 1927. Development of Gresley G.N. 180 lb. Pacific (introduced 1922, L.N.E.R. A1, later A10) with 220 lb. pressure (prototype and others rebuilt from A10). Some have G.N.-type tender† with coal rails, remainder L.N.E.R. pattern.
* Kylchap blast pipe and double chimney
Weights: Loco. 96 tons 5 cwt.
Tender { 56 tons 6 cwt.† / 57 tons 18 cwt.
Pressure: 220 lb. Su. Cyls.: 19" × 26"
Driving Wheels: 6' 8" T.E.: 32,910 lb.
Walschaerts gear and derived motion, P.V.

60035 Windsor Lad
60036 Colombo
60037 Hyperion
60038 Firdaussi
60039 Sandwich
60040 Cameronian
60041 Salmon Trout
60042 Singapore
60043 Brown Jack
60044 Melton
60045 Lemberg
60046 Diamond Jubilee
60047 Donovan
60048 Doncaster
60049 Galtee More
60050 Persimmon
60051 Blink Bonny
60052 Prince Palatine
60053 Sansovino
60054 Prince of Wales
60055 Woolwinder
60056 Centenary
60057 Ormonde
60058 Blair Athol
60059 Tracery
60060 The Tetrarch
60061 Pretty Polly

[J. P. Wilson

Class W1 4-6-4 No. 60700

[F. F. Moss

Class V2 2-6-2 No. 60800 *Green Arrow*

[P. Ransome-Wallis

Class B1 4-6-0 No. 61319

Top : Class A2 4-6-2 No. 60536 *Trimbush*
Centre : Class A2/3 4-6-2 No. 60515 *Sun Stream*
Bottom : Class A2/2 4-6-2 No. 502 *Ear' Marischal* (new No. 60502)

[C. C. B. Herbert, H. C. Casserley, P. Ransome-Wallis

Top : Class A1 4-6-2 No. 60136
Centre Class A4 4-6-2 No. 60027 *Merlin*
Bottom : Class A3 4-6-2 No. 60040 *Cameronian*
[*P. Ransome-Wallis (top and centre) E. Treacy*

Top : Class B16/2 4-6-0 No. 61438
Centre : Class B17/4 4-6-0 No. 61665 *Leicester City*
Bottom : Class B2 4-6-0 No. 61614 *Castle Hedingham*
[*H. C. Casserley, Roy E. Vincent, A. F. Cook*

60062 Minoru
60063 Isinglass
60064 Tagalie
60065 Knight of Thistle
60066 Merry Hampton
60067 Ladas
60068 Sir Visto
60069 Sceptre
60070 Gladiateur
60071 Tranquil
60072 Sunstar
60073 St. Gatien
60074 Harvester
60075 St. Frusquin
60076 Galopin
60077 The White Knight
60078 Night Hawk
60079 Bayardo
60080 Dick Turpin
60081 Shotover
60082 Neil Gow
60083 Sir Hugo
60084 Trigo
60085 Manna
60086 Gainsborough
60087 Blenheim
60088 Book Law
60089 Felstead
60090 Grand Parade
60091 Captain Cuttle
60092 Fairway
60093 Coronach
60094 Colorado
60095 Flamingo
60096 Papyrus
60097* Humorist
60098 Spion Kop
60099 Call Boy
60100 Spearmint
60101 Cicero
60102 Sir Frederick Banbury
60103 Flying Scotsman
60104 Solario
60105 Victor Wild
60106 Flying Fox
60107 Royal Lancer
60108 Gay Crusader
60109 Hermit
60110 Robert the Devil
60111 Enterprise
60112 St. Simon

Total 78

4-6-2 Class A1

A1/1* Introduced 1945. Thompson rebuild of A10.
A1 Peppercorn development of A1/1 for new construction.
Weights : Loco. {101 tons.* / 104 tons 2 cwt.}
Tender 60 tons 7 cwt.
Pressure : 250 lb. Su.
Cyls.: (3) 19″×26″
Driving Wheels : 6′ 8″ T.E.: 37,400 lb.
Walschaerts gear, P.V.

60113* Great Northern
60114 W. P. Allen

60115	60125	60135	60145
60116	60126	60136	60146
60117	60127	60137	60147
60118	60128	60138	60148
60119	60129	60139	60149
60120	60130	60140	60150
60121	60131	60141	60151
60122	60132	60142	60152
60123	60133	60143	60153
60124	60134	60144	

N.B. Locos of this class are still being delivered.

4-6-2 Class A2

A2/2* Introduced 1943. Original Thompson Pacific, rebuilt from Gresley Class P2 2-8-2 (introduced 1934).
Weight : Loco. 101 tons 10 cwt.
Pressure : 225 lb. Su.
Cyls.: (3) 20″×26″
Driving Wheels : 6′ 2″ T.E.: 40,320 lb.
A2/1† Introduced 1944. Development of Class A2/2, incorporating Class V2 2-6-2 type boiler.
Weight : Loco. 98 tons.
Pressure : 225 lb. Su.
Cyls.: (3) 19″×26″
Driving Wheels : 6′ 2″ T.E.: 36,385 lb.
A2/3‡ Introduced 1946. Development of Class A2/2 for new construction.
Weight : Loco. 101 tons 10 cwt.
Pressure : 250 lb. Su.
Cyls.: (3) 19″×26″
Driving Wheels : 6′ 2″ T.E.: 40,430 lb.
A2§ Introduced 1947. Peppercorn development of Class A2/3 with shorter wheelbase.
Weight : Loco. 101 tons.

Pressure : 250 lb. Su.
Cyls.: (3) 19" × 26"
Driving Wheels : 6' 2" T.E.: 40,430 lb.
Tender weight (all parts): 60 tons 7 cwt. (except Nos. 60508-10, 52 tons).
Walschaerts gear, P.V.

60500‡ Edward Thompson
60501* Cock o' the North
60502* Earl Marischal
60503* Lord President
60504* Mons Meg
60505* Thane of Fife
60506* Wolf of Badenoch
60507† Highland Chieftain
60508† Duke of Rothesay
60509† Waverley
60510† Robert the Bruce
60511‡ Airborne
60512‡ Steady Aim
60513‡ Dante
60514‡ Chamossaire
60515‡ Sun Stream
60516‡ Hycilla
60517‡ Ocean Swell
60518‡ Tehran
60519‡ Honeyway
60520‡ Owen Tudor
60521‡ Watling Street
60522‡ Straight Deal
60523‡ Sun Castle
60524‡ Herringbone
60525§ A. H. Peppercorn
60526§ Sugar Palm
60527§ Sun Chariot
60528§ Tudor Minstrel
60529§ Pearl Diver
60530§ Sayajirao
60531§ Bahram
60532§ Blue Peter
60533§ Happy Knight
60534§ Irish Elegance
60535§ Hornet's Beauty
60536§ Trimbush
60537§ Bachelor's Button
60538§ Velocity
60539§ Bronzino

Totals :
Class A2 15 Class A2/2 6
Class A2/1 4 Class A2/3 15

4-6-4 Class W1

Introduced 1937. Rebuilt from Gresley experimental high-pressure 4-cyl. compound with water-tube boiler, introduced 1929.
Weights : Loco. 107 tons 17 cwt.
Tender 60 tons 7 cwt.
Pressure : 250 lb. Su.
Cyls.: (3) 20" × 26"
Driving Wheels : 6' 8" T.E.: 41,435 lb.
Walschaerts gear and derived motion, P.V.

60700 **Total 1**

2-6-2 Class V2

Introduced 1936. Gresley design.
Weights : Loco. 93 tons 2 cwt.
Tender 52 tons.
Pressure : 220 lb. Su.
Cyls.: (3) $18\frac{1}{2}$" × 26"
Driving Wheels : 6' 2" T.E.: 33,730 lb
Walschaerts gear and derived motion, P.V.

60800 Green Arrow
60801
60802
60803
60804
60805
60806
60807
60808
60809 The Snapper, The East Yorkshire Regiment, The Duke of York's Own
60810
60811
60812
60813
60814
60815
60816
60817
60818
60819
60820
60821
60822
60823
60824
60825

60826
60827
60828
60829
60830
60831
60832
60833
60834
60835 The Green Howard, Alexandra, Princess of Wales's Own Yorkshire Regiment
60836
60837
60838
60839
60840
60841
60842
60843
60844
60845
60846
60847 St. Peter's School, York, A.D. 627
60848
60849
60850
60851
60852
60853
60854
60855
60856
60857
60858
60859
60860 Durham School
60861
60862
60863
60864
60865
60866
60867
60868
60869
60870
60871
60872 King's Own Yorkshire Light Infantry
60873 Coldstreamer

60874	60902	60930	60958
60875	60903	60931	60959
60876	60904	60932	60960
60877	60905	60933	60961
60878	60906	60934	60962
60879	60907	60935	60963
60880	60908	60936	60964
60881	60909	60937	60965
60882	60910	60938	60966
60883	60911	60939	60967
60884	60912	60940	60968
60885	60913	60941	60969
60886	60914	60942	60970
60887	60915	60943	60971
60888	60916	60944	60972
60889	60917	60945	60973
60890	60918	60946	60974
60891	60919	60947	60975
60892	60920	60948	60976
60893	60921	60949	60977
60894	60922	60950	60978
60895	60923	60951	60979
60896	60924	60952	60980
60897	60925	60953	60981
60898	60926	60954	60982
60899	60927	60955	60983
60900	60928	60956	
60901	60929	60957	

Total 184

4-6-0 Class B1

Introduced 1942. Thompson design.
Weights : Loco. 71 tons 3 cwt.
Tender 52 tons.
Pressure : 225 lb. Su.
Cyls.: (O) 20″ × 26″
Driving Wheels : 6′ 2″ T.E.: 26,880 lb.
Wa'schaerts gear, P.V.

61000 Springbok
61001 Eland
61002 Impala
61003 Gazelle
61004 Oryx
61005 Bongo

61006	Blackbuck
61007	Klipspringer
61008	Kudu
61009	Hartebeeste
61010	Wildebeeste
61011	Waterbuck
61012	Puku
61013	Topi
61014	
61015	Duiker
61016	Inyala
61017	Bushbuck
61018	Gnu
61019	Nilghai
61020	Gemsbok
61021	Reitbok
61022	Sassaby
61023	Hirola
61024	Addax
61025	Pallah
61026	Ourebi
61027	Madoqua
61028	Umseke
61029	Chamois
61030	Nyala
61031	Reedbuck
61032	Stembok
61033	Dibatag
61034	Chiru
61035	Pronghorn
61036	Ralph Assheton
61037	Jairou
61038	Blacktail
61039	Steinbok
61040	Roedeer

61041	61054	61067	61080
61042	61055	61068	61081
61043	61056	61069	61082
61044	61057	61070	61083
61045	61058	61071	61084
61046	61059	61072	61085
61047	61060	61073	61086
61048	61061	61074	61087
61049	61062	61075	61088
61050	61063	61076	61089
61051	61064	61077	61090
61052	61065	61078	61091
61053	61066	61079	61092

61093	61117	61141	61165
61094	61118	61142	61166
61095	61119	61143	61167
61096	61120	61144	61168
61097	61121	61145	61169
61098	61122	61146	61170
61099	61123	61147	61171
61100	61124	61148	61172
61101	61125	61149	61173
61102	61126	61150	61174
61103	61127	61151	61175
61104	61128	61152	61176
61105	61129	61153	61177
61106	61130	61154	61178
61107	61131	61155	61179
61108	61132	61156	61180
61109	61133	61157	61181
61110	61134	61158	61182
61111	61135	61159	61183
61112	61136	61160	61184
61113	61137	61161	61185
61114	61138	61162	61186
61115	61139	61163	61187
61116	61140	61164	61188

61189	Sir William Gray
61190	
61191	
61192	
61193	
61194	
61195	
61196	
61197	
61198	
61199	
61200	
61201	
61202	
61203	
61204	
61205	
61206	
61207	
61208	
61209	
61210	
61211	

61212
61213
61214
61215 William Henton Carver
61216
61217
61218
61219
61220
61221 Sir Alexander Erskine-Hill
61222
61223
61224
61225
61226
61227
61228
61229
61230
61231
61232
61233
61234
61235
61236
61237 Geoffrey H. Kitson
61238 Leslie Runciman
61239
61240 Harry Hinchliffe
61241 Viscount Ridley
61242 Alexander Reith Gray
61243 Sir Harold Mitchell
61244 Strang Steel
61245 Murray of Elibank
61246 Lord Balfour of Burleigh
61247 Lord Burghley
61248 Geoffrey Gibbs
61249 FitzHerbert Wright
61250 A. Harold Bibby
61251 Oliver Bury

61252	61259	61266	61273
61253	61260	61267	61274
61254	61261	61268	61275
61255	61262	61269	61276
61256	61263	61270	61277
61257	61264	61271	61278
61258	61265	61272	61279

61280	61303	61326	61349
61281	61304	61327	61350
61282	61305	61328	61351
61283	61306	61329	61352
61284	61307	61330	61353
61285	61308	61331	61354
61286	61309	61332	61355
61287	61310	61333	61356
61288	61311	61334	61357
61289	61312	61335	61358
61290	61313	61336	61359
61291	61314	61337	61360
61292	61315	61338	61361
61293	61316	61339	61362
61294	61317	61340	61363
61295	61318	61341	61364
61296	61319	61342	61365
61297	61320	61343	61366
61298	61321	61344	61367
61299	61322	61345	61368
61300	61323	61346	61369
61301	61324	61347	
61302	61325	61348	

N.B. Locomotives of this class are still being delivered.

4-6-0 Class B16

B16/1 Introduced 1920. Raven N.E. design with inside Stephenson gear.
B16/2* Introduced 1937. Gresley rebuild of B16/1 with outside Walschaerts' gear and derived motion for inside cylinder.
B16/3† Introduced 1944. Thompson rebuild of B16/1 with three Walschaerts' gears.

Weights : Loco. { 77 tons 14 cwt. / 79 tons 4 cwt.* / 78 tons 19 cwt.† }
Tender 46 tons 12 cwt.
Pressure : 180 lb. Su.
Cyls.: (3) $18\frac{1}{2}'' \times 26''$
Driving Wheels : 5' 8" T.E.: 30,030 lb.
P.V.

61400	61407†	61414	61421*
61401	61408	61415	61422
61402	61409	61416	61423
61403†	61410	61417†	61424
61404	61411	61418†	61425
61405	61412	61419	61426
61406*	61413	61420†	61427

61428	61439†	61450	61461†
61429	61440	61451	61462
61430	61441	61452	61463†
61431	61442	61453†	61464†
61432	61443	61454†	61465
61433	61444†	61455*	61466
61434	61445	61456	61467†
61435*	61446	61457*	61468†
61436	61447	61458	
61437*	61448†	61459	
61438*	61449†	61460	

Totals : Class B16/1 46
Class B16/2 7
Class B16/3 16

4-6-0 Class B4

B4/4* Introduced 1906. Robinson G.C. design with slide valves, later superheated.

B4/3 Introduced 1925. B4/3 rebuilt with piston valves and larger cyls. (B4/1 and B4/2 corresponded to B4/3 and B4/4 before cutting down to L.N.E.R. loading gauge.)

Weights : Loco. { 70 tons 14 cwt.* / 71 tons 15 cwt.
Tender 40 tons 6 cwt.
Pressure : 180 lb. Su.
Cyls.:(O) { 19" × 26"* / 21" × 26"
Driving Wheels : 6' 7"
T.E. { 18, 180 lb.* / 22,205 lb.

61482* Immingham
61483

Totals : Class B4/3 1
Class B4/4 1

4-6-0 Class B12

B12/1* Introduced 1911. S. D. Holden G.E. design with small Belpaire boiler.

B12/3 Introduced 1932. Gresley rebuild of B12/1 with large round-topped boiler and long-travel valves.

B12/1† Introduced 1943. Rebuild of B12/1 with small round-topped boiler, retaining original valves.
(B12/2 was a development of B12/1 with Lentz valves, since rebuilt to B12/3.)

Weights : Loco. { 63 tons.*† / 69 tons 10 cwt.
Tender 39 tons 6 cwt.
Pressure : 180 lb. Su. Cyls.: 20" × 28"
Driving Wheels : 6' 6" T.E.: 21,970 lb.
P.V.

61501*	61524†	61546	61566
61502*	61525	61547	61567
61503*	61526†	61549	61568
61504†	61528*	61550	61569
61505†	61529*	61552*	61570
61507†	61530	61553	61571
61508†	61532†	61554	61572
61510	61533	61555	61573
61511†	61535	61556	61574
61512	61536*	61557	61575
61513*	61537	61558	61576
61514	61538	61559	61577
61515	61539*	61560*	61578
61516	61540	61561	61579
61519	61541	61562	61580
61520	61542	61563*	
61521*	61543*	61564	
61523	61545	61565	

Totals : Class B12/1 21
Class B12/3 48

4-6-0 Classes B2 & B17

B17/1[1] Introduced 1928. Gresley design for G.E. section with G.E.-type tenders.

B17/6[2] Introduced 1947. B17/1 fitted with 100A (B1 type) boiler.

B17/4[3] Introduced 1936. Locos with L.N.E.R. 4200-gallon tenders.

B17/6[4] Introduced 1943. B17/4 fitted with 100A (B1 type) boiler.

B17/5[5] Introduced 1937. Rebuild of B17/4 with streamlined casing.
(B17/2 and B17/3 were variants of B17/1 now included in that part.)

Weights : Loco. { 77 tons 5 cwt.[1] / 77 tons 5 cwt.[2] / 77 tons 5 cwt.[3] / 77 tons 5 cwt.[4] / 80 tons 10 cwt.[5]
Tender { 39 tons 6 cwt.[1] / 39 tons 6 cwt.[2] / 52 tons [3] / 52 tons [4] / 52 tons 13 cwt.[5]

Pressure : { 180 lb.[1] / 225 lb.[2] / 180 lb.[3] / 225 lb.[4] / 180 lb.[5] } Su.

Cyls.: (3) 17½" × 26"
Driving Wheels : 6' 8"

T.E. : 22,485 lb.[1]; 28,555 lb.[2]; 22,485 lb.[3]; 28,555 lb.[4]; 22,485 lb.[5]

Walschaerts gear and derived motion, P.V.

B2[6] Introduced 1945. Thompson 2-cyl. re-build of B17, with 100A boiler and ex-N.E. tender.

B2[7] Introduced 1945, with L.N.E.R. tender.

Weights : Loco. 73 tons 10 cwt.
Tender 46 tons 12 cwt.[6] / 52 tons [7]

Pressure : 225 lb. Su.
Cyls.: (O) 20″ × 26″
Driving Wheels : 6′ 8″ T.E.: 24,865 lb.
Walschaerts gear and derived motion, P.V.

61600[1] Sandringham
61601[1] Holkham
61602[1] Walsingham
61603[6] Framlingham
61604[1] Elveden
61605[2] Lincolnshire Regiment
61606[1] Audley End
61607[6] Blickling
61608[1] Gunton
61609[1] Quidenham
61610[1] Honingham Hall
61611[1] Raynham Hall
61612[1] Houghton Hall
61613[1] Woodbastwick Hall
61614[6] Castle Hedingham
61615[7] Culford Hall
61616[6] Fallodon
61617[6] Ford Castle
61618[1] Wynyard Park
61619[1] Welbeck Abbey
61620[1] Clumber
61621[1] Hatfield House
61622[2] Alnwick Castle
61623[2] Lambton Castle
61624[1] Lumley Castle
61625[1] Raby Castle
61626[1] Brancepeth Castle
61627[2] Aske Hall
61628[2] Harewood House
61629[1] Naworth Castle
61630[2] Tottenham Hotspur
61631[1] Serlby Hall
61632[7] Belvoir Castle
61633[2] Kimbolton Castle
61634[1] Hinchingbrooke
61635[2] Milton
61636[1] Harlaxton Manor
61637[1] Thorpe Hall
61638[2] Melton Hall
61639[6] Norwich City
61640[1] Somerleyton Hall
61641[2] Gayton Hall
61642[2] Kilverstone Hall
61643[1] Champion Lodge
61644[6] Earlham Hall
61645[1] The Suffolk Regiment
61646[2] Gilwell Park
61647[3] Helmingham Hall
61648[3] Arsenal
61649[3] Sheffield United
61650[3] Grimsby Town
61651[3] Derby County
61652[4] Darlington
61653[3] Huddersfield Town
61654[4] Sunderland
61655[3] Middlesbrough
61656[3] Leeds United
61657[3] Doncaster Rovers
61658[1] The Essex Regiment
61659[5] East Anglian
61660[3] Hull City
61661[3] Sheffield Wednesday
61662[3] Manchester United
61663[3] Everton
61664[4] Liverpool
61665[3] Leicester City
61666[4] Nottingham Forest
61667[3] Bradford
61668[3] Bradford City
61669[3] Barnsley
61670[5] City of London
61671[7] Royal Sovereign
61672[3] West Ham United

Totals : Class B2 10
Class B17/1 27
Class B17/4 18
Class B17/5 2
Class B17/6 16

4-6-0 Class B5

Introduced 1902.
* Robinson G.C. design with slide valves.
† Rebuilt with piston valves.
(All later superheated.)
Weights: Loco. {64 tons 3 cwt.* / 65 tons 4 cwt.†}
Tender 48 tons 6 cwt.
Pressure: 180 lb. Su.
Cyls. (O) {19" × 26"* / 21" × 26"†}
Driving Wheels: 5' 8"
T.E.: {24,030 lb.* / 25,800 lb.†}

61686† 61688† 61689* **Total 3**

4-6-0 Class B13

Introduced 1899 (Survivor built 1906). Worsdell N.E. design later rebuilt to counter-pressure loco for loco testing purposes. Now maintained at Rugby Testing Plant.
Pressure: 160 lb. Cyls.: (O) 20" × 26"
Driving Wheels: 6' 1¼" T.E.: 19,310 lb.
P.V.

61699S **Total 1**

2-6-2 Class V4

Introduced 1941. Gresley design.
Weights: Loco. 70 tons 8 cwt.
Tender 42 tons 15 cwt.
Pressure: 250 lb. Su.
Cyls.: (3) 15" × 26"
Driving Wheels: 5' 8" T.E.: 27,420 lb.
Walschaerts gear and derived motion, P.V.

61700 Bantam Cock
61701 **Total 2**

4-6-0 Class B7

B7/1 Introduced 1921. Robinson G.C. design.
B7/2* Introduced 1923. Post-grouping locos. with smaller chimney and cab.
Weights: Loco. 79 tons 10 cwt.
Tender 48 tons 6 cwt.
Pressure: 180 lb. Su.
Cyls.: (4) 16" × 26"
Driving Wheels: 5' 8" T.E.: 29,950 lb.
P.V.

(First B.R. number is shown in brackets. This renumbering is not yet complete.)

61702 (61365)	61706 (61381)
61703 (61367)	61707 (61382)
61704 (61375)	61708 (61386)
61705 (61377)	61709 (61387)
61710*(61388)	61712*(61392)
61711*(61391)	61713*(61396)

Totals: Class B7/1 8
Class B7/2 4

2-6-0 Class K2

K2/2 Introduced 1914. Gresley G.N. design.
K2/1* Introduced 1931. Rebuilt from small-boilered K1 (introduced 1912).
† K2/2 fitted with side-window cab in Scottish Region.
Weights: Loco. 64 tons 8 cwt.
Tender 43 tons 2 cwt.
Pressure: 180 lb. Su.
Cyls.: (O) 20" × 26"
Driving Wheels: 5' 8" T.E.: 23,400 lb.
Walschaerts gear, P.V.

61720*	61731	61742	61753
61721*	61732	61743	61754
61722*	61733	61744	61755
61723*	61734	61745	61756
61724*	61735	61746	61757
61725*	61736	61747	61758
61726*	61737	61748	61759
61727*	61738	61749	61760
61728*	61739	61750	61761
61729*	61740	61751	61762
61730	61741	61752	61763

61764† Loch Arkaig

61765	61767	61769	61771
61766	61768	61770	

61772† Loch Lochy
61773
61774† Loch Garry
61775† Loch Treig

61776†	61778	61780
61777	61779†	

61781† Loch Morar
61782† Loch Eil
61783† Loch Sheil

61784†	61785†	61786†

61787† Loch Quoich
61788† Loch Rannoch
61789† Loch Laidon
61790† Loch Lomond
61791† Loch Laggan

61792†	61793†

61794† Loch Oich

Totals: Class K2/1 10
Class K2/2 65

Top : Class B12/3 4-6-0 No. 61523
Centre : Class B12/1 4-6-0 No. 61524
Bottom : Class B4/4 4-6-0 No. 1482 *Immingham* (new No. 61482)
[*M. E. Edwards, P. Ransome-Wallis (centre and bottom)*

Top : Class K2/2 2-6-0 No. 61730
Centre . Class K3/2 2-6-0 No. 61938
Bottom . Class C4/2 4-4-2 No. 2918 (new No. 62918)
[A. F. Cook, E. V. Fry, P. Ransome-Wallis

Top : Class D49/2 4-4-0 No. 62775 *The Tynedale*
Centre : Class D49/1 4-4-0 No. 62701 *Derbyshire*
Bottom : Class D49/4 4-4-0 No. 62768 *The Morpeth*
[*P. Ransome-Wallis (top and centre), H. C. Casserley*

Above : Class D16/2 4-4-0 No. 62547

Left : Class D16/3 4-4-0 No. 62617

Below : Class D16/3 4-4-0 No. 62522 with modified footplating

[H. C. Casserley, J. R. Eagles, A. F. Cook

2-6-0 Classes K3 & K5

K3/2 Introduced 1924. Development of Gresley G.N. design, built to L.N.E.R. loading gauge.

K3/3* Introduced 1929. Differ in details only, such as springs, from K3/2.

‡ K3/2 fitted with ex-G.N. tender.

(K3/1 were ex-G.N. locos (introduced 1920), with G.N. cabs, and K3/4, K3/5 and K3/6 were variations of K3/2, differing in weight and details. These locos have now been modified to K3/2.)

Weights : Loco. 72 tons 12 cwt.
Tender { 52 tons. / 43 tons 2 cwt.‡ }
Pressure : 180 lb. Su.
Cyls.: (3) 18½″ × 26″
Driving Wheels : 5′ 8″ T.E.: 30,030 lb.
Walschaerts gear and derived motion, P.V.

K5† Introduced 1945. Thompson 2-cyl. rebuild of K3.

Weights : Loco. 71 tons 5 cwt.
Tender 52 tons.
Pressure : 225 lb. Su.
Cyls.: (O) 20″ × 26″
Driving Wheels : 5′ 8″ T.E.: 29,250 lb.
Walschaerts gear, P.V.

61800	61825	61850	61875*
61801	61826	61851	61876*
61802	61827	61852	61877*
61803	61828	61853	61878*
61804	61829	61854‡	61879*
61805	61830	61855‡	61880*
61806	61831	61856‡	61881*
61807	61832	61857‡	61882*
61808	61833	61858‡	61883*
61809	61834	61859‡	61884*
61810	61835	61860	61885*
61811	61836	61861	61886*
61812‡	61837	61862	61887*
61813	61838	61863†	61888*
61814	61839	61864	61889*
61815	61840	61865	61890
61816	61841‡	61866	61891
61817	61842	61867	61892
61818	61843	61868	61893
61819	61844	61869	61894
61820	61845	61870*	61895
61821	61846	61871*	61896
61822	61847	61872*	61897
61823	61848	61873*	61898
61824	61849	61874*	61899

61900	61924	61948	61972
61901	61925	61949	61973
61902	61926	61950	61974
61903	61927	61951	61975
61904	61928	61952	61976
61905	61929	61953	61977
61906	61930	61954	61978
61907	61931	61955	61979
61908	61932	61956	61980
61909	61933	61957	61981
61910	61934	61958	61982
61911	61935	61959	61983
61912	61936	61960	61984
61913	61937	61961	61985
61914	61938	61962	61986
61915	61939	61963	61987
61916	61940	61964	61988
61917	61941	61965	61989
61918	61942	61966	61990
61919	61943	61967	61991
61920	61944	61968	61992
61921	61945	61969	
61922	61946	61970	
61923	61947	61971	

Totals : Class K3/2 172
Class K3/3 20
Class K5 1

2-6-0 K1 & K4

K4* Introduced 1937. Gresley loco for West Highland line.

Weights : Loco. 68 tons 8 cwt.
Tender 44 tons 4 cwt.
Pressure : 200 lb. Su.
Cyls.: (3) 18½″ × 26″
Driving Wheels : 5′ 2″ T.E.: 36,600 lb.
Walschaerts gear and derived motion, P.V.

K1/1† Introduced 1945. Thompson 2-cyl. loco. Rebuilt from K4.

K1 Introduced 1949. Peppercorn development of Thompson K1/1 (No. 61997) for new construction.

Weights : Loco. 66 tons 17 cwt.
Tender 44 tons 4 cwt.
Pressure : 225 lb. Su.
Cyls.: (O) 20″ × 26″
Driving Wheels : 5′ 8″ T.E.: 32,080 lb.
Walschaerts gear, P.V.

61993* Loch Long
61994* The Great Marquess
61995* Cameron of Locheil
61996* Lord of the Isles
61997† MacCailin Mor
61998* MacLeod of MacLeod

62001	62014	62027	62040
62002	62015	62028	62041
62003	62016	62029	62042
62004	62017	62030	62043
62005	62018	62031	62044
62006	62019	62032	62045
62007	62020	62033	62046
62008	62021	62034	62047
62009	62022	62035	62048
62010	62023	62036	62049
62011	62024	62037	62050
62012	62025	62038	
62013	62026	62039	

N.B. Locos of Class K1 are still being delivered.

Totals : Class K1/1 1
Class K4 5

4-4-0 Class D31

Introduced 1890. Holmes N.B. design. (Rebuilt from 1918.)
Weights : Loco. 46 tons 8 cwt.
Tender 33 tons 9 cwt.
Pressure : 175 lb. Cyls.: 18¼" × 26"
Driving Wheels : 6' 6" T.E.: 16,515 lb.

62059	62060	62072

Total 3

4-4-0 Class D3

Introduced 1896. Ivatt G.N. design. Rebuilt from 1912 with large boiler.) **(see note p. 7.)**
* Rebuilt with side-window cab for working officers' saloons.
Weights : Loco. 45 tons 14 cwt.
Tender 38 tons 10 cwt.
Pressure : 175 lb. Cyls.: 17½" × 26"
Driving Wheels : 6' 8" T.E.: 14,805 lb.

62000*	62128	62133	62140
62123	62131	62135	62148
62125	62132	62139	

Total 11

4-4-0 Class D2

Introduced 1897. Ivatt G.N. design. **(see note p. 7).**
* Rebuilt with superheater.
Weights : Loco. 47 tons 10 cwt.
Tender 40 tons 18 cwt.
Pressure : 175 lb. / 170 lb. Su.*
Cyls.: 17½" × 26"
Driving Wheels : 6' 8"
T.E.: 14,805 lb. / 14,380 lb.*

62154	62173	62181	62193
62161	62177*	62188	62194
62172	62180*	62190	62199*

Total 12

IMPORTANT NOTE
A careful reading of the explanation on page 7 is essential to understand the use of reference marks in this book.

4-4-0 Class D1

Introduced 1911 Ivatt G.N design **(see note p. 7).**
Weights : Loco. 53 tons 6 cwt.
Tender 43 tons 2 cwt.
Pressure : 170 lb. Su. Cyls.: 18¼" × 26"
Driving Wheels : 6' 8" T.E.: 16,075 lb.
P.V.

62203	62208	62209	62214
62215			

Total 5

4-4-0 Class D41

Introduced 1893. Pickersgill and Johnson G.N.o.S. design.
Weights : Loco. 45 tons.
Tender 37 tons 8 cwt.
Pressure : 165 lb. Cyls.: 18" × 26"
Driving Wheels : 6' 1" T.E.: 16,185 lb.

62225	62232	62243	62252
62227	62234	62246	62255
62228	62235	62247	62256
62229	62240	62248	
62230	62241	62249	
62231	62242	62251	

Total 21

4-4-0 Class D40

Introduced 1899. Pickersgill G.N.o.S. design.
* Introduced 1920. Heywood superheated locos.
Weights : Loco. { 46 tons 7 cwt. / 48 tons 13 cwt.* }
Tender 37 tons 8 cwt.
Pressure : 165 lb. SS. Cyls.: 18" × 26"
Driving Wheels : 6' 1" T.E.: 16,185 lb.

62260	62264	62268	62271
62261	62265	62269	62272
62262	62267	62270	

62273* George Davidson
62274* Benachie
62275* Sir David Stewart
62276* Andrew Bain
62277* Gordon Highlander
62278* Hatton Castle
62279* Glen Grant

Total 18

4-4-0 Class D9

Introduced 1901. Robinson G.C. design. Since rebuilt with superheater.
Pressure : 180 lb. Su. Cyls.: 19" × 26"
Driving Wheels : 6' 9" T.E.: 17,730 lb.
P.V.

62300	62308	62315	62324
62301	62309	62317	62325
62302	62311	62318	62330
62303	62312	62319	62332
62304	62313	62321	62333
62305			

62307 Queen Mary

Total 22

4-4-0 Class D20

D20/1 Introduced 1899. W. Worsdell N.E. design. Since superheated.
D20/2* Introduced 1936. D20/1 rebuilt with long-travel valves.
Weights : Loco. { 54 tons 2 cwt. / 55 tons 9 cwt.* }
Tender { 41 tons 4 cwt. / 43 tons.* }
Pressure : 175 lb. Su. Cyls.: 19" × 26"
Driving Wheels : 6' 10" T.E.: 17,025 lb.
P.V.

62340	62344	62349*	62354
62341	62345	62351	62355
62342	62347	62352	62357
62343	62348	62353	62358
62359	62370	62379	62388
62360*	62371*	62380	62389
62361	62372	62381	62391
62362	62373	62382	62392
62363	62374	62383	62395
62365	62375*	62384	62396
62366	62376	62386	62397
62369	62378	62387	

Totals : Class D20/1 43
Class D20/2 4

4-4-0 Class D29

Introduced 1909. Reid N.B. "Scott" class, later superheated.
Weights : Loco. 54 tons 4 cwt.
Tender 46 tons.
Pressure : 190 lb. Su. Cyls.: 19" × 26"
Driving Wheels : 6' 6" T.E.: 19,435 lb.
P.V.

62401 Dandie Dinmont
62402 Redgauntlet
62404 Jeanie Deans
62405 The Fair Maid
62406 Meg Merrilies
62410 Ivanhoe
62411 Lady of Avenel
62412 Dirk Hatteraick
62413 Guy Mannering

Total 9

4-4-0 Class D30

D30/1* Introduced 1912. Reid N.B. "Scott" class.
D30/2 Introduced 1914. Development of D30/1 with detail differences.
Weights : Loco. { 57 tons 6 cwt.* / 57 tons 16 cwt. }
Tender { 46 tons.* / 46 tons 13 cwt. }
Pressure : 165 lb. Su. Cyls.: 20" × 26"
Driving Wheels : 6' 6" T.E.: 18,700 lb.
P.V.

62417* Hal o' the Wynd
62418 The Pirate
62419 Meg Dods
62420 Dominie Sampson
62421 Laird o' Monkbarns
62422 Caleb Balderstone
62423 Dugald Dalgetty
62424 Claverhouse
62425 Ellangowan

62426 Cuddie Headrigg
62427 Dumbiedykes
62428 The Talisman
62429 The Abbot
62430 Jingling Geordie
62431 Kenilworth
62432 Quentin Durward
62434 Kettledrummle
62435 Norna
62436 Lord Glenvarloch
62437 Adam Woodcock
62438 Peter Poundtext
62439 Father Ambrose
62440 Wandering Willie
62441 Black Duncan
62442 Simon Glover

Totals : Class D30/1 1
Class D30/2 24

4-4-0 Class D32

Introduced 1906. Reid N.B. "Intermediate" class. Since superheated.
Weights : Loco. 53 tons 14 cwt.
Tender 40 tons.
Pressure : 180 lb. Su. Cyls.: 19" × 26"
Driving Wheels : 6' 0" T.E.: 19,945 lb
P.V.

62445 62451 **Total 2**

4-4-0 Class D33

Introduced 1909. Later Reid N.B. "Intermediate" class. Since superheated.
Weights : Loco. 54 tons 3 cwt.
Tender 44 tons 11 cwt.
Pressure : 180 lb. Su. Cyls.: 19" × 26"
Driving Wheels : 6' 0" T.E.: 19,945 lb.
P.V.

62455	62459	62461	62464
62457	62460	62462	62466
62458			**Total 9**

4-4-0 Class D34

Introduced 1913. Reid N.B. "Glen" class
Weights : Loco. 57 tons 4 cwt.
Tender 46 tons 13 cwt.
Pressure : 165 lb. Su. Cyls.: 20" × 26"
Driving Wheels : 6' 0" T.E.: 20,260 lb.
P.V.

62467 Glenfinnan
62468 Glen Orchy
62469 Glen Douglas
62470 Glen Roy
62471 Glen Falloch
62472 Glen Nevis
62474 Glen Croe
62475 Glen Beasdale
62476 Glen Sloy
62477 Glen Dochart
62478 Glen Quoich
62479 Glen Sheil
62480 Glen Fruin
62481 Glen Ogle
62482 Glen Mamie
62483 Glen Garry
62484 Glen Lyon
62485 Glen Murran
62487 Glen Arklet
62488 Glen Aladale
62489 Glen Dessary
62490 Glen Fintaig
62492 Glen Garvin
62493 Glen Gloy
62494 Glen Gour
62495 Glen Luss
62496 Glen Loy
62497 Glen Mallie
62498 Glen Moidart

Total 29

4-4-0 Classes D15 & D16

D15[1] Introduced 1904. Belpaire boiler development of original J. Holden (G.E.) "Claud Hamilton" class, some rebuilt from D14.

D16/2[2] Introduced 1923. Hill "Super Claud"—D15 with larger boiler, some rebuilt from D15.

D16/3[3] Introduced 1933. Gresley rebuild of D15 with larger round-topped boiler and modified footplating.

D16/3[4] Introduced 1933. Rebuild of D15 with larger round-topped boiler, modified footplating and 8" piston valves.

D16/3[5] Introduced 1936. Rebuild of D15 with larger round-topped boiler, modified footplating and 9½" piston valves.

D16/3[6] Introduced 1938. Rebuild of D16/2 with round-topped boiler, but retaining original footplating and slide valves.

D16/3[7] Introduced 1939. Rebuild of D16/2 with round-topped boiler and modified footplating, retaining slide valves.

(At grouping the remaining locos of the "Claud Hamilton" class retaining small round-topped boilers were classified D14. Saturated locos of D15 were originally classified D15, superheated locos with short smokeboxes D15/1 and superheated locos with extended smokeboxes D15/2. All the remaining locos were converted to D15/2 and then known simply as D15. D16/1 were the original D16 locos with short smokeboxes.)

Weights : Loco. { 52 tons 4 cwt.[1]
54 tons 18 cwt.[2]
55 tons 18 cwt. (all D16/3)
Tender 39 tons 5 cwt.
Pressure : 180 lb. Su. Cyls.: 19" × 26"
Driving Wheels : 7' 0" T.E.: 17,095 lb.

62501[1]	62530[3]	62561[3]	62591[2]
62502[1]	62531[3]	62562[6]	62592[6]
62503[1]	62532[5]	62564[6]	62593[3]
62505[1]	62533[3]	62565[6]	62596[6]
62506[1]	62534[3]	62566[3]	62597[3]
62507[1]	62535[5]	62567[3]	62598[3]
62508[1]	62536[5]	62568[4]	62599[5]
62509[1]	62538[1]	62569[6]	62601[6]
62510[3]	62539[3]	62570[2]	62603[2]
62511[3]	62540[3]	62571[3]	62604[3]
62512[1]	62541[3]	62572[3]	62605[6]
62513[3]	62542[6]	62573[6]	62606[6]
62514[3]	62543[6]	62574[3]	62607[6]
62515[3]	62544[6]	62575[3]	62608[3]
62516[3]	62545[3]	62576[5]	62609[4]
62517[3]	62546[4] *	62577[2]	62610[3]
62518[3]	62547[2]	62578[6]	62611[6]
62519[3]	62548[3]	62579[3]	62612[6]
62520[1]	62549[3]	62580[6]	62613[6]
62521[3]	62551[3]	62581[5]	62614[7]
62522[3]	62552[6]	62582[3]	62615[6]
62523[3]	62553[2]	62584[6]	62616[6]
62524[3]	62554[6]	62585[3]	62617[6]
62525[3]	62555[3]	62586[3]	62618[6]
62526[3]	62556[6]	62587[4]	62619[6]
62527[3]	62557[6]	62588[4]	62620[6]
62528[1]	62558[2]	62589[6]	
62529[3]	62559[3]	62590[2]	

Totals : Class D15 12
Class D16/2 8
Class D16/3 90

* Named *Claud Hamilton*

4-4-0 Class D10

Introduced 1913. Robinson G.C. "Director" class.
Weights : Loco. 61 tons.
Tender 48 tons 6 cwt.
Pressure : 180 lb. Su. Cyls.: 20" × 26"
Driving Wheels : 6' 9" T.E.: 19,645 lb.
P.V.

62650 Prince Henry
62651 Purdon Viccars
62652 Edwin A. Beazley
62653 Sir Edward Fraser
62654 Walter Burgh Gair
62655 The Earl of Kerry
62656 Sir Clement Royds
62657 Sir Berkeley Sheffield
62658 Prince George
62659 Worsley-Taylor

Total 10

4-4-0 Class D11

D11/1* Introduced 1920. Robinson G.C. "Large Director," development of D10.

D11/2 Introduced 1924. Post-grouping locos built to Scottish loading gauge. From 1938 the class has been rebuilt with long-travel valves.

Weights : Loco. 61 tons 3 cwt.
Tender 48 tons 6 cwt.
Pressure : 180 lb. Su. Cyls.: 20" × 26"
Driving Wheels : 6' 9" T.E.: 19,645 lb.
P.V.

62660* Butler-Henderson
62661* Gerard Powys Dewhurst
62662* Prince of Wales
62663* Prince Albert
62664* Princess Mary
62665* Mons
62666* Zeebrugge
62667* Somme
62668* Jutland
62669* Ypres
62670* Marne
62671 Bailie MacWheeble
62672 Baron of Bradwardine
62673 Evan Dhu
62674 Flora MacIvor
62675 Colonel Gardiner
62676 Jonathan Oldbuck
62677 Edie Ochiltree

62678 Luckie Mucklebackit
62679 Lord Glenallan
62680 Lucy Ashton
62681 Captain Craigengelt
62682 Haystoun of Bucklaw
62683 Hobbie Elliott
62684 Wizard of the Moor
62685 Malcolm Graeme
62686 The Fiery Cross
62687 Lord James of Douglas
62688 Ellen Douglas
62689 Maid of Lorn
62690 The Lady of the Lake
62691 Laird of Balmawhapple
62692 Allan-Bane
62693 Roderick Dhu
62694 James Fitzjames

Totals : Class D11/1 11
Class D11/2 24

4-4-0 Class D49

D49/1*† Introduced 1927. Gresley design with piston valves, Walschaerts gear and derived motion.

D49/2‡§ Introduced 1928. Development of D49/1 with Lentz Rotary Cam poppet valves.

D49/4ø Introduced 1942. Rebuild of D49/2 with two inside cyls. of D11 pattern, Stephenson gear and piston valves.
(D49/3 comprised locos 62720-4 as built with Lentz Oscillating Cam poppet valves. From 1938 these locos were converted to D49/1. 62751-75 have larger valves than the earlier D49/2, and were at first classified D49/4.)

* Fitted with ex-G.C. tender.
†§ Fitted with ex-N.E. tender.
The remainder (†ø) have L.N.E.R. tenders.

Weights : Loco. { 66 tons.*† / 64 tons 10 cwt.‡§ / 62 tons.ø
Tender { 48 tons 6 cwt.* / 44 tons 2 cwt.†§ / 52 tons. ‡ø
Pressure : 180 lb. Su.
Cyls. { (3) 17" × 26"*†‡§ / 20" × 26"ø
Driving Wheels : 6' 8"
T.E.: { 21,555 lb.*†‡§ / 19,890 lb.ø

62700* Yorkshire
62701* Derbyshire
62702* Oxfordshire
62703† Hertfordshire
62704* Stirlingshire
62705* Lanarkshire
62706* Forfarshire
62707* Lancashire
62708* Argyllshire
62709* Berwickshire
62710* Lincolnshire
62711* Dumbartonshire
62712* Morayshire
62713* Aberdeenshire
62714* Perthshire
62715* Roxburghshire
62716* Kincardineshire
62717* Banffshire
62718* Kinross-shire
62719* Peebles-shire
62720† Cambridgeshire
62721† Warwickshire
62722† Huntingdonshire
62723† Nottinghamshire
62724† Bedfordshire
62725* Inverness-shire
62726‡ The Meynell
62727§ The Quorn
62728* Cheshire
62729* Rutlandshire
62730* Berkshire
62731* Selkirkshire
62732* Dumfries-shire
62733* Northumberland
62734* Cumberland
62735* Westmorland
62736‡ The Bramham Moor
62737‡ The York and Ainsty
62738‡ The Zetland
62739‡ The Badsworth
62740‡ The Bedale
62741‡ The Blankney
62742‡ The Braes of Derwent
62743‡ The Cleveland
62744‡ The Holderness
62745‡ The Hurworth
62746‡ The Middleton
62747‡ The Percy
62748‡ The Southwold

62749‡	The Cottesmore
62750‡	The Pytchley
62751‡	The Albrighton
62752‡	The Atherstone
62753‡	The Belvoir
62754‡	The Berkeley
62755‡	The Bilsdale
62756‡	The Brocklesby
62757‡	The Burton
62758‡	The Cattistock
62759‡	The Craven
62760‡	The Cotswold
62761‡	The Derwent
62762‡	The Fernie
62763‡	The Fitzwilliam
62764‡	The Garth
62765‡	The Goathland
62766‡	The Grafton
62767‡	The Grove
62768ø	The Morpeth
62769‡	The Oakley
62770‡	The Puckeridge
62771‡	The Rufford
62772‡	The Sinnington
62773‡	The South Durham
62774‡	The Staintondale
62775‡	The Tynedale

Totals : Class D49/1 34
Class D49/2 41
Class D49/4 1

2-4-0 Class E4

Introduced 1891. J. Holden G.E. design.
* Fitted with side-window cab.
Weights : Loco. 40 tons 6 cwt.
Tender 30 tons 13 cwt.
Pressure : 160 lb. Cyls.: 17½" × 24"
Driving Wheels : 5' 8" T.E.: 14,700 lb.

62780	62785	62790	62795*
62781*	62786	62791	62796
62782	62787	62792	62797*
62783	62788*	62793*	
62784*	62789	62794	

Total 18

4-4-2 Class C1

Introduced 1902. (Oldest survivor built 1904.) G.N. Ivatt large Atlantic.
Weights : Loco. 69 tons 12 cwt.
Tender 43 tons 2 cwt.
Pressure : 170 lb. Su.
Cyls.:(O) 20" × 24"
Driving Wheels : 6' 8"
T.E.: 17,340 lb.
P.V.

62817	62828	62854	62885
62822	62839	62877	

Total 7

IMPORTANT NOTE

A careful reading of the notes on page 7 is essential to understand the use of reference marks in this book.

4-4-2 Class C4

C4/2* Introduced 1902. Robinson G.C. design. Slide valves, originally saturated.
C4/4† Introduced 1911. Rebuilt with superheater and piston valves.
(C4/1 and C4/3 were locos of C4/2 and C4/4 before cutting down to L.N.E.R. loading gauge.)
Weights : Loco. {70 tons 17 cwt.* / 71 tons 18 cwt.†}
Tender 48 tons 6 cwt.
Pressure : 180 lb. Su.
Cyls.:(O) {19" × 26"* / 21" × 26"†}
Driving Wheels : 6' 9"
T.E.: {17,730 lb.* / 21,660 lb.†}

62900†	62908*	62912*	62918*
62901†	62909†	62915†	62919†
62903†			

Totals : Class C4/2 3
Class C4/4 6

0-8-0 Class Q4

Q4/1* Introduced 1902. Robinson G.C. design. Saturated locos with slide valves.

Q4/2† Introduced 1914. Superheated rebuild, retaining slide valves.

Q4/2‡ Introduced 1914. Rebuilt with superheater and piston valves.

Weights : Loco. { 62 tons 8 cwt.* / 63 tons.† / 64 tons 1 cwt.‡ }
Tender 48 tons 6 cwt.

Pressure : 180 lb. SS.

Cyls.: (O) { 19″ × 26″*† / 21″ × 26″‡ }

Driving Wheels : 4′ 8″

T.E.: { 25,645 lb.*† / 31,325 lb.‡ }

63200†	63213‡	63226*	63235†
63201†	63216†	63227*	63236†
63202*	63217†	63228†	63238†
63203*	63219†	63229†	63240†
63204*	63220‡	63231†	63241*
63205*	63221‡	63232‡	63243†
63207†	63223†	63233†	
63210†	63225‡	63234*	

Totals : Class Q4/1 8
Class Q4/2 22

0-8-0 Class Q5

Q5/1 (Slide valve) Introduced 1901. Worsdell N.E. design.

Q5/1* (Piston valve) Introduced 1903.

Weights : Loco. 58 tons 8 cwt.
Tender 40 tons 8 cwt.

Pressure: 175 lb. Cyls.: (O) 20″ × 26″

Driving Wheels : 4′ 7¼″ T.E.: 28,000 lb.

63251	63262	63280*	63289*
63255	63267	63281*	63290*
63256	63270*	63282*	63293*
63257	63271*	63283*	63294*
63259	63272*	63284*	63296*
63260	63274*	63285*	63303
63261	63278*	63287*	63311

63312	63318	63328	63335
63313	63319	63330	63336
63314	63326	63333	63338

Total : 45

0-8-0 Class Q6

Introduced 1913. Raven N.E. design.
* Some locos are fitted with tenders from withdrawn B15 locos.

Weights : Loco. 65 tons 18 cwt.
Tender { 44 tons 2 cwt. / 44 tons.* }

Pressure : 180 lb. Su.
Cyls.: (O) 20″ × 26″
Driving Wheels : 4′ 7½″ T.E.: 28,800 lb.
P.V.

63340	63370	63400	63430
63341	63371	63401	63431
63342	63372	63402	63432
63343	63373	63403	63433
63344	63374	63404	63434
63345	63375	63405	63435
63346	63376	63406	63436
63347	63377	63407	63437
63348	63378	63408	63438
63349	63379	63409	63439
63350	63380	63410	63440
63351	63381	63411	63441
63352	63382	63412	63442
63353	63383	63413	63443
63354	63384	63414	63444
63355	63385	63415	63445
63356	63386	63416	63446
63357	63387	63417	63447
63358	63388	63418	63448
63359	63389	63419	63449
63360	63390	63420	63450
63361	63391	63421	63451
63362	63392	63422	63452
63363	63393	63423	63453
63364	63394	63424	63454
63365	63395	63425	63455
63366	63396	63426	63456
63367	63397	63427	63457
63368	63398	63428	63458
63369	63399	63429	63459

Total 120

0-8-0 Class Q7

Introduced 1919. Raven N.E. design.
Weights : Loco. 71 tons 12 cwt.
Tender 44 tons 2 cwt.
Pressure : 180 lb. Su.
Cyls.: (3) $18\frac{1}{2}'' \times 26''$
Driving Wheels : 4′ $7\frac{1}{4}''$ T.E.: 36,965 lb.
P.V.

63460	63464	63468	63472
63461	63465	63469	63473
63462	63466	63470	63474
63463	63467	63471	

Total 15

2-8-0 Class O3

Introduced 1913. Gresley G.N. design.
Weights : Loco. 76 tons 4 cwt.
Tender 43 tons 2 cwt.
Pressure : 180 lb. Su.
Cyls.: (O) $21'' \times 28''$
Driving Wheels : 4′ 8″ T.E.: 33,735 lb.
Walschaerts gear, P.V.

63475	63479	63483	63488
63476	63480	63484	63491
63477	63481	63485	63493
63478	63482	63486	

Total 15

2-8-0 Classes O1 & O4

O4/1[1] Introduced 1911. Robinson G.C. design with small Belpaire boiler, steam and vacuum brakes and water scoop.

O4/3[2] Introduced 1917. Ex-R.O.D. locos with steam brake only and no scoop. Taken into L.N.E.R. stock from 1924.

O4/2[3] Introduced 1925. O4/3 with cab and boiler mountings reduced to Scottish loading gauge.

O4/5[4] Introduced 1932. Rebuilt with shortened O2-type boiler and separate smokebox saddle.

O4/6[5] Introduced 1924. Rebuilt from O5, retaining higher cab (63912-20 with side-windows).

O4/7[6] Introduced 1939. Rebuilt with shortened O2-type boiler, retaining G.C. smokebox.

O4/8[7] Introduced 1944. Rebuilt with 100A(B1) boiler, retaining original cylinders.

(O4/4 were rebuilds with O2 boilers, since rebuilt again ; O5 was a G.C. development of O4 with larger Belpaire boiler.)

Weights: Loco.
- 73 tons 4 cwt.[1]
- 73 tons 4 cwt.[2]
- 73 tons 4 cwt.[3]
- 74 tons 13 cwt.[4]
- 73 tons 4 cwt.[5]
- 73 tons 17 cwt.[6]
- 72 tons 10 cwt.[7]

Tender
- 48 tons 6 cwt. (with scoop)
- 47 tons 6 cwt. (without scoop)

Pressure : 180 lb. Su.
Cyls.: (O) $21'' \times 26''$
Driving Wheels : 4′ 8″ T.E.: 31,325 lb.
P.V.

O1[8] Introduced 1944. Thompson rebuild with 100A boiler, Walschaerts valve gear and new cylinders.

Weights : Loco. 73 tons 6 cwt.
Tender as O4.
Pressure : 225 lb. Su.
Cyls.: (O) $20'' \times 26''$
Driving Wheels : 4′ 8″ T.E.: 35,520 lb.
Walschaerts gear, P.V.

63570[6]	63595[6]	63620[1]
63571[1]	63596[6]	63621[1]
63572[1]	63597[1]	63622[1]
63573[1]	63598[1]	63623[1]
63574[1]	63599[1]	63624[1]
63575[7]	63600[6]	63625[1]
63576[1]	63601[1]	63626[1]
63577[1]	63602[1]	63627[1]
63578[8]	63603[6]	63628[4]
63579[8]	63604[1]	63629[2]
63580[1]	63605[1]	63630[8]
63581[1]	63606[1]	63631[1]
63582[6]	63607[1]	63632[1]
63583[1]	63608[1]	63633[7]
63584[1]	63609[1]	63634[6]
63585[1]	63610[8]	63635[1]
63586[1]	63611[1]	63636[2]
63587[1]	63612[1]	63637[2]
63588[6]	63613[7]	63638[2]
63589[8]	63614[1]	63639[2]
63590[8]	63615[6]	63640[1]
63591[8]	63616[6]	63641[2]
63592[8]	63617[1]	63642[2]
63593[1]	63618[1]	63643[6]
63594[8]	63619[8]	63644[3]

63645-63920

63645[2]
63646[8]
63647[3]
63648[3]
63649[2]
63650[8]
63651[7]
63652[8]
63653[7]
63654[1]
63655[6]
63656[2]
63657[2]
63658[1]
63659[2]
63660[1]
63661[6]
63662[6]
63663[8]
63664[1]
63665[2]
63666[2]
63667[2]
63668[2]
63669[6]
63670[8]
63671[1]
63672[2]
63673[6]
63674[3]
63675[6]
63676[8]
63677[1]
63678[8]
63679[2]
63680[3]
63681[2]
63682[3]
63683[1]
63684[1]
63685[2]
63686[2]
63687[8]
63688[2]
63689[8]
63690[3]
63691[2]
63692[1]
63693[1]
63694[2]
63695[2]
63696[2]
63697[2]
63698[1]
63699[6]
63700[1]
63701[2]
63702[2]
63703[2]
63704[3]
63705[6]
63706[6]
63707[1]
63708[6]
63709[3]
63710[1]
63711[8]
63712[8]
63713[2]
63714[2]
63715[2]
63716[2]
63717[2]
63718[2]
63719[1]
63720[2]
63721[2]
63722[1]
63723[1]
63724[2]
63725[8]
63726[4]
63727[1]
63728[2]
63729[2]
63730[3]
63731[2]
63732[2]
63733[2]
63734[2]
63735[2]
63736[1]
63737[2]
63738[7]
63739[2]
63740[8]
63741[2]
63742[2]
63743[1]
63744[2]
63745[4]
63746[8]
63747[6]
63748[6]
63749[6]
63750[2]
63751[2]
63752[8]
63753[2]
63754[2]
63755[8]
63756[2]
63757[1]
63758[6]
63759[2]
63760[8]
63761[6]
63762[1]
63763[2]
63764[2]
63765[2]
63766[2]
63767[2]
63768[8]
63769[2]
63770[6]
63771[2]
63772[6]
63773[8]
63774[2]
63775[6]
63776[2]
63777[8]
63778[1]
63779[2]
63780[8]
63781[2]
63782[2]
63783[2]
63784[8]
63785[7]
63786[8]
63787[2]
63788[4]
63789[8]
63790[2]
63791[2]
63792[8]
63793[2]
63794[6]
63795[8]
63796[8]
63797[1]
63798[2]
63799[1]
63800[2]
63801[2]
63802[7]
63803[8]
63804[2]
63805[1]
63806[8]
63807[2]
63808[8]
63809[1]
63812[2]
63813[2]
63816[4]
63817[8]
63818[7]
63819[7]
63821[2]
63822[2]
63823[2]
63824[6]
63827[7]
63828[7]
63829[2]
63832[2]
63833[2]
63835[2]
63836[7]
63837[2]
63838[2]
63839[6]
63840[2]
63841[2]
63842[2]
63843[6]
63845[2]
63846[2]
63847[3]
63848[6]
63849[2]
63850[2]
63851[4]
63852[2]
63853[7]
63854[8]
63855[2]
63856[2]
63857[6]
63858[2]
63859[2]
63860[6]
63861[2]
63862[2]
63863[8]
63864[2]
63865[8]
63867[8]
63868[8]
63869[8]
63870[2]
63872[8]
63873[2]
63874[8]
63876[6]
63877[2]
63878[2]
63879[8]
63880[6]
63881[2]
63882[7]
63883[2]
63884[6]
63885[2]
63886[8]
63887[8]
63888[2]
63889[2]
63890[8]
63891[6]
63893[7]
63894[6]
63895[2]
63897[2]
63898[2]
63899[2]
63900[2]
63901[8]
63902[5]
63904[5]
63905[5]
63906[5]
63907[5]
63908[5]
63911[5]
63912[5]
63913[5]
63914[5]
63915[5]
63917[5]
63920[5]

Totals :	**Class O1**	**54**
	Class O4/1	**70**
	Class O4/2	**11**
	Class O4/3	**118**
	Class O4/5	**6**
	Class O4/6	**13**
	Class O4/7	**41**
	Class O4/8	**16**

2-8-0 Class O2

O2/1* Introduced 1921. Development of experimental Gresley G.N. 3-cyl. loco (L.N.E.R. 3921). Subsequently rebuilt with side-window cab, and reduced boiler mountings.

O2/2† Introduced 1924. Development of O2/1 with detail differences.

O2/3 Introduced 1932. Development of O2/2 with side-window cab and reduced boiler mountings.

O2/4‡ Introduced 1943. Rebuilt with 100A (B1 type) boiler and smokebox extended backwards (3924 retaining G.N. tender).

Weights: Loco. { 75 tons 16 cwt.*† / 78 tons 13 cwt. / 74 tons 2 cwt.‡
Tender { 43 tons 2 cwt. (63922-46) / 52 tons (63947-87)

Pressure: 180 lb. Su.

Cyls.: (3) 18½"×26"

Driving Wheels: 4' 8" T.E.: 36,470 lb.
Walschaerts gear and derived motion, P.V.

63922*	63939†	63956	63973
63923*	63940†	63957	63974
63924‡	63941†	63958	63975
63925*	63942†	63959	63976
63926*	63943†	63960	63977
63927*	63944†	63961	63978
63928*	63945†	63962‡	63979
63929*	63946†	63963	63980
63930*	63947‡	63964	63981
63931*	63948	63965	63982
63932‡	63949	63966	63983
63933†	63950‡	63967	63984
63934†	63951	63968	63985
63935†	63952	63969	63986
63936†	63953	63970	63987
63937†	63954	63971	
63938†	63955	63972	

Totals: Class O2 (100A) 5
Class O2/1 9
Class O2/2 14
Class O2/3 38

0-6-0 Classes J3 & J4

J4* Introduced 1896. Ivatt G.N. development of standard Stirling 0-6-0.

J3 Introduced 1912. Larger boilered rebuild of J4 (some rebuilt from Stirling domeless locos, oldest survivor built 1892) (**see note p. 7**).

Weights: Loco. { 41 tons 5 cwt.* / 42 tons 12 cwt.
Tender { 34 tons 18 cwt.* / 38 tons 10 cwt.

Pressure: 175 lb. Cyls.: 17½"×26"
Driving Wheels: 5' 2" T.E.: 19,105 lb.

64105	64119	64129	64142
64109*	64120*	64131	64148
64112*	64121*	64132	64150
64114	64122	64133	64151
64115	64123	64135	64153
64116	64124	64137	64158
64117	64125	64140	64160*
64118	64128	64141	64162*

Totals: Class J3 26
Class J4 6

0-6-0 Class J6

Introduced 1911 Gresley G.N. design (**see note p. 7**).
Weights: Loco. 50 tons 10 cwt.
Tender 43 tons 2 cwt.
Pressure: 170 lb. Su. Cyls.: 19"×26"
Driving Wheels: 5' 2" T.E.: 21,875 lb.
P.V.

64170	64188	64206	64224
64171	64189	64207	64225
64172	64190	64208	64226
64173	64191	64209	64227
64174	64192	64210	64228
64175	64193	64211	64229
64176	64194	64212	64230
64177	64195	64213	64231
64178	64196	64214	64232
64179	64197	64215	64233
64180	64198	64216	64234
64181	64199	64217	64235
64182	64200	64218	64236
64183	64201	64219	64237
64184	64202	64220	64238
64185	64203	64221	64239
64186	64204	64222	64240
64187	64205	64223	64241

64242	64252	64262	64272
64243	64253	64263	64273
64244	64254	64264	64274
64245	64255	64265	64275
64246	64256	64266	64276
64247	64257	64267	64277
64248	64258	64268	64278
64249	64259	64269	64279
64250	64260	64270	
64251	64261	64271	

Total 110

0-6-0 Class J11

Introduced 1901. Robinson G.C. design. Parts 1 and 4 have 3,250 gallon tenders; Parts 2 and 5 4,000 gallon. Parts 1 and 2 have high boiler mountings; Parts 4 and 5 low. All Parts 4 and 5 are superheated, and some of Parts 1 and 2. There are frequent changes between these parts

J11/3* Introduced 1942. Rebuilt with long-travel piston valves and boiler higher pitched.

Weights: Loco. { 51 tons 19 cwt. (Sat.) / 52 tons 2 cwt. (Su.) / 53 tons 6 cwt.*

Tender { 44 tons 3 cwt. (3,250 gall.) / 48 tons 6 cwt. (4,000 gall.)

Pressure: 180 lb. SS. Cyls.: 18½" × 26"
Driving Wheels: 5' 2" T.E.: 21,960 lb.

64280	64300	64320	64340
64281	64301	64321	64341
64282	64302	64322	64342
64283*	64303	64323	64343
64284*	64304*	64324	64344
64285	64305	64325	64345
64286	64306	64326	64346*
64287	64307	64327	64347
64288	64308	64328	64348
64289	64309	64329	64349
64290	64310	64330	64350
64291	64311	64331	64351
64292	64312	64332	64352*
64293	64313	64333	64353
64294	64314*	64334	64354*
64295	64315	64335	64355
64296	64316*	64336	64356
64297	64317*	64337	64357
64298	64318*	64338	64358
64299	64319	64339	64359*

64360	64384	64408	64432
64361	64385	64409	64433
64362*	64386*	64410	64434
64363	64387	64411	64435
64364*	64388	64412	64436
64365	64389	64413	64437
64366	64390	64414	64438
64367	64391	64415	64439*
64368	64392	64416	64440
64369	64393	64417*	64441*
64370	64394	64418	64442*
64371	64395	64419	64443
64372	64396	64420	64444
64373*	64397	64421	64445
64374	64398	64422	64446
64375*	64399	64423	64447
64376	64400	64424	64448
64377	64401	64425	64449
64378	64402*	64426	64450*
64379*	64403	64427*	64451
64380	64404	64428	64452
64381	64405	64429	64453
64382	64406*	64430	
64383	64407	64431	

Totals: Class J11/3 25
Class J11 (other parts) 149

0-6-0 Class J35

J35/5* Introduced 1906. Reid N.B. design with piston valves.

J35/4 Introduced 1908. Slide valves. (Parts 1, 2 and 3 were variations of Parts 4 and 5 before superheating.)

Weights: Loco. { 51 tons.* / 50 tons 15 cwt.

Tender { 38 tons 1 cwt.* / 37 tons 15 cwt.

Pressure: 180 lb. Su. Cyls.: 18¼" × 26"
Driving Wheels: 5' 0" T.E.: 22,080 lb.

64460*	64473*	64484	64494
64461*	64474*	64485	64495
64462*	64475*	64486	64496
64463*	64476*	64487	64497
64464*	64477*	64488	64498
64466*	64478	64489	64499
64468*	64479	64490	64500
64470*	64480	64491	64501
64471*	64482	64492	64502
64472*	64483	64493	64504

64505	64514	64522	64530
64506	64515	64523	64531
64507	64516	64524	64532
64509	64517	64525	64533
64510	64518	64526	64534
64511	64519	64527	64535
64512	64520	64528	
64513	64521	64529	

Totals : Class J35/4 55
Class J35/5 15

0-6-0 Class J37

Introduced 1914. Reid N.B. design. Superheated development of J35.
Weights : Loco. 54 tons 14 cwt.
Tender 40 tons 19 cwt.
Pressure : 180 lb. Su. Cyls.: 19½" × 26"
Driving Wheels : 5' 0" T.E.: 25,210 lb.
P.V.

64536	64562	64588	64614
64537	64563	64589	64615
64538	64564	64590	64616
64539	64565	64591	64617
64540	64566	64592	64618
64541	64567	64593	64619
64542	64568	64594	64620
64543	64569	64595	64621
64544	64570	64596	64622
64545	64571	64597	64623
64546	64572	64598	64624
64547	64573	64599	64625
64548	64574	64600	64626
64549	64575	64601	64627
64550	64576	64602	64628
64551	64577	64603	64629
64552	64578	64604	64630
64553	64579	64605	64631
64554	64580	64606	64632
64555	64581	64607	64633
64556	64582	64608	64634
64557	64583	64609	64635
64558	64584	64610	64636
64559	64585	64611	64637
64560	64586	64612	64638
64561	64587	64613	64639

Total 104

0-6-0 Class J19

Introduced 1912. S. Holden G.E. design rebuilt with round-topped boiler from 1934.
* Rebuilt with 19" cyls. and 180 lb. pressure.
† Rebuilt with 19" cyls. and 160 lb pressure.
Weights : Loco. 50 tons 7 cwt.
Tender 38 tons 5 cwt.
Pressure : { 170 lb. Su. / 180 lb. Su.* / 160 lb. Su.† }
Cyls.: { 20" × 26" / 19" × 26"*† }
Driving Wheels : 4' 11"
T.E.: { 27,430 lb. / 26, 215 lb.* / 23,300 lb.† }
P.V.

64640	64649	64658	64667
64641	64650	64659	64668
64642	64651	64660	64669
64643	64652	64661	64670
64644	64653	64662	64671*
64645	64654	64663	64672†
64646	64655	64664*	64673
64647	64656	64665	64674
64648	64657	64666	

Total 35

0-6-0 Class J20

J20* Introduced 1920. Hill G.E. design with Belpaire boiler.
J20/1 Introduced 1943. Rebuilt with B12/1 type round-topped boiler.
Weights : Loco. 54 tons 15 cwt.
Tender 38 tons 5 cwt.
Pressure : 180 lb. Su. Cyls.: 20" × 28"
Driving Wheels : 4' 11" T.E.: 29,045 lb.
P.V.

64675*	64682	64689*	64696*
64676*	64683*	64690*	64697
64677	64684	64691	64698*
64678	64685	64692*	64699
64679	64686	64693	
64680	46687*	64694	
64681	64688	64695	

Totals : Class J20 9
Class J20/1 16

0-6-0 Class J39

Introduced 1926. Gresley design.
J39/1 Standard 3,500 gallon tender.
J39/2* Standard 4,200 gallon tender
J39/3† Various ex-N.E. tenders (3,940 gallon on 64843-5, 4,125 gallon on 64855-9)
Weights : Loco. 57 tons 17 cwt.
Tender {44 tons 4 cwt. / 52 tons 13 cwt.*} and others
Pressure : 180 lb. Su. Cyls.: 20" × 26"
Driving Wheels : 5' 2" T.E.: 25,665 lb.
P.V.

64700	64738	64776	64814
64701	64739	64777	64815
64702	64740	64778	64816
64703	64741	64779	64817
64704	64742	64780	64818
64705	64743	64781	64819
64706	64744	64782	64820*
64707	64745	64783	64821*
64708	64746	64784*	64822*
64709	64747	64785*	64823
64710	64748	64786*	64824
64711	64749	64787*	64825
64712	64750	64788*	64826
64713	64751	64789*	64827
64714	64752	64790*	64828
64715	64753	64791*	64829
64716	64754	64792*	64830
64717	64755	64793*	64831
64718	64756	64794*	64832
64719	64757	64795*	64833
64720	64758	64796	64834
64721	64759	64797	64835
64722	64760	64798	64836
64723	64761	64799	64837
64724	64762	64800	64838*
64725	64763	64801	64839*
64726	64764	64802	64840*
64727	64765	64803	64841*
64728	64766	64804	64842†
64729	64767	64805	64843†
64730	64768	64806	64844†
64731	64769	64807	64845†
64732	64770	64808	64846
64733	64771	64809	64847
64734	64772	64810	64848
64735	64773	64811	64849
64736	64774	64812	64850
64737	64775	64813	64851

64852	64887*	64922*	64957*
64853	64888*	64923*	64958*
64854	64889*	64924*	64959*
64855†	64890*	64925*	64960*
64856†	64891*	64926*	64961*
64857†	64892*	64927*	64962*
64858†	64893*	64928*	64963*
64859†	64894*	64929*	64964*
64860	64895*	64930*	64965*
64861	64896*	64931*	64966*
64862	64897*	64932*	64967*
64863	64898*	64933	64968*
64864	64899*	64934	64969*
64865	64900*	64935	64970*
64866	64901*	64936	64971†
64867	64902*	64937	64972†
64868	64903*	64938	64973†
64869	64904*	64939	64974†
64870	64905*	64940	64975†
64871	64906*	64941	64976†
64872*	64907*	64942	64977†
64873*	64908*	64943	64978†
64874*	64909*	64944	64979†
64875*	64910*	64945*	64980†
64876*	64911*	64946*	64981†
64877*	64912*	64947*	64982†
64878*	64913*	64948*	64983†
64879*	64914*	64949*	64984†
64880*	64915*	64950*	64985†
64881*	64916*	64951*	64986†
64882*	64917*	64952*	64987†
64883*	64918*	64953*	64988†
64884*	64919*	64954*	
64885*	64920*	64955*	
64886*	64921*	64956*	

Totals : Class J39/1 156
Class J39/2 106
Class J39/3 27

0-6-0 Class J1

Introduced 1908 (**see note p. 7**). Ivatt G.N. design.
Weights : Loco. 46 tons 14 cwt.
Tender 43 tons 2 cwt.
Pressure : 175 lb. Cyls.: 18" × 26"
Driving Wheels : 5' 8" T.E.: 18,430 lb.

65002	65005	65008	65013
65003	65006	65009	65014
65004	65007	65010	**Total 11**

0-6-0 Class J2

Introduced 1912 (see note p. 7). Ivatt/Gresley G.N. design.
Weights: Loco. 50 tons 10 cwt.
Tender 43 tons 2 cwt.
Pressure: 170 lb. Su. Cyls.: 19" × 26"
Driving Wheels: 5' 8" T.E.: 19,945 lb.
P.V.

65015	65018	65020	65022
65016	65019	65021	65023
65017			

Total 9

0-6-0 Class J21

Introduced 1886. T. W. Worsdell N.E. design. Majority built as 2-cyl. compounds and later rebuilt as simple locos. (see note p. 6).
* Saturated with Joy's gear and slide valves.
† Rebuilt with superheater, Stephenson gear and piston valves.
‡ Rebuilt with piston valves, superheater removed, 24" piston stroke.
§ Rebuilt with piston valves, superheater removed, 26" piston stroke.

Weights: Loco. 42 tons 1 cwt.* / 43 tons 15 cwt.† / 42 tons 9 cwt.‡§
Tender 36 tons 19 cwt.
Pressure: 160 lb. SS.
Cyls.: 18" × 24"* / 19" × 24"†‡ / 19" × 26"§ T.E.: 17,265 lb.* / 19,240 lb.†‡ / 20,840 lb.§
Driving Wheels: 5' 1¼"

65025‡	65052†	65079‡	65101‡
65026‡	65057†	65080‡	65102‡
65027‡	65058‡	65081‡	65103†
65028†	65059‡	65082†	65105‡
65030‡	65060‡	65083‡	65108‡
65033†	65061†	65084†	65110†
65035‡	65062†	65088†	65111‡
65036‡	65064†	65089†	65112*
65037†	65066‡	65090†	65116*
65038†	65067‡	65091†	65117‡
65039‡	65068†	65092†	65118‡
65040†	65070‡	65093‡	65119†
65041*	65072‡	65094‡	65120*
65042‡	65073*	65095†	65121†
65043§	65075†	65097†	65122*
65044*	65076‡	65098†	65123†
65047†	65077†	65099‡	
65051*	65078†	65100‡	

Total 70

0-6-0 Class J10

J10/2* Introduced 1892. Parker M.S. & L. design with small tenders.
J10/4† Introduced 1896. Pollitt development of J10/2 with larger bearings and larger tenders.
J10/6 Introduced 1901. Robinson locos with larger bearings and small tenders.

Weights: Loco. 41 tons 6 cwt.
Tender 37 tons 6 cwt. / 43 tons.†
Pressure: 160 lb. Cyls.: 18" × 26"
Driving Wheels: 5' 1" T.E.: 18,780 lb.

65126*	65147†	65168	65188
65127*	65148†	65169†	65189
65128*	65149†	65170†	65190
65130*	65151†	65171†	65191
65131	65153†	65172	65192
65132†	65154†	65173	65193
65133†	65155†	65175	65194
65134†	65156†	65176	65196
65135†	65157†	65177	65197
65136†	65158†	65178†	65198
65137†	65159†	65179	65199
65138†	65160†	65180	65200
65139	65161†	65181	65201
65140†	65162	65182	65202
65141†	65163	65183	65203
65142†	65164†	65184	65204
65143†	65165†	65185	65205
65144†	65166†	65186	65208
65145†	65167†	65187	65209
65146†			

Totals: Class J10/2 4
Class J10/4 35
Class J10/6 38

0-6-0 Class J36

Introduced 1888. Holmes N.B. design.
Weights: Loco. 41 tons 19 cwt.
Tender 33 tons 9 cwt.
Pressure: 165 lb. Cyls.: 18¼" × 26"
Driving Wheels: 5' 0" T.E.: 19,690 lb.

65210	65221	65229	65237
65211	65222	65230	65238
65213	65224	65231	65239
65214	65225	65232	65240
65215	65226	65233 Plumer	
65216	Haig	65234	65241
65217	65227	65235	65242
65218	65228	65236 Horne	

65243 Maude		65294	65320
65244	65270	65295	65321
65245	65271	65296	65322
65246	65273	65297	65323
65247	65274	65298	65324
65248	65275	65300	65325
65249	65276	65303	65327
65250	65277	65304	65329
65251	65278	65305	65330
65252	65279	65306	65331
65253	65280	65307	65333
65254	65281	65308	65334
65255	65282	65309	65335
65257	65283	65310	65338
65258	65285	65311	65339
65259	65286	65312	65340
65260	65287	65313	65341
65261	65288	65314	65342
65264	65290	65315	65343
65265	65291	65316	65344
65266	65292	65317	65345
65267	65293	65318	65346
65268 Allenby		65319	

Total 118

0-6-0 Class J15

Intro. 1883. Worsdell G.E. design, modified by J. Holden. (Oldest survivor built 1886.)

* Fitted with side-window cab for Colne Valley line.

Weights : Loco. 37 tons 2 cwt.
Tender 30 tons 13 cwt.

Pressure : 160 lb. Cyls.: 17½"×24"

Driving Wheels : 4' 11" T.E.: 16,940 lb.

65350	65370	65389	65412
65353	65371	65390	65413
65354	65372	65391*	65414
65355	65373	65393	65415
65356	65374	65396	65416
65357	65375	65397	65417
65359	65376	65398	65419
65361	65377	65401	65420
65362	65378	65402	65422
65363	65379	65404	65423
65364	65382	65405*	65424*
65365	65384	65406	65425
65366	65386	65407	65426
65367	65387	65408	65427
65369	65388	65409	65428

65429	65442	65455	65468
65430	65443	65456	65469
65431	65444	65457	65470
65432*	65445	65458	65471
65433	65446	65459	65472
65434	65447	65460	65473
65435	65448	65461	65474
65436	65449	65462	65475
65437	65450	65463	65476
65438*	65451	65464	65477
65439	65452	65465	65478
65440	65453	65466	65479
65441	65454	65467	

Total 111

0-6-0 Class J5

Introduced 1909 (**see note p. 7**). Ivatt G.N. design.

* Rebuilt with superheater.

Weights : Loco. 47 tons 6 cwt.
Tender 43 tons 2 cwt.

Pressure : { 175 lb. / 170 lb. Su.* } Cyls.: 18"×26"

Driving Wheels : 5' 2"

T.E.: { 20,210 lb. / 19,630 lb.* }

65480*	65485	65490	65495
65481	65486	65491	65496
65482	65487	65492	65497
65483	65488	65493	65498
65484	65489*	65494	65499

Total 20

0-6-0 Class J17

Introduced 1901. J. Holden G. E. design. Many rebuilt from round-top boiler J16, introduced 1900.

*Fitted with small tender.

Weights : Loco. 45 tons 8 cwt.
Tender { 30 tons 12 cwt.* / 38 tons 5 cwt. }

Pressure : 180 lb. Su. Cyls.: 19"×26"

Driving Wheels : 4' 11" T.E.: 24,340 lb.

65500*	65508*	65516*	65524
65501*	65509	65517*	65525
65502*	65510*	65518*	65526
65503*	65511*	65519*	65527
65504*	65512*	65520	65528*
65505*	65513*	65521	65529
65506*	65514*	65522	65530
65507*	65515*	65523	65531

Above : Class D31 4-4-0 No. 62060

Right : Class D9 4-4-0 No. 62325

Below : Class D11/2 4 - 4 - 0 No. 62671 *Bailie MacWheeble*

[H. C. Casserley, J. F. Ayland, B. V. Franey

Top : Class O4/1 2-8-0 No. 63574. *Centre Upper :* Class O4/6 2-8-0 No. 63920. *Centre Lower :* Class O4/7 2-8-0 No. 63708. *Bottom* · Class O1 2-8-0 No. 63773
[P. L. Melvill, P. Ransome-Wallis, W. Beckerlegge, C. C. B. Herbert

Class WD 2-8-0 No. 90028 [*A. F. Cook*

Class Q4/2 0-8-0 No. 63217 [*P. Ransome-Wallis*

Class Q6 0-8-0 No. 63449 [*H. C. Casserley*

N
O
BC

Scen
Scot

Above : Class J35 0-6-0 No. 4523 (new No. 64523) rouses the echoes near Wormit (Fife) at the head of an Edinburgh-Aberdeen freight

Below : Class A3 4-6-2 No. 60057 *Ormonde* passes St. Fort Junction with the 1.40 p.m. Aberdeen-King's Cross fast fish

[*Photos : Gavin L. Wilson*

Above
headir
Mallai
expr
Monas
Class
61790
and C
No.

TH
HE
ER

n the
Region

Above : On the West Highland Section—Class K4 2-6-0 No. 61993 *Loch Long* arrives at Ardlui with a restaurant car express

[*B. V. Franey*

Below : Class V2 2-6-2 No. 60822 pulls out of Aberdeen with an up express

[*P. Ransome-Wallis*

ouble-
up
asgow
ough
e are
0 No.
omond
4-4-0
Glen

Franey

Top . Class J25 0-6-0 No. 65650 *[B. V. Franey*

Centre : Class J21 0-6-0 No. 65098 *[H. C. Casserley*

Bottom Class J26 0-6-0 No. 65768 with new boiler *[B. V. Franey*

Top : Class J11 0-6-0 No. 64337 — *[M. P. Mileham*
Centre : Class J15 0-6-0 No. 65424 — *[P. Ransome-Wallis*
Bottom : Class J17 0-6-0 No. 65532 — *[B. V. Franey*

Class J6 0-6-0 No. 64233 *[H. Casserley*

[P. Ransome-Wallis
Class J36 0-6-0 No. 5287 (new No. 65287) with cut down mountings

Class J36 0-6-0 No. 65237 *[C. C. B. Herbert*

65532	65547	65563	65578
65533	65548	65564	65579
65534	65549	65565	65580
65535	65551	65566	65581
65536	65552	65567	65582
65537	65553	65568	65583
65538	65554	65569	65584
65539	65555	65570	65585
65540	65556	65571*	65586
65541	65557	65572	65587
65542	65558	65573	65588
65543	65559	65574	65589
65544	65560	65575	
65545	65561	65576	
65546	65562	65577	

Total 89

IMPORTANT NOTE

A careful reading of the notes on page 7 is essential to understand the use of reference marks in this book.

0-6-0 Class J24

Introduced 1894 (**see note p. 6**).

* W. Worsdell N.E. design, saturated with slide valves.

† Rebuilt with superheater and piston valves.

‡ Rebuilt with piston valves, super heater removed.

Weights : Loco. { 38 tons 10 cwt.* / 39 tons 11 cwt.†‡
Tender 36 tons 19 cwt.

Pressure : 160 lb. SS.

Cyls.: { 18" × 24"* / 18½" × 24"†‡

Driving Wheels : 4' 7¼"

T.E.: { 19,140 lb.* / 20,220 lb. †‡

65600*	65611†	65622*	65632*
65601*	65614*	65623*	65634*
65603†	65615*	65624†	65636†
65604*	65617†	65627‡	65640*
65608*	65619*	65628‡	65642*
65609*	65621‡	65631†	65644‡

Total 24

0-6-0 Class J25

Introduced 1898 (**see note p. 6**). W. Worsdell N.E. design.

*Original design, saturated with slide valves.

† Rebuilt with superheater and piston valves.

‡ Rebuilt with piston valves, superheater removed.

Weights : Loco. { 39 tons 11 cwt.* / 41 tons 14 cwt.† / 40 tons 17 cwt.‡
Tender 36 tons 19 cwt.

Pressure : 160 lb. SS. Cyls.: 18½" × 26"

Driving Wheels : 4' 7¼" T.E.: 21,905 lb.

65645†	65665†	65688*	65710*
65646†	65666*	65689*	65712*
65647*	65667*	65690*	65713*
65648*	65669†	65691*	65714*
65650*	65670*	65692‡	65716*
65651*	65671*	65693*	65717†
65653*	65672*	65694*	65718*
65654‡	65673‡	65695*	65720*
65655*	65675*	65696*	65721*
65656*	65676*	65697*	65723*
65657*	65677‡	65698*	65724*
65658*	65679*	65699*	65725*
65659†	65680*	65700*	65726*
65660*	65681‡	65702‡	65727*
65661*	65683‡	65705*	65728*
65662†	65685*	65706†	
65663*	65686*	65707*	
65664*	65687*	65708*	

Total 69

0-6-0 Class J26

Introduced 1904 (**see note p. 6**). W. Worsdell N. E. design.

Weights : Loco. 46 tons 16 cwt.
Tender 36 tons 19 cwt.

Pressure : 180 lb. Cyls.: 18½" × 26"

Driving Wheels : 4' 7¼" T.E.: 24,640 lb.

65730	65740	65750	65760
65731	65741	65751	65761
65732	65742	65752	65762
65733	65743	65753	65763
65734	65744	65754	65764
65735	65745	65755	65765
65736	65746	65756	65766
65737	65747	65757	65767
65738	65748	65758	65768
65739	65749	65759	65769

65770	65773	65776	65778
65771	65774	65777	65779
65772	65775		

Total 50

0-6-0 Class J27

Introduced 1906 (**see note p. 71**). W. Worsdell N.E. design developed from J26.
* Introduced 1921. Raven locos superheated with piston valves.
† Introduced 1943. Piston valves, superheater removed.
Weights : Loco. { 47 tons Sat. / 49 tons 10 cwt. Su.
Tender 36 tons 19 cwt.
Pressure : 180 lb. SS. Cyls.: 18½″ × 26″
Driving Wheels : 4′ 7¼″ T.E.: 24,640 lb.

65780	65809	65838	65867†
65781	65810	65839	65868†
65782	65811	65840	65869*
65783	65812	65841	65870†
65784	65813	65842	65871*
65785	65814	65843	65872*
65786	65815	65844	65873†
65787	65816	65845	65874*
65788	65817	65846	65875†
65789	65818	65847	65876†
65790	65819	65848	65877†
65791	65820	65849	65878*
65792	65821	65850	65879†
65793	65822	65851	65880*
65794	65823	65852	65881*
65795	65824	65853	65882†
65796	65825	65854	65883*
65797	65826	65855	65884†
65798	65827	65856	65885*
65799	65828	65857	65886*
65800	65829	65858	65887*
65801	65830	65859	65888†
65802	65831	65860†	65889*
65803	65832	65861†	65890*
65804	65833	65862†	65891†
65805	65834	65863*	65892*
65806	65835	65864†	65893*
65807	65836	65865†	65894*
65808	65837	65866*	

Total 115

0-6-0 Class J38

Introduced 1926. Gresley design. Predecessor of J39, with 4′ 8″ wheels, boiler 6″ longer than J39 and smokebox 6″ shorter.
* Rebuilt with J39 boiler.
Weights : Loco. 58 tons 19 cwt.
Tender 44 tons 4 cwt.
Pressure : 180 lb. Su. Cyls.: 20″ × 26″
Driving Wheels : 4′ 8″ T.E.: 28,415 lb.
P.V.

65900	65909	65918*	65927*
65901	65910	65919	65928
65902	65911	65920	65929
65903*	65912	65921	65930
65904	65913	65922	65931
65905	65914	65923	65932
65906*	65915	65924	65933
65907	65916	65925	65934
65908*	65917*	65926*	

Total 35

2-4-2T Class F2

Introduced 1898. Pollitt G.C. design.
* Push-and-pull fitted.
Weight : 62 tons 6 cwt.
Pressure : 160 lb. Cyls.: 18″ × 26″
Driving Wheels : 5′ 7″ T.E.: 17,100 lb.

67108 | 67109* | 67111*

Total 3

2-4-2T Class F3

Introduced 1893. J. Holden G.E. design. (Oldest survivor built 1895) (**see note p. 6**).
Weight : 58 tons 12 cwt.
Pressure : 160 lb. Cyls.: 17½″ × 24″
Driving Wheels : 5′ 8″ T.E.: 14,710 lb.

67124	67127	67139	67150
67126	67128	67149	

Total 7

2-4-2T Class F4

Introduced 1884. Worsdell G.E. design, modified by J. Holden. (Oldest survivor built 1906) (see note p. 6).
* Push-and-pull fitted.
Weight : 53 tons 19 cwt.
Pressure : 160 lb. Cyls.: 17½" × 24"
Driving Wheels : 5' 4" T.E.: 15,620 lb.

67151*	67158	67167	67182
67152	67160	67171	67183
67153	67162	67174	67184
67154	67163	67175	67186
67155	67164	67176	67187
67156	67165	67177	
67157	67166	67178	

Total 26

2-4-2T Class F5

Introduced 1911. S. D. Holden design. (Rebuilt from F4, oldest survivor originally built 1903.) (see note p. 6).
Weight : 53 tons 19 cwt.
Pressure : 180 lb. Cyls.: 17½" × 24"
Driving Wheels : 5' 4" T.E.: 17,570 lb.

67188	67196	67204	67212
67189	67197	67205	67213
67190	67198	67206	67214
67191	67199	67207	67215
67192	67200	67208	67216
67193	67201	67209	67217
67194	67202	67210	67218
67195	67203	67211	67219

Total 32

2-4-2T Class F6

Introduced 1911 S. D. Holden design, development of F4 with higher pressure and larger tanks (see note p. 6).
Weight : 56 tons 9 cwt.
Pressure : 180 lb. Cyls.: 17½" × 24"
Driving Wheels : 5' 4" T.E.: 17,570 lb.

67220	67222	67224	67226
67221	67223	67225	67227
67228	67231	67234	67237
67229	67232	67235	67238
67230	67233	67236	67239

Total 20

0-4-4T Class G5

Introduced 1894. W. Worsdell N.E. design.
*†Push-and pull fitted and rebuilt with larger tanks.
Weight : 54 tons 4 cwt.
Pressure : 160 lb. Cyls.: 18" × 24"
Driving Wheels : 5' 1¼" T.E.: 17,265 lb.

67240	67268	67296	67325
67241	67269	67297*	67326
67242	67270	67298	67327
67243	67271	67299	67328
67244	67272	67300	67329
67245	67273*	67301	67330
67246	67274	67302	67331
67247	67275	67303	67332
67248	67276	67304	67333
67249	67277	67305*	67334
67250*	67278	67307	67335
67251	67279*	67308	67336
67252	67280*	67309	67337*
67253*	67281*	67310	67338
67254	67282*	67311*	67339*
67255	67283	67312	67340†
67256	67284	67313	67341
67257	67285	67314	67342
67258	67286*	67315	67343
67259	67287	67316	67344
67260	67288	67317	67345
67261*	67289	67318	67346
67262	67290	67319	67347
67263	67291	67320	67348
67264	67292	67321	67349
67265	67293	67322*	
67266	67294	67323*	
67267	67295	67324	

Total 109

4-4-2T Class C12

Introduced 1898. Ivatt G.N. design.
* Boiler pressure reduced to 170 lb.
† Boiler pressure reduced to 170 lb. and push and pull fitted.
Weight : 62 tons 6 cwt.
Pressure : { 175 lb. / 170 lb.*† Cyls.: 18" × 26'
Driving Wheels : 5' 8"
T.E.: { 18,425 lb. / 17,900 lb.*†

67350	67364	67376	67389
67352	67365	67377	67390
67353	67366	67379	67391
67354*	67367	67380	67392
67356	67368	67381	67393
67357	67369	67382	67394
67359	67371	67383	67395
67360	67372	67384	67397
67361	67373	67385	67398*
67362	67374†	67386	67399*
67363*	67375	67387	Total 43

4-4-2T Class C13

Introduced 1903. Robinson G.C. design, later rebuilt with superheater.
* Push-and-pull fitted.
Weight : 66 tons 13 cwt.
Pressure : 160 lb. Su. Cyls.: 18" × 26"
Driving Wheels : 5' 7" T.E.: 17,100 lb.

67400	67410	67420*	67430
67401	67411	67421*	67431
67402	67412	67422	67432
67403	67413	67423	67433*
67404	67414	67424	67434
67405	67415	67425	67435
67406	67416*	67426	67436*
67407	67417*	67427	67437
67408	67418*	67428	67438*
67409	67419	67429	67439

Total 40

4-4-2T Class C14

Introduced 1907. Robinson G.C. design later superheated, development of C13. With detail differences.
Weight : 71 tons.
Pressure : 160 lb. Su. Cyls.: 18" × 26"
Driving Wheels : 5' 7" T.E.: 17,100 lb.

67440	67443	67446	67449
67441	67444	67447	67450
67442	67445	67448	67451

Total 12

4-4-2T Class C15

Introduced 1911. Reid N.B. design.
* Push-and-pull fitted.
Weight : 68 tons 15 cwt.
Pressure : 175 lb. Cyls.: 18" × 26"
Driving Wheels : 5' 9" T.E.: 18,160 lb.

67452	67460*	67468	67475
67453	67461	67469	67476
67454	67462	67470	67477
67455	67463	67471	67478
67456	67464	67472	67479
67457	67465	67473	67480
67458	67466	67474	67481
67459	67467		Total 30

4-4-2T Class C16

Introduced 1915. Reid N.B. design, superheated development of C15.
* Superheater removed.
Weight : 72 tons 10 cwt.
Pressure : 165 lb. SS. Cyls.: 19" × 26"
Driving Wheels : 5' 9" T.E.: 19,080 lb.
P.V.

67482	67488	67494	67499
67483*	67489	67495	67500
67484	67490	67496	67501
67485	67491	67497	67502
67486	67492	67498	
67487	67493		Total 21

2-6-2T Classes V1 & V3

V1 Introduced 1930. Gresley design.
V3* Introduced 1939. Development of V1 with higher pressure (locos numbered below 67682 rebuilt from V1).
Weights : 84 tons.
86 tons 16 cwt.*
Pressure : { 180 lb. Su. / 200 lb. Su.*
Cyls.: (3) 16" × 26"
Driving Wheels : 5' 8"
T.E.: { 22,465 lb. / 24,960 lb.*
Walschaerts gear, derived motion, P.V.

67600	67609	67618	67627
67601	67610	67619	67628
67602	67611	67620	67629
67603	67612	67621	67630
67604	67613	67622	67631
67605	67614	67623	67632
67606	67615	67624	67633
67607	67616	67625	67634*
67608	67617	67626	67635

67636	67650	67664	67678
67637	67651	67665	67679
67638	67652	67666	67680
67639	67653	67667	67681
67640	67654	67668	67682*
67641	67655	67669*	67683*
67642	67656	67670	67684*
67643	67657	67671	67685*
67644	67658	67672*	67686*
67645	67659	67673	67687*
67646	67660	67674	67688*
67647	67661	67675*	67689*
67648	67662	67676	67690*
67649	67663	67677	67691*

Totals : Class V1 78
Class V3 14

2-6-4T Class L1

Introduced 1945. Thompson design.
Weight : 89 tons 9 cwt.
Pressure : 225 lb. Cyls.: (O) 20" × 26"
Driving Wheels : 5' 2" T.E.: 32,080 lb.
Walschaerts gear, P.V.

67701	67725	67749	67773
67702	67726	67750	67774
67703	67727	67751	67775
67704	67728	67752	67776
67705	67729	67753	67777
67706	67730	67754	67778
67707	67731	67755	67779
67708	67732	67756	67780
67709	67733	67757	67781
67710	67734	67758	67782
67711	67735	67759	67783
67712	67736	67760	67784
67713	67737	67761	67785
67714	67738	67762	67786
67715	67739	67763	67787
67716	67740	67764	67788
67717	67741	67765	67789
67718	67742	67766	67790
67719	67743	67767	67791
67720	67744	67768	67792
67721	67745	67769	67793
67722	67746	67770	67794
67723	67747	67771	67795
67724	67748	67772	67796
67797	67798	67799	67800

N.B.—**Locos of this class are still being delivered.**

0-6-0ST Class J94

Introduced 1943. Riddles M.o.S. design. (Bought from M.o.S. 1946.)
Weight : 48 tons 5 cwt.
Pressure : 170 lb. Cyls.: 18" × 26"
Driving Wheels : 4' 3" T.E.: 23,870 lb.

68006	68025	68044	68063
68007	68026	68045	68064
68008	68027	68046	68065
68009	68028	68047	68066
68010	68029	68048	68067
68011	68030	68049	68068
68012	68031	68050	68069
68013	68032	68051	68070
68014	68033	68052	68071
68015	68034	68053	68072
68016	68035	68054	68073
68017	68036	68055	68074
68018	68037	68056	68075
68019	68038	68057	68076
68020	68039	68058	68077
68021	68040	68059	68078
68022	68041	68060	68079
68023	68042	68061	68080
68024	68043	68062	**Total 75**

0-4-0T (Tram Locos) Class Y6

Introduced 1883. Worsdell G.E. design. (Oldest survivor built 1897.)
Weight : 21 tons 5 cwt.
Pressure : 140 lb. Cyls.: 11" × 15"
Driving Wheels : 3' 1" T.E.: 5,835 lb.

68082 | 68083 **Total 2**

0-4-0T Class Y7

Introduced 1888. T. W. Worsdell N.E. design. (Survivors built 1923.)
Weight : 22 tons 14 cwt.
Pressure : 140 lb. Cyls.: 14" × 20"
Driving Wheels : 3' 6½" T.E.: 11,040 lb.

68088S | 68089 **Total 2**

0-4-0T Class Y8

Introduced 1890. T. W. Worsdell N.E. design.
Weight : 15 tons 10 cwt.
Pressure : 140 lb. Cyls.: 11" × 15"
Driving Wheels : 3' 0" T.E.: 6,000 lb.

68091 **Total 1**

0-4-0ST Class Y9

Introduced 1882. Holmes N.B. design.
* Many of these locos run permanently attached to wooden tenders, some by loose couplings and others by central drawgear.
Weights: Loco. 27 tons 16 cwt. Tender 6 tons.*
Pressure: 130 lb. Cyls.: (O) 14" × 20"
Driving Wheels: 3' 8" T.E.: 9,845 lb.

68092	68101	68110	68119
68093	68102	68111	68120
68094	68103	68112	68121
68095	68104	68113	68122
68096	68105	68114	68123
68097	68106	68115	68124
68098	68107	68116	
68099	68108	68117	
68100	68109	68118	

Total 33

0-4-0T Class Y4

Introduced 1913. Hill G.E. design.
Weight: 38 tons 1 cwt.
Pressure: 180 lb. Cyls.: (O) 17" × 20"
Driving Wheels: 3' 10" T.E.: 19,225 lb.
Walschaerts gear.

68125	68127	68128	68129S
68126			

Total 5

0-4-0T Class Y1

Sentinel Wagon Works design. Single-speed Geared Sentinel Locomotives. The four parts of this class differ in details, including size of boiler and fuel capacity.
Y1/1* Introduced 1925.
Y1/2† Introduced 1927.
Y1/3** Introduced 1926.
Y1/4‡ Introduced 1927.
§ Sprocket gear ratio 9 : 25 (remainder 11 : 25).
Weights: 20 tons 17 cwt.* / 19 tons 16 cwt.† / 14 tons.** / 19 tons 7 cwt.‡
Pressure: 275 lb. Su. Cyls.: 6¾" × 9"
Driving Wheels: 2' 6"
T.E.: 7,260 lb. / 8,870 lb.§
Poppet valves.

68130S*	68133S*	68138†
68131S*	68136S‡	68139**
68132S*	68137†	68140†
68141†	68146†§	68150†§
68142†	68147†§	68151†§
68143†§	68148†§	68152S*
68144†§	68149†§	68153S†
68145†§		

Totals: Class Y1/1 4
Class Y1/2 15
Class Y1/3 2
Class Y1/4 1

0-4-0T Class Y3

Sentinel Wagon Works design. Two-speed Geared Sentinel Locos.
Introduced 1927.
* Sprocket gear ratio 15 : 19 (remainder 19 : 19).
Weight: 20 tons 16 cwt.
Pressure: 275 lb. Su. Cyls.: 6¾" × 9"
Driving Wheels: 2' 6"
T.E.: Low Gear: 12,600 lb. / High Gear: 4,705 lb. / Low Gear: 15,960 lb.* / High Gear: 5,960 lb.*
Poppet valves.

68154	68162	68171	68179
68155	68163	68172	68180*
68156	68164	68173S	68181*
68157	68165	68174	68182*
68158	68166S	68175	68183*
68159	68167	68176	68184
68160	68168	68177S	68185
68161	68169	68178S	

Total 31

0-4-0T Class Y10

Sentinel Wagon Works design. Double-ended Two-speed Geared Sentinel Loco.
Introduced 1930.
Weight: 23 tons 19 cwt.
Pressure: 275 lb. Su. Cyls.: 6¾" × 9"
Driving Wheels: 3' 2"
T.E.: Low Gear: 11,435 lb. / High Gear: 7,965 lb.
Poppet valves.

68186 **Total 1**

0-4-0T (Petrol) Class Y11

Introduced 1921. Motor, Rail and Tram Car Co. design.
Weight: 8 tons. H.P.: 40.

68188	68189

Total 2

0-4-2T Class Z4

Introduced 1915. Manning-Wardle design for G.N. of S.
Weight : 25 tons 17 cwt.
Pressure : 160 lb. Cyls.: (O) 13″ × 20″
Driving Wheels : 3′ 6″ T.E.: 10,945 lb.

68190	68191

Total 2

0-4-2T Class Z5

Introduced 1915. Manning-Wardle design for G.N. of S.
Weight : 30 tons 18 cwt.
Pressure : 160 lb. Cyls.: (O) 14″ × 20″
Driving Wheels : 4′ 0″ T.E.: 11,105 lb.

68192	68193

Total 2

0-6-0ST Class J62

Introduced 1897. Pollitt M.S. & L. design.
Weight : 30 tons 17 cwt.
Pressure : 150 lb. Cyls.: (O) 13″ × 20″
Driving Wheels : 3′ 6″ T.E.: 10,260 lb.

68200

Total 1

0-6-0T Class J63

Introduced 1906. Robinson G.C. design.
Weight : 37 tons 9 cwt.
Pressure : 150 lb. Cyls.: (O) 13″ × 20″
Driving Wheels : 3′ 6″ T.E.: 10,260 lb.

68204	68206	68208	68210
68205	68207	68209	

Total 7

0-6-0T Class J65

Introduced 1889. J. Holden G.C. design **(see note p. 6).**
Weight : 36 tons 11 cwt.
Pressure : 160 lb. Cyls.: 14″ × 20″
Driving Wheels : 4′ 0″ T.E.: 11,105 lb.

68211	68214

Total 2

0-6-0T (Tram Locos) Class J70

Introduced 1903. J. Holden G.E. design.
Weight : 27 tons 1 cwt.
Pressure : 180 lb. Cyls.: (O) 12″ × 15″
Driving Wheels : 3′ 1″ T.E.: 8,930 lb.
Walschaerts gear.

68216	68219	68222	68225
68217	68220	68223	68226
68218	68221	68224	

Total 11

0-6-0T Class J71

Introduced 1886. T. W. Worsdell N.E. design.
* † Altered cylinder dimensions.
Weight : 37 tons 12 cwt.
Pressure : 140 lb. Dr. Wheels : 4′ 7½″
Cyls.: 16″ × 22″; 16¾″ × 22″*; 18″ × 22″†
T.E.: 12,130 lb.; 13,300 lb.*; 15,355 lb.†

68230*	68253*	68277	68297
68231	68254	68278	68298
68232	68255	68279	68299
68233	68256	68280*	68300
68234*	68258*	68281	68301
68235	68259*	68282	68302*
68236	68260	68283	68303*
68238	68262	68284	68304*
68239	68263	68286*	68305*
68240	68264	68287*	68306*
68242	68265	68288	68307*
68243	68266	68289*	68308*
68244	68267	68290	68309*
68245	68268	68291	68310*
68246*	68269	68292	68311*
68247	68270	68293*	68312†
68248	68271	68294	68313*
68249	68272	68295	68314
68250*	68273	68296	68316*
68251	68275		
68252*	68276		

Total 80

0-6-0ST Class J55

Introduced 1912. Gresley G.N. rebuild from domeless locos, introduced 1891. Pressure reduced to 160 lb.
Weight : 45 tons 16 cwt.
Pressure : 160 lb. Cyls.: 17½″ × 26″
Driving Wheels: 4′ 8″ T.E.: 19,340 lb.

68319S

Total 1

0-6-0T Class J88

Introduced 1904. Reid N.B. design with short wheelbase.

Weight : 38 tons 14 cwt.

Pressure : 130 lb. Cyls.: (O) 15″×22″

Driving Wheels : 3′ 9″ T.E.: 12,155 lb.

68320	68329	68338	68347
68321	68330	68339	68348
68322	68331	68340	68349
68323	68332	68341	68350
68324	68333	68342	68351
68325	68334	68343	68352
68326	68335	68344	68353
68327	68336	68345	68354
68328	68337	68346	

Total 35

0-6-0T Class J73

Introduced 1891. W. Worsdell N.E. design.

Weight : 46 tons 15 cwt.

Pressure : 160 lb. Cyls.: 19″×24″

Driving Wheels : 4′ 7¼″ T.E.: 21,320 lb.

68355	68358	68361	68363
68356	68359	68362	68364
68357	68360		

Total 10

0-6-0T Class J66

Introduced 1886. J. Holden G.E. design.

Weight : 40 tons 6 cwt.

Pressure : 160 lb. Cyls.: 16½″×22″

Driving Wheels : 4′ 0″ T.E.: 16,970 lb.

68370S	68375	68380	68385
68371	68376	68381	68386
68372	68377	68382	68387
68373	68378	68383	68388
68374	68379	68384	

Total 19

0-6-0T Class J77

Introduced 1899. W. Worsdell N.E. rebuild of Fletcher 0-4-4T originally built 1874-84.

* Darlington rebuilds with square-cornered cab roof (remainder York rebuilds with rounded cab).

Weight : 43 tons.

Pressure : 160 lb. Cyls.: 17″×22″

Driving Wheels : 4′ 1¼″ T.E.: 17,560 lb.

68391	68405*	68417	68430
68392*	68406	68420*	68431
68393*	68407	68421	68432*
68395*	68408	68422	68433
68396	68409	68423	68434
68397*	68410	68424	68435
68398	68412*	68425	68436
68399	68413	68426	68437
68401	68414	68427	68438
68402	68415	68428	68440*
68404*	68416	68429	

Total 43

0-6-0T Class J83

Introduced 1900. Holmes N.B. design.

Weight : 45 tons 5 cwt.

Pressure : 150 lb. Cyls.: 17″×26″

Driving Wheels : 4′ 6″ T.E.: 17,745 lb.

68442	68452	68463	68473
68443	68453	68464	68474
68444	68454	68465	68475
68445	68455	68466	68476
68446	68456	68467	68477
68447	68457	68468	68478
68448	68458	68469	68479
68449	68459	68470	68480
68450	68460	68471	68481
68451	68461	68472	

Total 39

0-6-0T Class J93

Introduced 1897. Marriott M. & G.N. design.

Weight : 37 tons 14 cwt.

Pressure : 150 lb. Cyls.: (O) 16″×20″

Driving Wheels : 3′ 7″ T.E.: 15,180 lb.

68489 **Total 1**

0-6-0T Classes J67 & J69

(See note p. 6)

J67/1* Introduced 1890. J. Holden G.E. design with 160 lb. pressure.

J69 Introduced 1902. Development of J67 with 180 lb. pressure and larger tanks (some rebuilt from J67).

J67/2† Introduced 1937. Rebuild of J69 with 160 lb. boiler.

Weights: 40 tons.* / 42 tons 9 cwt. / 41 tons 8 cwt.†

Pressure: 160 lb.*† / 180 lb. Cyls.: 16½" × 22"

Driving Wheels: 4' 0"

T.E.: 16,970 lb.*† / 19,090 lb.

68490*	68522*	68554	68588*
68491	68523*	68555	68589*
68492*	68524	68556	68590*
68493*	68525	68557	68591
68494	68526	68558	68592*
68495	68527	68559	68593*
68496*	68528	68560	68594*
68497	68529†	68561	68595*
68498*	68530	68562	68596
68499	68531†	68563	68597†
68500	68532	68565	68598
68501	68533	68566	68599
68502	68534	68567	68600
68503	68535	68568	68601
68504	68536†	68569	68602
68505	68537	68570	68603
68507	68538	68571	68605
68508	68540†	68572†	68606*
68509*	68541	68573	68607
68510*	68542	68574	68608*
68511*	68543	68575	68609†
68512*	68544	68576	68610†
68513*	68545	68577	68611*
68514*	68546	68578	68612
68515*	68547†	68579	68613
68516*	68548	68581	68616*
68517*	68549	68583*	68617
68518*	68550	68584*	68618
68519*	68551	68585	68619
68520*	68552	68586*	68621
68521*	68553	68587	68623
68625	68629	68632	68635
68626	68630	68633	68636
68628†	68631		

Totals: Class J67/1 34
Class J67/2 10
Class J69 90

0-6-0T Class J68

Introduced 1912. Hill G.E. development of J69 with side-window cab (see note p. 6).

Weight: 42 tons 9 cwt.
Pressure: 180 lb. Cyls.: 16½" × 22"
Driving Wheels: 4' 0" T.E.: 19 090 lb.

68638	68646	68654	68662
68639	68647	68655	68663
68640	68648	68656	68664
68641	68649	68657	68665
68642	68650	68658	68666
68643	68651	68659	
68644	68652	68660	
68645	68653	68661	

Total 29

0-6-0 Crane Tank Class J92

Introduced 1891. J. Holden G.E. rebuild of Ruston & Proctor 0-6-0T (originally built 1868.)

Weight: 40 tons 8 cwt.
Pressure: 140 lb. Cyls.: 16" × 22"
Driving Wheels: 4' 0" T.E.: 13,960 lb.

68667S | 68668S | 68669S

Total 3

0-6-0T Class J72

Introduced 1898. W. Worsdell N.E. design.
* Altered cylinder dimensions.

Weight: 38 tons 12 cwt.
Pressure: 140 lb. Cyls.: 17" × 24" / 18" × 24"*
Driving Wheels: 4' 1¼"
T.E.: 16,760 lb. / 18,790 lb.*

68670	68675	68680	68685*
68671	68676	68681	68686
68672	68677	68682	68687
68673	68678	68683	68688
68674	68679	68684	68689

68690	68707	68723	68739
68691	68708	68724	68740
68692	68709	68725	68741
68693	68710	68726	68742
68694	68711	68727	68743
68695	68712	68728	68744
68696	68713	68729	68745
68697	68714	68730	68746
68698	68715	68731	68747
68699	68716	68732	68748
68700	68717	68733	68749
68701	68718	68734	68750
68702	68719	68735	68751
68703	68720	68736	68752
68704	68721	68737	68753
68705	68722	68738	68754
68706			

Total 81

0-6-0ST Class J52

J52/2 Introduced 1897. Ivatt standard G.N. saddletank with domed boiler.
J52/1* Introduced 1922. Rebuild of Stirling domeless saddletank (introduced 1892)—non-condensing.
J52/1† Introduced 1922. Condensing rebuild of Stirling locos.
‡ J52/2 with boiler pressure raised to 175 lb. Weight : 51 tons 14 cwt.
Pressure : { 170 lb. / 175 lb ‡ } Cyls.: 18″ × 26″
Driving Wheels: 4′ 8″ T.E. { 21,735 lb. / 22,370 lb.‡ }

68757†	68775*	68793†	68811
68758†	68776†	68794†	68812
68759†	68777†	68795†	68813
68760†	68778†	68796†	68814
68761†	68779*	68797*	68815
68762*	68780*	68798*	68816
68763*	68781†	68799*	68817
68764*	68782S*	68800*	68818
68765*	68783†	68801*	68819
68766*	68784†	68802*	68820
68767*	68785†	68803*	68821
68768*	68786*	68804*	68822
68769*	68787†	68805	68823
68770*	68788†	68806	68824
68771*	68789*	68807	68825
68772*	68790*	68808	68826
68773†	68791†	68809	68827
68774†	68792*	68810	68828

68829	68845	68861	68877
68830	68846	68862	68878
68831	68847	68863	68879
68832	68848	68864	68880
68833	68849	68865	68881
68834	68850	68866	68882
68835	68851	68867	68883
68836	68852	68868	68884
68837	68853	68869	68885
68838	68854	68870	68886
68839	68855	68871	68887
68840‡	68856	68872	68888
68841	68857	68873	68889
68842	68858	68874	
68843	68859	68875	
68844	68860‡	68876‡	

Totals : Class J52/1 48
Class J52/2 85

0-6-0T Class J50

J50/2* Introduced 1922. Gresley G.N. design (68900-19 rebuilt from smaller J51, built 1915-22).
J50/3† Introduced 1926. Post-grouping development with detail differences.
J50/1‡ Introduced 1929. Rebuilt from smaller J51, built 1913-4.
J50/4§ Introduced 1937. Development of J50/3 with larger bunker.
Weights : { 56 tons 6 cwt.‡ / 58 tons 3 cwt.†§ / 57 tons.* }
Pressure : 175 lb. Cyls.: 18½″ × 26″
Driving Wheels : 4′ 8″ T.E.: 23,635 lb.

68890‡	68905*	68920*	68935*
68891‡	68906*	68921*	68936*
68892‡	68907*	68922*	68937*
68893‡	68908*	68923*	68938*
68894‡	68909*	68924*	68939*
68895‡	68910*	68925*	68940†
68896‡	68911*	68926*	68941†
68897‡	68912*	68927*	68942†
68898‡	68913*	68928*	68943†
68899‡	68914*	68929*	68944†
68900*	68915*	68930*	68945†
68901*	68916*	68931*	68946†
68902*	68917*	68932*	68947†
68903*	68918*	68933*	68948†
68904*	68919*	68934*	68949†

68950†	68961†	68972†	68983§
68951†	68962†	68973†	68984§
68952†	68963†	68974†	68985§
68953†	68964†	68975†	68986§
68954†	68965†	68976†	68987§
68955†	68966†	68977†	68988§
68956†	68967†	68978§	68989§
68957†	68968†	68979§	68990§
68958†	68969†	68980§	68991§
68959†	68970†	68981§	
68960†	68971†	68982§	

Totals : Class J50/1 10
Class J50/2 40
Class J50/3 38
Class J50/4 14

2-6-4T Class L3

Introduced 1914. Robinson G.C. design.
* Altered cylinder dimensions.
Weight : 97 tons 9 cwt.
Pressure : 180 lb. Su. Cyls. {21" × 26" / 20" × 26"*}
Driving Wheels: 5' 1" T.E. {28,760 lb. / 26,085 lb.*}

69050	69055	69060	69066
69051	69056	69061*	69067
69052	69057	69062	69068
69053	69058	69064	69069
69054	69059	69065	

Total 19

0-6-2T Class N10

Introduced 1902. W. Worsdell N.E. design.
Weight : 57 tons 14 cwt.
Pressure : 160 lb. Cyls.: 18½" × 26"
Driving Wheels : 4' 7¼" T.E.: 21,905 lb.

69090	69095	69100	69106
69091	69096	69101	69107
69092	69097	69102	69108
69093	69098	69104	69109
69094	69099	69105	

Total 19

0-6-2T Class N13

Introduced 1913. Stirling H. & B. design.
Pressure : 175 lb. Cyls.: 18" × 26"
Driving Wheels : 4' 6" T.E.: 23,205 lb.

69111	69114	69116	69118
69112	69115	69117	69119
69113			

Total 9

0-6-2T Class N14

Introduced 1909. Reid N.B. design.
Pressure : 175 lb. Cyls.: 18" × 26"
Driving Wheels : 4' 6" T.E.: 23,205 lb.

69120 | 69124 | 69125

Total 3

0-6-2T Class N15

N15/2* Introduced 1910. Reid N.B. design developed from N14. Cowlairs incline banking locos.
N15/1 Introduced 1910. Development of N15/2 with smaller bunker for normal duties.
Weight : {62 tons 1 cwt.* / 60 tons 18 cwt.}
Pressure : 175 lb. Cyls.: 18" × 26"
Driving Wheels : 4' 6" T.E.: 23,205 lb.

69126*	69147	69168	69189
69127*	69148	69169	69190
69128*	69149	69170	69191
69129*	69150	69171	69192
69130*	69151	69172	69193
69131*	69152	69173	69194
69132	69153	69174	69195
69133	69154	69175	69196
69134	69155	69176	69197
69135	69156	69177	69198
69136	69157	69178	69199
69137	69158	69179	69200
69138	69159	69180	69201
69139	69160	69181	69202
69140	69161	69182	69203
69141	69162	69183	69204
69142	69163	69184	69205
69143	69164	69185	69206
69144	69165	69186	69207
69145	69166	69187	69208
69146	69167	69188	69209

69210	69214	69218	69222
69211	69215	69219	69223
69212	69216	69220	69224
69213	69217	69221	

Totals : Class N15/1 93
Class N15/2 6

0-6-2T Class N4

N4/2 Introduced 1889. Parker M.S. & L. design.

N4/4* Introduced 1892. Development of N4/2 with larger bunker.
N4/1 and N4/3 were N4/2 and N4/4 with longer chimney.

Weights : { 61 tons 10 cwt. / 61 tons 19 cwt.* }
Pressure : 160 lb. Cyls.: 18" × 26"
Driving Wheels : 5' 1" T.E.: 18,780 lb.
Joy gear.

69225	69231	69237	69244*
69226	69232	69239	69245*
69227	69233	69240	69246*
69228	69234	69241	69247*
69229	69235	69242*	
69230	69236	69243*	

Totals : Class N4/2 16
Class N4/4 6

0-6-2T Class N5

N5/2 Introduced 1891. Parker M.S. & L. design developed from N4.

N5/3* Introduced 1915. N5/2 rebuilt with larger tanks, bunker and cyls.
(N5/1 was N5/2 with longer chimney).

Weights : { 62 tons 7 cwt. / 64 tons 13 cwt.* }
Pressure : 160 lb. Cyls.: { 18" × 26" / 18½" × 26"* }
Driving Wheels: 5' 1" T.E. { 18,780 lb. / 19,840 lb.* }

69250	69261	69272	69283
69251	69262	69273	69284
69252	69263	69274	69285
69253	69264	69275	69286
69254	69265	69276	69287
69255	69266	69277	69288
69256	69267	69278	69289
69257	69268	69279	69290
69258	69269	69280	69291
69259	69270	69281	69292
69260	69271	69282	69293

69294	69314	69333	69352
69295	69315	69334	69353
69296	69316	69335	69354
69297	69317	69336	69355
69298	69318	69337	69356
69299	69319	69338	69357
69300	69320	69339	69358
69301	69321	69340	69359
69302	69322	69341	69360
69303	69323	69342	69361
69304	69324	69343	69362
69305	69325	69344	69363
69306	69326	69345	69364
69307	69327	69346	69365
69308	69328	69347	69366
69309	69329	69348	69367
69310	69330	69349	69368
69311*	69331	69350	69369
69312	69332	69351	69370
69313			

Totals : Class N5/2 120
Class N5/3 1

0-6-2T Class N8

* Introduced 1886. T. W. Worsdell N.E. design, saturated with Joy's gear and slide valves (majority rebuilt from compounds).

† Rebuilt with superheater, Stephenson gear and piston valves, 24" piston stroke.

‡ As † but with 26" stroke.

§ Rebuilt with Stephenson gear and piston valves, superheater removed, 24" stroke.

¶ As § but with 26" piston stroke.

Weights : { 56 tons 5 cwt.* §¶ / 58 tons 14 cwt.† ‡ }
Pressure : 160 lb. SS.
Cyls.: { 18" × 24"* / 19" × 24"†§ / 19" × 26"‡¶ }
Driving Wheels : 5' 1¼"
T.E.: { 17,265 lb.* / 19,235 lb.† § / 20,840 lb.‡ ¶ }

69371†	69377†	69381¶	69386‡
69372§	69378§	69382¶	69387§
69373†	69379†	69383§	69389*
69376†	69380†	69385†	69390†

69391†	69394†	69397§	69400¶
69392*	69395†	69398†	69401‡
69393†	69396*		

Total 26

0-6-2T Class N9

Introduced 1893. T. W. Worsdell N.E. design.
Weight : 56 tons 10 cwt.
Pressure : 160 lb. Cyls.: 19" × 26"
Driving Wheels : 5' 1¼" T.E.: 20,840 lb.

69410	69415	69422	69426
69411	69418	69423	69427
69413	69420	69424	69428
69414	69421	69425	69429

Total 16

0-6-2T Class N1

* Introduced 1907. Ivatt G.N. design, prototype of class.

†‡§¶ Introduced 1907. Standard design with shorter tanks and detail differences (**see note p. 7**).

§¶ Rebuilt with superheater and reduced pressure.

‡¶ Fitted with condensing gear.

Weights : { 64 tons 14 cwt.* / 65 tons 17 cwt.

Pressure : { 175 lb. / 170 lb. Su. §¶ Cyls.: 18" × 26"

Driving Wheels: 5' 8" T.E. { 18,430 lb. / 17,900 lb. §¶

69430*	69445‡	69459†	69473†
69431‡	69446†	69460‡	69474†
69432‡	69447†	69461‡	69475‡
69433‡	69448†	69462‡	69476‡
69434‡	69449†	69463‡	69477‡
69435¶	69450‡	69464¶	69478¶
69436§	69451‡	69465‡	69479¶
69437¶	69452§	69466‡	69480‡
69439¶	69453‡	69467‡	69481‡
69440†	69454†	69468‡	69482¶
69441‡	69455‡	69469‡	69483§
69442‡	69456‡	69470‡	69484‡
69443†	69457‡	69471‡	69485‡
69444†	69458‡	69472§	

Total 55

0-6-2T Class N2

(**see note p. 7**).

N2/2* Introduced 1925. Post-grouping development of Gresley ex-G.N. N2/1, introduced 1920, which class is now included in N2/2. Condensing gear and small chimney.

N2/2† Condensing gear removed, retaining small chimney.

N2/3‡ Introduced 1925. Locos built non-condensing, orginally fitted with large chimney. Some now with small chimney.

N2/4§ Introduced 1928. Development of N2/2, slightly heavier. Condensing gear and small chimney.
(The small chimneys are to suit the Metropolitan loading gauge, for working to Moorgate St. Condensing gear has been removed from or added to certain locos transferred from or to the London area.)

Weights : { 70 tons 5 cwt.*† / 70 tons 8 cwt.‡ / 71 tons 9 cwt.§

Pressure : 170 lb. Su. Cyls.: 19" × 26"
Driving Wheels : 5' 8" T.E.: 19,945 lb.
P.V.

69490*	69515†	69540*	69565‡
69491*	69516†	69541*	69566‡
69492*	69517*	69542*	69567‡
69493*	69518†	69543*	69568§
69494*	69519†	69544*	69569§
69495*	69520*	69545*	69570§
69496*	69521*	69546*	69571§
69497*	69522*	69547*	69572§
69498*	69523*	69548*	69573§
69499*	69524*	69549*	69574§
69500†	69525*	69550†	69575§
69501†	69526*	69551†	69576§
69502†	69527*	69552†	69577§
69503†	69528*	69553†	69578§
69504*	69529*	69554†	69579§
69505†	69530*	69555§	69580§
69506*	69531*	69556§	69581§
69507†	69532*	69557†	69582§
69508†	69533*	69558†	69583§
69509†	69534*	69559†	69584§
69510†	69535*	69560†	69585§
69511†	69536*	69561†	69586§
69512*	69537*	69562‡	69587§
69513†	69538*	69563‡	69588§
69514†	69539*	69564‡	69589§

69590§	69592§	69594‡	69596‡
69591§	69593§	69595‡	

Totals : Class N2/2 70
Class N2/3 9
Class N2/4 28

0-6-2T Class N7

N7 (G.E.)[1] Introduced 1914. Hill G.E. design.
N7/1[2] Introduced 1925. Post-grouping development of N7 (G.E.) with detail differences.
N7/2[3] Introduced 1926. Development of N7/1 with long-travel valves.
N7/3[4] Introduced 1927. Doncaster-built version of N7/2 with round-topped boiler.
N7/4[5] Introduced 1940. N7 (G.E.) rebuilt with round-topped boiler, retaining short-travel valves.
N7/3[6] Introduced 1943. N7/1 rebuilt with round-topped boiler, retaining short-travel valves.
N7/3[7] Introduced 1943. N7/2 rebuilt with round-topped boiler.

Weights :
- 62 tons 5 cwt.[1]
- 63 tons 13 cwt.[2]
- 64 tons 17 cwt.[3]
- 64 tons [4]
- 61 tons 16 cwt.[5]
- 64 tons [6]
- 64 tons [7]

Pressure : 180 lb. Su. Cyls.: 18″ × 24″
Driving Wheels : 4′ 10″ T.E.: 20,515 lb.
Walschaerts gear, P.V.

69600[5]	69618[5]	69636[6]	69654[2]
69601[5]	69619[5]	69637[2]	69655[2]
69602[1]	69620[5]	69638[2]	69656[6]
69603[5]	69621[5]	69639[6]	69657[2]
69604[5]	69622[6]	69640[2]	69658[2]
69605[5]	69623[2]	69641[2]	69659[2]
69606[5]	69624[2]	69642[2]	69660[6]
69607[5]	69625[2]	69643[2]	69661[2]
69608[5]	69626[2]	69644[2]	69662[2]
69609[5]	69627[2]	69645[2]	69663[6]
69610[5]	69628[2]	69646[2]	69664[6]
69611[5]	69629[2]	69647[6]	69665[2]
69612[5]	69630[2]	69648[6]	69666[6]
69613[5]	69631[2]	69649[6]	69667[2]
69614[5]	69632[6]	69650[6]	69668[2]
69615[5]	69633[6]	69651[6]	69669[6]
69616[5]	69634[2]	69652[6]	69670[2]
69617[5]	69635[6]	69653[2]	69671[2]
69672[3]	69688[3]	69704[4]	69720[4]
69673[3]	69689[3]	69705[4]	69721[4]
69674[3]	69690[3]	69706[4]	69722[4]
69675[7]	69691[7]	69707[4]	69723[4]
69676[7]	69692[7]	69708[4]	69724[4]
69677[7]	69693[7]	69709[4]	69725[4]
69678[7]	69694[3]	69710[4]	69726[4]
69679[7]	69695[3]	69711[4]	69727[4]
69680[3]	69696[7]	69712[4]	69728[4]
69681[3]	69697[7]	69713[4]	69729[4]
69682[7]	69698[3]	69714[4]	69730[4]
69683[3]	69699[7]	69715[4]	69731[4]
69684[3]	69700[3]	69716[4]	69732[4]
69685[7]	69701[7]	69717[4]	69733[4]
69686[7]	69702[4]	69718[4]	
69687[7]	69703[4]	69719[4]	

Totals : Class N7 1
Class N7/1 32
Class N7/2 14
Class N7/3 66
Class N7/4 21

4-6-2T Class A7

Introduced 1910. Raven N.E. design, later rebuilt with superheater and reduced pressure.
* Saturated.
Weight : 87 tons 10 cwt.
Pressure : 160 lb. Su. / 180 lb.*
Cyls.: (3) 16½″ × 26″
Driving Wheels : 4′ 7¼″
T.E.: 26,140 lb. / 29,405 lb.*
P.V.

69770	69775*	69780	69785
69771	69776	69781	69786
69772	69777	69782	69787*
69773	69778*	69783	69788
69774	69779	69784	69789

Total 20

4-6-2T Class A6

Introduced 1915. Raven N.E. design. (Rebuild of Worsdell Class "W" 4-6-0T, introduced 1907.) Later superheated.
* Saturated.
Weights : 79 tons. / 78 tons.*
Pressure : 175 lb. SS. Cyls.: 19″ × 26″
Driving Wheels : 5′ 1¼″ T.E.: 23,830 lb.
P.V.

69791	69793	69794*	69795*

69796	69797	69798*	69799*

Total 8

4-6-2T Class A5

A5/1 Introduced 1911. Robinson G.C. design.

A5/2* Introduced 1925. Post-grouping development of A5/1 with reduced boiler mountings and detail differences.

Weights: 85 tons 18 cwt. / 90 tons 11 cwt.*

Pressure: 180 lb. Su. Cyls: 20" × 26"

Driving Wheels: 5' 7" T.E.: 23,750 lb.

P.V.

69800	69811	69822	69833*
69801	69812	69823	69834*
69802	69813	69824	69835*
69803	69814	69825	69836*
69804	69815	69826	69837*
69805	69816	69827	69838*
69806	69817	69828	69839*
69807	69818	69829	69840*
69808	69819	69830*	69841*
69809	69820	69831*	69842*
69810	69821	69832*	

Totals: Class A5/1 30
Class A5/2 13

4-6-2T Class A8

Introduced 1931. Gresley rebuild of Raven Class "D" 4-4-4T (introduced 1913.)

Weight: 86 tons 18 cwt.

Pressure: 175 lb. Su.

Cyls.: (3) 16½" × 26"

Driving Wheels: 5' 9" T.E.: 22,940 lb.

P.V.

69850	69862	69874	69885
69851	69863	69875	69886
69852	69864	69876	69887
69853	69865	69877	69888
69854	69866	69878	69889
69855	69867	69879	69890
69856	69868	69880	69891
69857	69869	69881	69892
69858	69870	69882	69893
69859	69871	69883	69894
69860	69872	69884	
69861	69873		

Total 45

0-8-4T Class S1

S1/1* Introduced 1907. Robinson G.C. design, since rebuilt with superheater.

S1/2† Introduced 1932. S1/1 rebuilt with booster and superheater, booster since removed.

S1/3‡ Introduced 1932. New locos built with booster, booster later removed.

Weights: 99 tons 6 cwt.* / 99 tons 2 cwt.† / 99 tons 1 cwt.‡

Pressure: 180 lb. Su.

Cyls.: (3) 18" × 26"

Driving Wheels: 4' 8" T.E.: 34,525 lb.

69900*	69902*	69904‡	69905‡
69901†	69903*		

Totals: Class S1/1 3
Class S1/2 1
Class S1/3 2

4-8-0T Class T1

Introduced 1909. W. Worsdell N.E. design.

* Rebuilt with superheater.

Weight: 85 tons 8 cwt.

Pressure: 175 lb. SS.

Cyls.: (3) 18" × 26"

Driving Wheels: 4' 7¼" T.E.: 34,080 lb.

P.V.

69910	69914*	69917	69920
69911	69915	69918	69921
69912	69916	69919	69922
69913			

Total 13

0-8-0T Class Q1

Thompson rebuild of Q4 0-8-0, introduced 1902.

Q1/1* Introduced 1942. 1,500 gallon tanks.

Q1/2 Introduced 1943. 2,000 gallon tanks.

Weights: 69 tons 18 cwt.* / 73 tons 13 cwt.

Pressure: 180 lb. Cyls.: (O) 19" × 26"

Driving Wheels: 4' 8" T.E.: 25,645 lb.

69925*	69929	69932	69935
69926*	69930	69933	69936
69927*	69931	69934	69937
69928*			

Total 13

2-8-8-2T Class U1 (Beyer-Garratt Loco)

Introduced 1925. Gresley/Beyer Peacock design.
Weight : 178 tons 1 cwt.
Pressure : 180 lb. Su.
Cyls.: (6) 18½″ × 26″
Driving Wheels : 4′ 8″ T.E.: 72,940 lb.
Walschaerts gear, derived motion, P.V.

69999 **Total 1**

2-8-0 Class WD

Ministry of Supply "Austerity" 2-8-0 locomotives purchased by British Railways, 1948.

Introduced 1943. Riddles M.o.S. design.
Weights : Loco. 70 tons 5 cwt.
Tender 55 tons 10 cwt.
Pressure: 225 lb. Cyls.: (O) 19″ × 28″.
Driving Wheels : 4′ 8½″ T.E. 34,215 lb.
Walschaerts gear, P.V.

Notes.

RENUMBERING.—This class, which includes engines formerly on loan and Eastern Region Class "O7," is being renumbered in series 90000-90732. In the list below the new number is given first, with tha former W.D. number in the second column (except in the case of locomotives Nos. 90000-100, 90422-520, of which the former Eastern Region Class O7 number is shown).

LOCATION.—The third column shows the Region on which the engine is located, at 31st May, 1949, the following abbreviations being used.

- E. Eastern Region.
- L.M.—London Midland Region.
- N.E.—North Eastern Region.
- S. —Southern Region.
- Sc. —Scottish Region.
- W. —Western Region.

Many of these locos., although allocated to a Region, are still stored awaiting overhaul after service on the continent.

New No.	Former No.	Region
90000	63000	E.
90001	63001	N.E.
90002	63002	E.
90003	63003	E.
90004	63004	Sc.
90005	63005	E.
90006	63006	N.E.
90007	63007	N.E.
90008	63008	N.E.
90009	63009	N.E.
90010	63010	N.E.
90011	63011	N.E.
90012	63012	N.E.
90013	63013	E.
90014	63014	N.E.
90015	63015	E.
90016	63016	N.E.
90017	63017	Sc.
90018	63018	E.
90019	63019	Sc.
90020	63020	Sc.
90021	63021	N.E.
90022	63022	N.E.
90023	63023	E.
90024	63024	E.
90025	63025	E.
90026	63026	N.E.
90027	63027	N.E.
90028	63028	E.
90029	63029	E.
90030	63030	N.E.
90031	63031	E.
90032	63032	E.
90033	63033	E.
90034	63034	E.
90035	63035	E.
90036	63036	E.
90037	63037	E.
90038	63038	Sc.
90039	63039	E.
90040	63040	E.
90041	63041	Sc.
90042	63042	E.
90043	63043	E.
90044	63044	N.E.
90045	63045	N.E.
90046	63046	E.
90047	63047	N.E.
90048	63048	N.E.
90049	63049	Sc.
90050	63050	E.
90051	63051	E.
90052	63052	N.E.
90053	63053	E.
90054	63054	N.E.
90055	63055	E.
90056	63056	N.E.

Top : Class G5 0-4-4T No. 67265 *[P. Ransome-Wallis*
Centre : Class C14 4-4-2T No. 67446 *[H. C. Casserley*
Bottom : Class C15 4-4-2T No. 67458 *[H. C. Casserley*

Left : Class J83 0-6-0T No. 68472

[P. Ransome-Wallis

Right : Class J71 0-6-0T No. 68278

[B. V. Franey

Left : Class J77 0-6-0T No. 68391

[B. V. Franey

Right : Class J72 0-6-0T No. 68671

[P Ransome-Wallis

Right : Class J50 0-6-0T No. 68947

[*P. Ransome-Wallis*

Left : Class J69 0-6-0T No. 68577

[*P. Ransome-Wallis*

Right : Class J67/1 0-6-0T No. 68592

[*A. F. Cook*

Left : Class J88 0-6-0T No. 68350

[*D. R. Inglis*

Above : Class N2/3
0-6-2T No. 69567

Left : Class N1
0-6-2T No. 69470

[*Photos :*
W. Beckerlegge

Below : Class N7/3
0-6-2T No. 69725

[*A. F. Cook*

New No.	Former No.	Region	New No.	Former No.	Region
90057	63057	N.E.	90104	77004	E.
90058	63058	Sc.	90105	77005	W.
90059	63059	E.	90106	77006	N.E.
90060	63060	E.	90107	77007	S.
90061	63061	N.E.	90108	77008	E.
90062	63062	E.	90109	77010	L.M.
90063	63063	L.M.	90110	77012	W.
90064	63064	E.	90111	77013	E.
90065	63065	E.	90112	77014	L.M.
90066	63066	E.	90113	77015	W.
90067	63067	N.E.	90114	77016	Sc.
90068	63068	N.E.	90115	77017	E.
90069	63069	N.E.	90116	77018	N.E.
90070	63070	E.	90117	77019	Sc.
90071	63071	Sc.	90118	77020	E.
90072	63072	N.E.	90119	77022	E.
90073	63073	E.	90120	77023	E.
90074	63074	N.E.	90121	77024	Sc.
90075	63075	E.	90122	77025	W.
90076	63076	N.E.	90123	77026	W.
90077	63077	Sc.	90124	77027	W.
90078	63078	N.E.	90125	77028	W.
90079	63079	E.	90126	77029	L.M.
90080	63080	E.	90127	77030	S.
90081	63081	N.E.	90128	77031	Sc.
90082	63082	N.E.	90129	77032	E.
90083	63083	E.	90130	77034	E.
90084	63084	E.	90131	77035	E.
90085	63085	E.	90132	77036	N.E.
90086	63086	N.E.	90133	77037	E.
90087	63087	E.	90134	77039	Sc.
90088	63088	E.	90135	77040	L.M.
90089	63089	N.E.	90136	77041	E.
90090	63090	N.E.	90137	77042	E.
90091	63091	N.E.	90138	77044	L.M.
90092	63092	N.E.	90139	77047	E.
90093	63093	E.	90140	77048	W.
90094	63094	N.E.	90141	77049	L.M.
90095	63095	E.	90142	77150	S.
90096	63096	E.	90143	77151	L.M.
90097	63097	Sc.	90144	77152	E.
90098	63098	N.E.	90145	77155	Sc.
90099	63099	N.E.	90146	77157	E.
90100	63100	N.E.	90147	77160	W.
90101	77000	W.	90148	77161	W.
90102	77001	W.	90149	77162	Sc.
90103	77003	N.E.	90150	77163	E.

New No.	Former No.	Region	New No.	Former No.	Region
90151	77164	E.	90198	77230	Sc.
90152	77165	W.	90199	77231	Sc.
90153	77166	E.	90200	77232	N.E.
90154	77167	E.	90201	77234	W.
90155	77169	N.E.	90202	77235	E.
90156	77170	N.E.	90203	77237	Sc.
90157	77171	W.	90204	77239	W.
90158	77173	E.	90205	77241	W.
90159	77174	L.M.	90206	77242	L.M.
90160	77175	N.E.	90207	77247	W.
90161	77176	E.	90208	77248	N.E.
90162	77178	E.	90209	77249	E.
90163	77179	W.	90210	77252	N.E.
90164	77180	S.	90211	77253	E.
90165	77181	E.	90212	77255	W.
90166	77182	E.	90213	77256	S.
90167	77184	W.	90214	77257	W.
90168	77185	Sc.	90215	77258	E.
90169	77186	E.	90216	77259	S.
90170	77187	Sc.	90217	77260	N.E.
90171	77192	L.M.	90218	77261	E.
90172	77195	N.E.	90219	77302	Sc.
90173	77196	W.	90220	77303	E.
90174	77198	Sc.	90221	77305	E.
90175	77199	E.	90222	77306	Sc.
90176	77200	W.	90223	77307	E.
90177	77201	Sc.	90224	77309	E.
90178	77202	L.M.	90225	77310	W.
90179	77203	W.	90226	77311	S.
90180	77204	E.	90227	77312	L.M.
90181	77205	S.	90228	77313	Sc.
90182	77206	Sc.	90229	77314	E.
90183	77207	L.M.	90230	77315	N.E.
90184	77208	N.E.	90231	77317	L.M.
90185	77209	E.	90232	77319	E.
90186	77210	W.	90233	77320	N.E.
90187	77212	W.	90234	77321	S.
90188	77214	W.	90235	77323	N.E.
90189	77215	E.	90236	77324	Sc.
90190	77218	E.	90237	77325	W.
90191	77221	E.	90238	77326	W.
90192	77222	Sc.	90239	77327	E.
90193	77225	Sc.	90240	77328	N.E.
90194	77226	S.	90241	77329	L.M.
90195	77227	E.	90242	77330	W.
90196	77228	E.	90243	77332	W.
90197	77229	W.	90244	77334	E.

New No.	Former No.	Region
90245	77335	W.
90246	77338	E.
90247	77340	S.
90248	77342	Sc.
90249	77348	W.
90250	77350	E.
90251	77351	E.
90252	77352	E.
90253	77353	E.
90254	77355	S.
90255	77356	E.
90256	77358	E.
90257	77359	S.
90258	77362	L.M.
90259	77364	E.
90260	77365	Sc.
90261	77368	W.
90262	77371	Sc.
90263	77372	E.
90264	77374	L.M.
90265	77375	Sc.
90266	77378	L.M.
90267	77379	S.
90268	77380	W.
90269	77381	E.
90270	77386	E.
90271	77388	W.
90272	77390	N.E.
90273	77392	N.E.
90274	77393	L.M.
90275	77394	E.
90276	77395	E.
90277	77398	W.
90278	77399	Sc.
90279	77401	E.
90280	77402	E.
90281	77404	Sc.
90282	77406	Sc.
90283	77407	L.M.
90284	77408	W.
90285	77411	E.
90286	77413	E.
90287	77414	E.
90288	77415	E.
90289	77416	Sc.
90290	77418	E.
90291	77419	Sc.

New No.	Former No.	Region
90292	77421	W.
90293	77424	Sc.
90294	77425	E.
90295	77426	L.M.
90296	77428	E.
90297	77429	W.
90298	77431	Sc.
90299	77432	E.
90300	77433	Sc.
90301	77434	E.
90302	77436	E.
90303	77439	N.E.
90304	77440	E.
90305	77441	N.E.
90306	77442	Sc.
90307	77443	W.
90308	77444	S.
90309	77445	N.E.
90310	77447	E.
90311	77449	E.
90312	70801	W.
90313	70802	Sc.
90314	70807	L.M.
90315	70808	W.
90316	70809	W.
90317	70811	S.
90318	70814	W.
90319	70817	Sc.
90320	70825	L.M.
90321	70829	W.
90322	70833	W.
90323	70834	E.
90324	70836	W.
90325	70838	W.
90326	70839	L.M.
90327	70843	W.
90328	70845	L.M.
90329	70849	E.
90330	70850	E.
90331	70851	L.M.
90332	70853	S.
90333	70857	E.
90334	70859	E.
90335	70860	L.M.
90336	70864	W.
90337	70865	W.
90338	70866	W.

New No.	Former No.	Region	New No.	Former No.	Region
90339	70867	E.	90386	78592	E.
90340	70871	E.	90387	78594	L.M.
90341	70874	E.	90388	78595	W.
90342	70875	W.	90389	78596	S.
90343	70876	W.	90390	78597	S.
90344	70877	N.E.	90391	78598	E.
90345	70878	S.	90392	78599	E.
90346	77263	N.E.	90393	78600	E.
90347	77270	S.	90394	78601	N.E.
90348	77271	L.M.	90395	78602	W.
90349	77274	E.	90396	78604	W.
90350	77278	Sc.	90397	78605	E.
90351	77280	W.	90398	78606	L.M.
90352	77283	N.E.	90399	78607	L.M.
90353	77285	E.	90400	78609	E.
90354	77286	S.	90401	78610	E.
90355	77288	W.	90402	78612	E.
90356	77289	W.	90403	78614	N.E.
90357	77291	W.	90404	78615	W.
90358	77292	E.	90405	78616	N.E.
90359	77294	W.	90406	78621	W.
90360	77296	S.	90407	78624	W.
90361	77297	W.	90408	78531	S.
90362	77299	E.	90409	78532	N.E.
90363	78510	W.	90410	78537	E.
90364	78512	L.M.	90411	78538	N.E.
90365	78514	E.	90412	78541	W.
90366	78521	W.	90413	78542	W.
90367	78522	L.M.	90414	78543	W.
90368	78525	E.	90415	78544	W.
90369	78526	E.	90416	78546	L.M.
90370	78560	E.	90417	78551	W.
90371	78561	L.M.	90418	78553	E.
90372	78563	W.	90419	78554	W.
90373	78564	N.E.	90420	78556	W.
90374	78568	L.M.	90421	78559	E.
90375	78569	S.	90422	63101	E.
90376	78572	Sc.	90423	63102	N.E.
90377	78575	N.E.	90424	63103	N.E.
90378	78578	N.E.	90425	63104	E.
90379	78580	E.	90426	63105	N.E.
90380	78581	E.	90427	63106	N.E.
90381	78583	E.	90428	63107	E.
90382	78585	N.E.	90429	63108	N.E.
90383	78587	N.E.	90430	63109	N.E.
90384	78588	E.	90431	63110	E.
90385	78590	W.	90432	63111	N.E.

New No.	Former No.	Region	New No.	Former No.	Region
90433	63112	E.	90480	63159	E.
90434	63113	N.E.	90481	63160	N.E.
90435	63114	N.E.	90482	63161	N.E.
90436	63115	Sc.	90483	63162	N.E.
90437	63116	E.	90484	63163	E.
90438	63117	E.	90485	63164	N.E.
90439	63118	E.	90486	63165	E.
90440	63119	Sc.	90487	63166	N.E.
90441	63120	Sc.	90488	63167	N.E.
90442	63121	E.	90489	63168	Sc.
90443	63122	E.	90490	63169	E.
90444	63123	Sc.	90491	63170	E.
90445	63124	N.E.	90492	63171	E.
90446	63125	N.E.	90493	63172	Sc.
90447	63126	L.M.	90494	63173	E.
90448	63127	E.	90495	63174	E.
90449	63128	N.E.	90496	63175	Sc.
90450	63129	N.E.	90497	63176	N.E.
90451	63130	N.E.	90498	63177	Sc.
90452	63131	N.E.	90499	63178	E.
90453	63132	E.	90500	63179	N.E.
90454	63133	E.	90501	63180	Sc.
90455	63134	Sc.	90502	63181	E.
90456	63135	E.	90503	63182	N.E.
90457	63136	N.E.	90504	63183	E.
90458	63137	N.E.	90505	63184	Sc.
90459	63138	N.E.	90506	63185	E.
90460	63139	E.	90507	63186	E.
90461	63140	N.E.	90508	63187	E.
90462	63141	N.E.	90509	63188	E.
90463	63142	Sc.	90510	63189	E.
90464	63143	Sc.	90511	63190	N.E.
90465	63144	N.E.	90512	63191	E.
90466	63145	E.	90513	63192	Sc.
90467	63146	N.E.	90514	63193	E.
90468	63147	Sc.	90515	63194	Sc.
90469	63148	Sc.	90516	63195	E.
90470	63149	N.E.	90517	63196	N.E.
90471	63150	E.	90518	63197	N.E.
90472	63151	Sc.	90519	63198	E.
90473	63152	E.	90520	63199	E.
90474	63153	E.	90521	77050	N.E.
90475	63154	N.E.	90522	77051	E.
90476	63155	E.	90523	77052	S.
90477	63156	E.	90524	77053	W.
90478	63157	N.E.	90525	77054	W.
90479	63158	N.E.	90526	77055	N.E.

New No.	Former No.	Region	New No.	Former No.	Region
90527	77056	S.	90574	77118	E.
90528	77057	E.	90575	77119	Sc.
90529	77058	W.	90576	77120	L.M.
90530	77059	S.	90577	77121	E.
90531	77060	W.	90578	77122	S.
90532	77061	E.	90579	77123	W.
90533	77062	S.	90580	77124	E.
90534	77063	Sc.	90581	77126	W.
90535	77064	W.	90582	77127	E.
90536	77066	Sc.	90583	77128	E.
90537	77067	E.	90584	77129	L.M.
90538	77068	E.	90585	77130	W.
90539	77070	Sc.	90586	77135	N.E.
90540	77071	E.	90587	77138	E.
90541	77072	L.M.	90588	77141	W.
90542	77073	Sc.	90589	77142	W.
90543	77074	S.	90590	77144	E.
90544	77075	E.	90591	77145	W.
90545	77076	Sc.	90592	77147	L.M.
90546	77077	W.	90593	77148	W.
90547	77078	Sc.	90594	77149	E.
90548	77079	W.	90595	77451	L.M.
90549	77080	Sc.	90596	77452	E.
90550	77081	N.E.	90597	77453	E.
90551	77085	E.	90598	77454	E.
90552	77086	S.	90599	77455	L.M.
90553	77087	Sc.	90600	77456	Sc.
90554	77088	E.	90601	77457	E.
90555	77089	L.M.	90602	77458	E.
90556	77090	S.	90603	77459	N.E.
90557	77092	W.	90604	77460	S.
90558	77094	S.	90605	77461	N.E.
90559	77095	N.E.	90606	77462	N.E.
90560	77096	Sc.	90607	77463	W.
90561	77097	W.	90608	77464	E.
90562	77098	S.	90609	77465	N.E.
90563	77099	W.	90610	77466	W.
90564	77101	S.	90611	77467	N.E.
90565	77102	W.	90612	77468	E.
90566	77103	S.	90613	77469	E.
90567	77104	N.E.	90614	77470	Sc.
90568	77106	W.	90615	77471	W.
90569	77107	Sc.	90616	77476	Sc.
90570	77108	S.	90617	77479	W.
90571	77111	N.E.	90618	77480	N.E.
90572	77115	W.	90619	77481	S.
90573	77116	W.	90620	77482	E.

New No.	Former No.	Region	New No.	Former No.	Region
90621	77484	L.M.	90668	79198	E.
90622	77485	S.	90669	79199	S.
90623	77488	N.E.	90670	79202	N.E.
90624	77489	W.	90671	79203	S.
90625	77492	N.E.	90672	79204	E.
90626	77494	L.M.	90673	79205	E.
90627	77497	N.E.	90674	79206	N.E.
90628	77499	E.	90675	79207	S.
90629	77503	N.E.	90676	79208	E.
90630	77508	W.	90677	79209	N.E.
90631	78626	E.	90678	79210	S.
90632	78629	E.	90679	79213	E.
90633	78632	W.	90680	79214	W.
90634	78637	E.	90681	79215	L.M.
90635	78638	E.	90682	79219	W.
90636	78643	E.	90683	79220	N.E.
90637	78644	E.	90684	79221	W.
90638	78650	E.	90685	79224	W.
90639	78652	E.	90686	79225	W.
90640	78658	L.M.	90687	79226	L.M.
90641	78666	S.	90688	79227	N.E.
90642	78671	W.	90689	79228	L.M.
90643	78672	E.	90690	79229	Sc.
90644	78675	E.	90691	79232	L.M.
90645	78681	W.	90692	79233	E.
90646	78682	E.	90693	79234	W.
90647	78683	E.	90694	79235	W.
90648	78684	E.	90695	79239	N.E.
90649	78685	W.	90696	79242	E.
90650	78688	S.	90697	79243	E.
90651	78689	E.	90698	79244	W.
90652	78695	W.	90699	79254	W.
90653	78700	E.	90700	79259	E.
90654	78704	E.	90701	79261	W.
90655	78705	S.	90702	79262	S.
90656	78714	W.	90703	79263	E.
90657	78715	E.	90704	79264	N.E.
90658	78717	W.	90705	79265	Sc.
90659	79178	E.	90706	79266	W.
90660	79181	E.	90707	79268	W.
90661	79182	N.E.	90708	79269	W.
90662	79184	E.	90709	79271	E.
90663	79186	N.E.	90710	79272	W.
90664	79190	W.	90711	79273	W.
90665	79194	E.	90712	79274	W.
90666	79195	W.	90713	79275	L.M.
90667	79196	E.	90714	79276	E.

New No.	Former No.	Region	New No.	Former No.	Region
90715	79278	W.	90724	79302	W.
90716	79279	W.	90725	79303	L.M.
90717	79280	E.	90726	79304	W.
90718	79281	S.	90727	79306	Sc.
90719	79282	W.	90728	79307	W.
90720	79283	L.M.	90729	79309	L.M.
90721	79294	W.	90730	79310	N.E.
90722	79298	W.	90731	79311	W.
90723	79301	L.M.	90732	79312	E.

2-10-0 Class WD

Min'stry of Supply "Austerity" 2-10-0 locomotives purchased by British Railways, 1948.

Introduced 1943. Riddles M.o.S. design.
Weights: Loco. 78 tons 6 cwt.
Tender 55 tons 10 cwt.
Pressure: 225 lb. Cyls. (O) 19″ × 28″.
Driving Wheels: 4′ 8½″ T.E. 34,215 lb.
Walschaerts gear, P.V.

Notes.

RENUMBERING.—The first column shows new British Railways number, the second the former W.D. number.

LOCATION.—The third column shows the Region on which the engines were located as at 31st May, 1949. Key as for Class W.D. 2-8-0 above. Some of these locos, have not yet been put into traffic on British Railways.

New No.	Former W.D. No.	Region
90750	73774	Sc.
90751	73775	Sc.
90752	73776	Sc.
90753	73777	Sc.
90754	73778	Sc.
90755	73779	Sc.
90756	73780	Sc.
90757	73781	Sc.
90758	73782	Sc.
90759	73783	Sc.
90760	73784	Sc.
90761	73785	Sc.
90762	73786	Sc.
90763	73787	Sc.
90764	73788	Sc.
90765	73789	Sc.
90766	73790	Sc.
90767	73791	Sc.
90768	73792	Sc.
90769	73793	Sc.
90770	73794	Sc.
90771	73795	Sc.
90712	73796	Sc.
90773	73798	Sc.
90774	73799	C.M.E., Rugby

Above : Class N13 0-6-2T No. E9118 (new No. 69118)

[P. Ransome-Wallis

Right : Class N5/3 0-6-2T No. 69311

[M. P. Mileham

Below : Class N8 0-6-2T No. 69371

[P. Ransome-Wallis

Above : Class A5
4-6-2T No. 69829
[*C. R. L. Coles*

Left : Class L3
2-6-4T No. 69054
[*B. V. Franey*

Right : Class A7
4-6-2T No. 69771
[*B. V. Franey*

Below : Class A6
4-6-2T No. 69798
[*E. V. Fry*

Facing Page

Top : Class V1
2-6-2T No. 67629
[*B. V. Franey*

Centre : Class L1
2-6-4T No. 67724
[*E. R. Wethersett*

Bottom : Class Q1
0-8-0T No. 69936
[*J. F. Ayland*

BRITISH RAILWAYS
67629

67724
BRITISH RAILWAYS

BRITISH RAILWAYS

Left : Class Y7 0-4-0T No. 68088

[A. F. Cook

Below right : Class Y11 petrol engine No. 68189

[E. V. Fry

Above left : Class Y11 petrol engine No. 8188 (new No. 68188)

[E. V. Fry

Right : Class J92 0-6-0T No. 68667

[P. Ransome-Wallis

PRINCIPAL DIMENSIONS OF EX-L.N.E.R. LOCOMOTIVES AND INDEX TO CLASSES

Tractive effort calculated to nearest 5lb. S—Superheated. SS—Some Superheated.

Class	Type	Designer	Originating Pre-Grouping Owner (if any)	Building or Re-building Date	Weight of Loco.	Boiler Pressure	Cylinders	Driving Wheels	Tractive Effort at 85% B.P.	Page
					T. Cwt.	Lb. per sq. in.	Ins.		Lb.	
A–1	4–6–2	Peppercorn	—	1948–9	104 2	250S	(3) 19 × 26	6′ 8″	37,400	13
A–1/1	4–6–2	Gresley (1922) ... Reb. Thompson	G.N.R.	1945	101 0	250S	(3) 19 × 26	6′ 8″	37,400	13
A–2	4–6–2	Peppercorn	—	1947–48	101 0	250S	(3) 19 × 26	6′ 2″	40,430	13
A–2/1	4–6–2	Thompson	—	1944–45	98 0	225S	(3) 19 × 26	6′ 2″	36,385	13
A–2/2	4–6–2	Gresley (Cl.P2. 1934-36) Reb. Thompson	—	1943–44	101 10	225S	(3) 20 × 26	6′ 2″	40,320	13
A–2/3	4–6–2	Thompson	—	1946–47	101 10	250S	(3) 19 × 26	6′ 2″	40,430	13
A–3	4–6–2	Gresley	—	1927–34	96 5	250S	(3) 19 × 26	6′ 8″	32,910	8
A–4	4–6–2	Gresley	—	1935–38	102 19	250S	(3) 18½ × 26	6′ 8″	{35,455 / 33,616‡}	8
A–5/1	4–6–2T	Robinson	G.C.R.	1911–23	85 18	180S	20 × 26	5′ 7″	23,750	63
A–5/2	4–6–2T	Robinson-Gresley	—	1925–26	90 11	180S	20 × 26	5′ 7″	23,750	63
A–6*	4–6–2T	W. Worsdell (1907-08) Reb. Raven	N.E.R.	1915–16	{78 0 / 79 0S}	175SS	19 × 26	5′ 1¼″	23,830	62
A–7	4–6–2T	Raven	N.E.R.	1910–11	87 10	{180 / 160S}	(3) 16½ × 26	4′ 7¼″	{29,405 / 26,140}	62
A–8†	4–6–2T	Raven (1913-22) ... Reb. Gresley	N.E.R.	1931–6	86 18	175	(3) 16½ × 26	5′ 9″	22,940	63
B–1	4–6–0	Thompson ...	—	1942–49	71 3	225S	O 20 × 26	6′ 2″	26,880	15
B–2	4–6–0	Gresley (1928-37) ... Reb. Thompson	—	1945–49	73 10	225S	O 20 × 26	6′ 8″	24,865	19

*Class A6 rebuilt from Worsdell 4-6-0T, N.E.R., Class W. †Class A8 rebuilt from N.E.R. 4-4-4T, Class D. (L.N.E.R. H1)
‡ With 17″ × 26″ inside cylinder.

Class	Type	Designer	Originating Pre-Grouping Owner (if any)	Building or Re-building Date	Weight of Loco.	Boiler Pressure	Cylinders	Driving Wheels	Tractive Effort at 85% B.P.	Page
					T. Cwt.	Lb. per sq. in.	Ins.		Lb.	
B-4/3	4-6-0	Robinson	G.C.R.	1906	71 15	180S	O 21 ×26	6′ 7″	22,205	18
B-4/4	4-6-0	Robinson	G.C.R.	1906	70 14	180S	O 19 ×26	6′ 7″	18,180	18
B-5	4-6-0	Robinson	G.C.R.	1902-04	64 3 65 4	180S	O 19 ×26 O 21 ×26	6′ 1″	19,670 24,030	20
B-7	4-6-0	Robinson	G.C.R.	1921-24	79 10	180S	(4) 16 ×26	5′ 8″	29,950	20
B-12/1	4-6-0	S. D. Holden	G.E.R.	1911-20	63 0	180S	20 ×28	6′ 6″	21,970	18
B-12/3	4-6-0	B-12, Reb. Gresley ...	—	1932-44	69 10	180S	20 ×28	6′ 6″	21,970	18
B-13*	4-6-0	W. Worsdell ...	N.E.R.	1906	62 10	160S	O 20 ×26	6′ 1¼″	19,310	20
B-16	4-6-0	Raven	N.E.R.	1919-24	77 14	180S	(3) 18½ ×26	5′ 8″	30,030	17
B-16/2	4-6-0	B-16, Reb. Gresley ...	—	1937-40	79 4	180S	(3) 18½ ×26	5′ 8″	30,030	17
B-16/3	4-6-0	B-16, Reb. Thompson	—	1944-48	78 19	180S	(3) 18½ ×26	5′ 8″	30,030	17
B-17	4-6-0	Gresley	—	1928-37	77 5	180S 225S	(3) 17½ ×26	6′ 8″	22,480 28,555	18
B-17/5	4-6-0	Gresley	—	1937	80 10	180S	(3) 17½ ×26	6′ 8″	22,480	18
C-1	4-4-2	Ivatt	G.N.R.	1904-10	69 12	170S	O 19 ×24 O 20 ×24	6′ 8″ 6′ 8″	15,650 17,340	31
C-4/2	4-4-2	Robinson	G.C.R.	1903-06	70 17	180S	O 19 ×26	6′ 9″	17,730	31
C-4/4	4-4-2	Robinson	G.C.R.	1903-06	71 18	180S	O 21 ×26	6′ 9″	21,660	31
C-12	4-4-2T	Ivatt	G.N.R.	1898-07	62 6	170 175	18 ×26	5′ 8″	17,900 18,425	52 52
C-13	4-4-2T	Robinson	G.C.R.	1903-05	66 13	160S	18 ×26	5′ 7″	17,100	52
C-14	4-4-2T	Robinson	G.C.R.	1907	71 0	160S	18 ×26	5′ 7″	17,100	52
C-15	4-4-2T	Reid	N.B.R.	1911-13	68 15	175	18 ×26	5′ 9″	18,160	52
C-16	4-4-2T	Reid	N.B.R.	1915-21	72 10	165SS	19 ×26	5′ 9″	19,080	52
D-1	4-4-0	Ivatt	G.N.R.	1911	53 6	170S	18½ ×26	6′ 8″	16,075	26
D-2	4-4-0	Ivatt	G.N.R.	1897-09	47 10	170S 175	17½ ×26	6′ 8″	14,380 14,805	26
D-3	4-4-0	Ivatt (1896-9) Reb. Gresley ...	G.N.R.	1912-28	45 14	175	17½ ×26	6′ 8″	14,805	26

D–9	4–4–0	Robinson	G.C.R.	1901–04	55	14	180S	19 × 26	6′ 9″	17,730	27
D–10	4–4–0	Robinson	G.C.R.	1913	61	0	180S	20 × 26	6′ 9″	19,645	29
D–11	4–4–0	Robinson	G.C.R.	1920–24	61	3	180S	20 × 26	6′ 9″	19,645	29
D–15	4–4–0	J. Holden	G.E.R.	1900–03	52	4	180S	19 × 26	7′ 0″	17,095	28
D–16/2	4–4–0	Reb. Holden J. Holden	G.E.R.	1923–30	54	18	180S	19 × 26	7′ 0″	17,095	28
D–16/3	4–4–0	Reb. Hill & Hill D–15 & D–16/2 Reb. Gresley	—	1933–48	55	18	180S	19 × 26	7′ 0″	17,095	28
D–20	4–4–0	W. Wordsell ...	N.E.R.	1899–07	54	2	175S	19 × 26	6′ 10″	17,025	27
D–20/2	4–4–0	D–20 Reb. Gresley ...	—	1936–48	55	9	175S	19 × 26	6′ 10″	17,025	27
D–29	4–4–0	Reid	N.B.R.	1909–11	54	4	190S	19 × 26	6′ 6″	19,435	27
D30/1	4–4–0	Reid	N.B.R.	1912	57	6	165S	20 × 26	6′ 6″	18,700	27
D30/2				1914–20	57	16					27
D–31	4–4–0	Holmes (1890-9) ... Reb. Reid & Chalmers	N.B.R.	1918–24	46	8	175S	18½ × 26	6′ 6″	16,515	26
D–32	4–4–0	Reid	N.B.R.	1906	53	14	180S	19 × 26	6′ 0″	19,945	28
D–33	4–4–0	Reid	N.B.R.	1909–10	54	3	180S	19 × 26	6′ 0″	19,945	28
D–34	4–4–0	Reid	N.B.R.	1913–20	57	4	165S	20 × 26	6′ 0″	20,260	28
D–40	4–4–0	Pickersgill	G.N. of S.R.	1899–15	46	7	165	18 × 26	6′ 1″	16,185	27
		Heywood	—	1920–21	48	13	165S	18 × 26	6′ 1″	16,185	27
D–41	4–4–0	Pickersgill and J. Johnson	G.N. of S.R.	1893–98	45	0	165	18 × 26	6′ 1″	16,185	26
D–49/1	4–4–0	Gresley	—	1927–29	66	0	180S	(3) 17 × 26	6′ 8″	21,555	30
D–49/2	4–4–0	Gresley	—	1928–35	64	10	180S	(3) 17 × 26	6′ 8″	21,555	30
D–49/4	4–4–0	Reb. Thompson ...	—	1942	62	0	180S	20 × 26	6′ 8″	19,890	30
E–4	2–4–0	J. Holden	G.E.R.	1891–02	40	6	160	17½ × 24	5′ 8″	14,700	31
F–2	2–4–2T	Pollitt	G.C.R.	1898	62	6	160	18 × 26	5′ 7″	17,100	50
F–3	2–4–2T	J. Holden	G.E.R.	1895–02	58	12	160	17½ × 24	5′ 8″	14,710	50
F–4	2–4–2T	J. Holden	G.E.R.	1906–09	53	19	160	17½ × 24	5′ 4″	15,620	51
F–5	2–4–2T	J. Holden	G.E.R.	1903–09	53	19	180	17½ × 24	5′ 4″	17,570	51
F–6	2–4–2T	J. and S. D. Holden ...	G.E.R.	1911	56	9	180	17½ × 24	5′ 4″	17,570	51
G–5	0–4–4T	W. Worsdell ...	N.E.R.	1894–01	54	4	160	18 × 24	5′ 1½″	17,265	51
J–1	0–6–0	Ivatt	G.N.R.	1908	46	14	175	18 × 26	5′ 8″	18,430	38
J–2	0–6–0	Ivatt	G.N.R.	1912	50	10	170S	19 × 26	5′ 8″	19,945	39

* Counter pressure locomotive for testing purposes.

Class	Type	Designer	Originating Pre-Grouping Owner (if any)	Building or Re-building Date	Weight of Loco.	Boiler Pressure	Cylinders	Driving Wheels	Tractive Effort at 85% B.P	Page
					T. Cwt.	Lb. per sq. in.	Ins.		Lb.	
J–3	0–6–0	P. Stirling and Ivatt (1892-01) Reb. Gresley	G.N.R.	1912–28	42 12	175	17½ × 26	5′ 2″	19,105	35
J–4	0–6–0	P. Stirling and Ivatt ...	G.N.R.	1896–01	41 5	175	17½ × 26	5′ 2″	19,105	35
J–5	0–6–0	Ivatt	G.N.R.	1909–10	47 6	{175 170S}	18 × 26	5′ 2″	{20,210 19,630	40
J–6	0–6–0	Ivatt and Gresley ...	G.N.R.	1911–22	50 10	170S	19 × 26	5′ 2″	21,875	35
J–10	0–6–0	Parker and Pollitt ...	M.S. & L.R.	1892–02	41 6	160	18 × 26	5′ 1″	18,780	39
J–11	0–6–0	Robinson	G.C.R.	1901–10	{51 19 52 2}	180SS	18½ × 26	}5′ 2″	21,960	36
J–11/3	0–6–0	Reb. Thompson	—	1942–8	53 6	180S	18½ × 26	}		36
J–15	0–6–0	J. Holden	G.E.R.	1886–13	37 2	160	17½ × 24	4′ 11″	16,940	40
J–17	0–6–0	J. Holden	G.E.R.	1900–10	45 8	180S	19 × 26	4′ 11″	24,340	40
J–19	0–6–0	Hill (1912-20) ... Reb. Gresley	G.E.R.	1934–9	50 7	{170S 180S 160S	20 × 28 19 × 28	4′ 11″ 4′ 11″	27,430 {26,215 23,300	37
J–20	0–6–0	Hill	G.E.R.	1920–22	54 15	180	20 × 28	4′ 11″	29,045	37
J–21	0–6–0	{T. W. Worsdell ... Reb. W. Worsdell T. W. Worsdell ... Reb. Raven}	N.E.R.	1886–95	{42 1 42 19 43 15S	}160	{18 × 24 19 × 24 19 × 26	}5′ 1¼″	{17,265 19,240 20,840	39
J–24	0–6–0	{W. Worsdell ... W. Worsdell ... Reb. Raven}	N.E.R.	1894–98	{38 10 39 11S	}160	{18 × 24 18½ × 24	}4′ 7¼″	{19,140 20,220	49
J–25	0–6–0	{W. Worsdell ... W. Worsdell ... Reb. Raven}	N.E.R.	1898–02	{39 11 40 17 41 14S	}160	18½ × 26	4′ 7¼″	21,905	49
J–26	0–6–0	W. Worsdell ..	N.E.R.	1904–05	46 16	180	18½ × 26	4′ 7¼″	24,640	49
J–27	0–6–0	{W. Worsdell ... Raven ... ...}	N.E.R.	1906–23	{47 0 49 10S	}180	18½ × 26	4′ 7¼″	24,640	50
J–35/4 J–35/5}	0–6–0	Reid	N.B.R.	{1908-13 1906–8	50 15 51 0	}180S	18½ × 26	5′ 0″	22,080	36 36

J-36	0-6-0	Holmes (1888 - 1900) Reb. Reid and Chalmers	N.B.R.	1913-22	41 19	165		18 × 26	5′ 0″	19,690	39
J-37	0-6-0	Reid	N.B.R.	1914-21	54 14	180S		19½ × 26	5′ 0″	25,210	37
J-38	0-6-0	Gresley	—	1926	58 19	180S		20 × 26	4′ 8″	28,415	50
J-39	0-6-0	Gresley	—	1926-41	57 17	180S		20 × 26	5′ 2″	25,665	38
J-50/1	0-6-0T	Gresley	—	1913-14	56 6	175		18½ × 26	4′ 8″	23,635	58
J-50/2	0-6-0T	Gresley	—	1914-24	57 0	175		18½ × 26	4′ 8″	23,635	58
J-50/3 J-50/4	0-6-0T	Gresley	—	1926-39	58 3	175		18½ × 26	4′ 8″	23,635	58 58
J-52/1 J-52/2	0-6-0ST	P. Stirling (1892-97) Reb. Gresley Ivatt	G.N.R.	1922-32 1897-09	51 14	170 170 175		18 × 26	4′ 8″	21,735 21,735 22,370	58 58
J-55	0-6-0T	P. Stirling (1891-2) ... Reb. Gresley	G.N.R.	1934	45 16	175 160		17½ × 26	4′ 8″	21,150 19,340	55
J-62	0-6-0ST	Pollitt	G.C.R.	1897	30 17	150	O	13 × 20	3′ 6″	10,260	55
J-63	0-6-0T	Robinson	G.C.R.	1906-14	37 9	150	O	13 × 20	3′ 6″	10,260	55
J-65	0-6-0T	J. Holden	G.E.R.	1889-93	36 11	160		14 × 20	4′ 0″	11,105	55
J-66	0-6-0T	J. Holden	G.E.R.	1886-88	40 6	160		16½ × 22	4′ 0″	16,970	56
J-67/1	0-6-0T	J. Holden	G.E.R.	1890-01	40 0	160		16½ × 22	4′ 0″	16,970	57
J-67/2	0-6-0T	J. and S. D. Holden ...	G.E.R.	1890-04	41 8	160		16½ × 22	4′ 0″	16,970	57
J-68	0-6-0T	S. D. Holden	G.E.R.	1912-23	42 9	180		16½ × 22	4′ 0″	19,090	57
J-69	0-6-0T	J. Holden	G.E.R.	1902-04	42 9	180		16½ × 22	4′ 0″	19,090	57
J-70	0-6-0T	J. Holden	G.E.R.	1903-21	27 1	180	O	12 × 15	3′ 1″	8,930	55
J-71	0-6-0T	T. W. Worsdell ...	N.E.R.	1886-95	37 12	140		16 × 22 18 × 22 16⅝ × 22	4′ 7¼″	12,130 15,355 13,300	55
J-72	0-6-0T	W. Worsdell ...	N.E.R.	1898-1925	38 12	140		17 × 24 18 × 24	4′ 1¼″	16,760 18,790	57
J-73	0-6-0T	W. Worsdell ...	N.E.R.	1891-92	46 15	160		19 × 24	4′ 7¼″	21,320	56
J-77	0-6-0T	Fletcher and T. W. Worsdell (1874-84) Reb. W. Worsdell and Raven	N.E.R.	1899-21	43 0	160		17 × 22	4′ 1¼″	17,560	56
J-83	0-6-0T	Holmes	N.B.R.	1900-01	45 5	150		17 × 26	4′ 6″	17,745	56
J-88	0-6-0T	Holmes	N.B.R.	1904-19	38 14	130	O	15 × 22	3′ 9″	12,155	56
J-92	0-6-0CT	Ruston and Proctor (1868) Rebuilt by J. Holden	G.E.R.	1891-4	40 8	140		16 × 22	4′ 0″	13,960	57

Class	Type	Designer	Originating Pre-Grouping Owner (if any)	Building or Re-building Date	Weight of Loco.	Boiler Pressure	Cylinders	Driving Wheels	Tractive Effort at 85% B.P.	Page
					T. Cwt.	Lb. per sq. in.	Ins.		Lb.	
J–93	0–6–0T	W. Marriott	M. & G.N.J.R.	1897–05	37 14	150	O 16 × 20	3′ 7″	15,180	56
J–94	0–6–0ST	Riddles (M.O.S.) ...	—	1943–46	48 5	170	18 × 26	4′ 3″	23,870	53
K–1/1, K–1	2–6–0	K–4, Reb. Thompson; Peppercorn ...	—	1945–9	66 17	225S	O 20 × 26	5′ 2″	32,080	25
K–2	2–6–0	Gresley	G.N.R.	1914–21	64 8	180S	O 20 × 26	5′ 8″	23,400	20
K–3	2–6–0	Gresley	G.N.R.	1920–37	72 12	180S	(3) 18½ × 26	5′ 8″	30,030	25
K–4	2–6–0	Gresley	—	1937–38	68 8	200S	(3) 18½ × 26	5′ 2″	36,600	25
K–5	2–6–0	K–3, Reb. Thompson	—	1945	71 5	225S	O 20 × 26	5′ 8″	29,250	25
L–1	2–6–4T	Thompson	—	1945–49	89	225S	O 20 × 26	5′ 2″	32,080	53
L–3	2–6–4T	Robinson	G.C.R.	1914–17	97 9	180S	21 × 26; 20 × 26	5′ 1″	28,760; 26,085	59
N–1	0–6–2T	Ivatt	G.N.R.	1907–12	64 14; 65 17	175; 170S	18 × 26	5′ 8″	18,430; 17,900	61
N–2	0–6–2T	Gresley	G.N.R.	1920–29	*	170S	19 × 26	5′ 8″	19,945	61
N4/2, N4/4	0–6–2T	Parker	M.S. & L.R.	1889–92	61 10; 61 19	160	18 × 26	5′ 1″	18,780	60
N–5/2	0–6–2T	Parker and Pollitt ...	M.S. & L.R.	1891–01	62 7	160	18 × 26	5′ 1″	18,780	60
N–5/3	0–6–2T	Pollitt (1898) ... Reb. Robinson	G.C.R.	1915	64 13	160	18½ × 26	5′ 1″	19,840	60
N–7	0–6–2T	Hill and Gresley ...	G.E.R.	1914–28	†	180S	18 × 24	4′ 10″	20,515	62
N–8	0–6–2T	T. W. Worsdell ... Reb. W. Worsdell	N.E.R.	1886–90	56 5	160	18 × 24	5′ 1¼″	17,265	60
		Reb. Raven ...	N.E.R.	1886–90	58 14	160S	19 × 24; 19 × 26	5′ 1¼″	19,235; 20,840	
N–9	0–6–2T	W. Worsdell ...	N.E.R.	1893–94	56 10	160	19 × 26	5′ 1¼″	20,840	61
N–10	0–6–2T	W. Worsdell ...	N.E.R.	1902–03	57 14	160	18½ × 26	4′ 7¼″	21,905	59
N–13	0–6–2T	M. Stirling	H. & B.R.	1913–14	61 9	175	18 × 26	4′ 6″	23,205	59
N–14	0–6–2T	Reid	N.B.R.	1909	62 19	175	18 × 26	4′ 6″	23,205	59
N–15/1, N–15/2	0–6–2T	Reid	N.B.R.	1910–24	60 18; 62 1	175	18 × 26	4′ 6″	23,205	59

O–1	2–8–0	Robinson (1911-20) ... Reb. Thompson	—	1944–48	73 6	225S	O 20 × 26	4′ 8″	35,520	33
O–2/1/2	2–8–0	Gresley	G.N.R.	1921–4	75 16	180S	18½ × 26	4′ 8″	36,470	35
O–2/3		Gresley	—	1923–43	78 13					
O–2/4		Reb. Thompson	—	1943–5	74 2					
O–3	2–8–0	Gresley	G.N.R.	1913–19	76 4	180S	O 21 × 28	4′ 8″	33,735	33
O–4/1, /2, /3, /6	2–8–0	Robinson	G.C.R.	1911–20	73 4	180S	O 21 × 26	4′ 8″	31,325	33
O–4/5	2–8–0	O–4 Reb. Gresley ...	—	1932–39	74 13	180S	O 21 × 26	4′ 8″	31,325	33
O–4/7	2–8–0	,, Reb. Gresley ...	—	1939–44	73 17	180S	O 21 × 26	4′ 8″	31,325	33
O–4/8	2–8–0	,, Reb. Thompson	—	1944–8	72 10	180S	O 21 × 26	4′ 8″	31,325	33
Q–1/1 / Q–1/2	0–8–0T	Q–4 Reb. Thompson	—	1942–43	69 18 / 73 13	180	O 19 × 26	4′ 8″	25,645	33
Q–4/1	0–8–0	Robinson	G.C.R.	1902–11	62 8	180	O 19 × 26	4′ 8″	25,645	32
Q4/2	0–8–0	Robinson	G.C.R.	1902–11	63 0 / 64 1	180S	O 19 × 26 / O 21 × 26	4′ 8″	25,645 / 31,325	32
Q–5/1	0–8–0	W. Worsdell ...	N.E.R.	1901–11	58 8	175	O 20 × 26	4′ 7½″	28,000	32
Q–6	0–8–0	Raven	N.E.R.	1913–21	65 18	180S	O 20 × 26	4′ 7½″	28,800	32
Q–7	0–8–0	Raven	N.E.R.	1919–24	71 12	180S	(3) 18½ × 26	4′ 7½″	36,965	33
S–1/1	0–8–4T	Robinson	G.C.R.	1907–08	99 6	180S	(3) 18 × 26	4′ 8″	34,525	63
S–1/2	0–8–4T	S1/1 Reb. Gresley ...	—	1932	99 2	180S	(3) 18 × 26	4′ 8″	34,525	63
S–1/3	0–8–4T	Gresley	—	1932	99 1	180S	(3) 18 × 26	4′ 8″	34,525	63
T–1	4–8–0T	Raven	N.E.R.	1909–25	85 8	175SS	(3) 18 × 26	4′ 7½″	34,080	63
U–1	2–8–8–2T	Beyer-Garratt-Gresley	—	1925	178 1	180S	(6) 18½ × 26	4′ 8″	72,940	64
V–1	2–6–2T	Gresley	—	1930–39	84 0	180S	(3) 16 × 26	5′ 8″	22,465	52
V–2	2–6–2	Gresley	—	1936–44	93 2	220S	(3) 18½ × 26	6′ 2″	33,730	14
V–3	2–6–2T	Gresley	—	1939–40	86 16	200S	(3) 16 × 26	5′ 8″	24.960	52
V–4	2–6–2	Gresley	—	1941	70 8	250S	(3) 15 × 26	5′ 8″	27,420	20
W–1‡	4–6–4	Gresley	—	1937	107 17	250S	(3) 20 × 26	6′ 8″	41,435	63
Y–1/1§	0–4–0T	Sentinel Co. ...	—	1925–33	20 17	275S	6¾ × 9	2′ 6″	7,260 / 8.870¶	54
Y–1/2§	0–4–0T		—	1927–9	19 16					54
Y–1/3§	0–4–0T		—	1926	14 0					54
Y–1/4§	0–4–0T		—	1927	19 7					54

* For weights see p. 61.

† For weights see p. 62.

‡ Originally designed as 4-6-4 compound engine with water tube boiler, and rebuilt as 3-cylinder simple engine with a Stephenson-type boiler in 1937.

§ Geared Locomotives (single speed).

¶ With gear ratio 9 : 25 (remainder 11 : 25).

Class	Type	Designer	Originating Pre-Grouping Owner (if any)	Building or Re-building Date	Weight of Loco.	Boiler Pressure	Cylinders	Driving Wheels	Tractive Effort at 85% B.P.	Page
					T. Cwt.	Lb. per sq. in.	Ins.		Lb.	
Y-3‡	0-4-0T	Sentinel Co. ...	—	1927-31	20 16	275S	6¾ × 9	2' 6"	§4,705† ‡12,600† §5,960 ‡15,960	54
Y-4	0-4-0T	Hill	G.E.R.	1913-21	38 1	180	O 17 × 20	3' 10"	19,225	54
Y-6	0-4-0T	J. Holden	G.E.R.	1897	21 5	140	11 × 15	3' 1"	5,835	53
Y-7	0-4-0T	T. W. Worsdell ...	N.E.R.	1923	22 14	140	14 × 20	3' 6½"	11,040	53
Y-8	0-4-0T	T. W. Worsdell ...	N.E.R.	1890	15 10	140	11 × 15	3' 0"	6,000	53
Y-9	0-4-0ST	Holmes	N.B.R.	1882-99	27 16	130	O 14 × 20	3' 8"	9,845	54
Y-10*	0-4-0T	Sentinel Co. ...	—	1930	23 19	275S	6¾ × 9	3' 2"	§7,965 ‡11,435	54
Z-4	0-4-2T	Manning-Wardle ...	G.N. of S.R.	1915	25 17	160	O 13 × 20	3' 6"	10,945	55
Z-5	0-4-2T	Manning-Wardle ...	G.N. of S.R.	1915	30 18	160	O 14 × 20	4' 0"	11,105	55
WD	2-8-0	Riddles (M.o.S.) ...	—	1943-45	70 5	225S	O 19 × 28	4' 8½"	34,215	64

NOTES. O—Outside cylinders (2). T—Tank. ST—Saddle Tank. C—Crane engines.
* Geared Locomotives (two speeds). † With sprocket gears 15 : 19 (remainder 19 : 19).
§ High gear. ‡ Low gear.

PETROL FREIGHT

Class	Type	Designer	Date Built	Weight of Loco.	Horse Power	Page
				T. C.		
Y-11	0-4-0	Motor, Rail & Tram Car Co.	1921	8 0	40	54